SAFETY, HEALTH, AND SECURITY IN WASTEWATER SYSTEMS

Prepared by the **Safety, Health, and Security in Wastewater Systems Task Force**
of the **Water Environment Federation**®

Tim Page-Bottorff, CSP, *Chair*	Jorj Long
Robert E. Adamski, P.E., BCEE, F.SAME, F.ASCE	Timothy Lum Yee
Bruce Anderson	Christopher Marlowe, CIH, CSP
John Bannen	Lorri McAuliffe, CET, CIT
Wesley Bauer	Ron Moeller
Nellie J. Brown, MS, CIH	Kevin M. Morley
Robin Burch	James Newton, P.E., BCEE
Gary Burrows, B.Sc., CIM	Robert C. O'Day, CHMM QEP
Alan J. Callier, P.E.	Eileen J. O'Neill, Ph.D.
Leonard W. Casson, Ph.D., P.E., BCEE	Patricia C. Passariello, P.E.
Rita Cheng	Peter Petersen
Pat Coleman, Ph.D., P.Eng.	Annette Pleis
James Covel, CPP	Douglas B. Prentiss, Sr.
Shannon Eyler, CSP	Douglas B. Prentiss, Jr.
Ronald Eyma, P.E., D.WRE	David L. Russell, P.E.
Chris Finton	Randy Schmidt
Nancy V. Halverson	Karen Shanley
Michelle Hatcher	Shannon D. Spence, P.E.
Diane M. Hinson, R.E.H.S.	Tom Stow
Nicole L. Ivers, CIH	Steve Walker, CWP
Hari Kapalavai, P.E.	Michel Wanna
Jack Keys	Leo M. Weinberg, P.E., BCEE
Myles Killar	Matthew J. Wheeler, P.E.
Stephen Laren	

Under the Direction of the **Safety, Occupational Health, and Security Subcommittee** of the
Technical Practice Committee

2012

Water Environment Federation
601 Wythe Street
Alexandria, VA 22314–1994 USA
http://www.wef.org

SAFETY, HEALTH, AND SECURITY IN WASTEWATER SYSTEMS

WEF Manual of Practice No. 1
Sixth Edition

*Prepared by the Safety, Health, and Security in Wastewater Systems
Task Force of the Water Environment Federation®*

WEF Press

Water Environment Federation   Alexandria, Virginia

New York   Chicago   San Francisco   Lisbon   London   Madrid
Mexico City   Milan   New Delhi   San Juan   Seoul
Singapore   Sydney   Toronto

McGraw-Hill books are available at special quantity discounts to use as premiums and sales promotions, or for use in corporate training programs. To contact a representative, please e-mail us at bulksales@mcgraw-hill.com.

Safety, Health, and Security in Wastewater Systems, Sixth Edition

1 2 3 4 5 6 7 8 9 0   DOC/DOC   1 8 7 6 5 4 3 2

ISBN 978-0-07-178093-3
MHID 0-07-178093-9

Water Environment Research, WEF, and *WEFTEC* are registered trademarks of the Water Environment Federation®.

Printed and bound by RR Donnelley.

This book is printed on acid-free paper.

IMPORTANT NOTICE

The material presented in this publication has been prepared in accordance with generally recognized engineering principles and practices and is for general information only. This information should not be used without first securing competent advice with respect to its suitability for any general or specific application.

The contents of this publication are not intended to be a standard of the Water Environment Federation® (WEF®) and are not intended for use as a reference in purchase specifications, contracts, regulations, statutes, or any other legal document.

No reference made in this publication to any specific method, product, process, or service constitutes or implies an endorsement, recommendation, or warranty thereof by WEF.

WEF makes no representation or warranty of any kind, whether expressed or implied, concerning the accuracy, product, or process discussed in this publication and assumes no liability.

Anyone using this information assumes all liability arising from such use, including but not limited to infringement of any patent or patents.

About WEF

Formed in 1928, the Water Environment Federation® (WEF®) is a not-for-profit technical and educational organization with members from varied disciplines who work toward WEF's vision to preserve and enhance the global water environment.

For information on membership, publications, and conferences, contact

Water Environment Federation
601 Wythe Street
Alexandria, VA 22314-1994 USA
(703) 684-2400
http://www.wef.org

Manuals of Practice of the Water Environment Federation®

The WEF Technical Practice Committee (formerly the Committee on Sewage and Industrial Wastes Practice of the Federation of Sewage and Industrial Wastes Associations) was created by the Federation Board of Control on October 11, 1941. The primary function of the Committee is to originate and produce, through appropriate subcommittees, special publications dealing with technical aspects of the broad interests of the Federation. These publications are intended to provide background information through a review of technical practices and detailed procedures that research and experience have shown to be functional and practical.

Contents

Chapter 1   Introduction to Health and Safety

Chapter 2   Safety and Health Programs

Chapter 3   Identifying and Predicting Hazards

Chapter 4 Safety and Health in Wastewater Treatment Plant Operation

Chapter 5 Safety and Health in Wastewater Treatment Plant Maintenance

Chapter 6   Safety and Health in Sewer Collections and Remote Locations

Chapter 7   Commercial and Powered Industrial Vehicles

Chapter 8   Biological Hazards at Wastewater Treatment Facilities

Chapter 9   Hazardous Materials and Waste Management

Chapter 10   Personal Protective Equipment

Chapter 11 Coordination with Other Agencies and Officials

Chapter 12 Security and Emergency Preparedness

List of Figures

List of Tables

Preface

Since the Triangle Shirtwaist Factory fire in 1911, health and safety has been an upfront management tool spoken in the same context as productivity, quality, and cost. The fire showed that fatalities and injuries, if prevented, have a direct effect on the bottom line and the workforce.

This Manual of Practice will serve as an injury-reduction tool to all those working in the wastewater field. There are guidelines for creating written programs and procedures as well as guidelines that describe how to perform a confined space entry, lockout/tagout, and chemical deliveries. From the laboratory to sewer system collection applications, this manual has recommendations that could help you reduce injuries and mishaps to ensure the ultimate safety of employees.

This publication was produced under the direction of Tim Page-Bottorff, CSP, *Chair*.

The principal authors of this publication are as follows:

Chapter 1	John Bannen
Chapter 2	John Bannen
Chapter 3	Christopher Marlowe, CIH, CSP
	Michelle Hatcher
Chapter 4	Lorri McAuliffe, CET, CIT
	Chris Finton
	Timothy Lum Yee
Chapter 5	Stephen Laren
	Bruce Anderson
	Jorj Long
	Annette Pleis
	David L. Russell, P.E.
Chapter 6	Matthew J. Wheeler, P.E.
Chapter 7	Hari Kapalavai, P.E.
	Nicole L. Ivers, CIH
Chapter 8	Alan J. Callier, P.E.

Chapter 9	Diane M. Hinson, R.E.H.S.
	Rita Cheng
	Randy Schmidt
Chapter 10	Tim Page-Bottorff, CSP
	Michelle Hatcher
Chapter 11	Douglas B. Prentiss, Sr.
	Douglas B. Prentiss, Jr.
Chapter 12	Leonard W. Casson, Ph.D., P.E., BCEE
	Robert E. Adamski, P.E., BCEE, F.SAME, F.ASCE
	Myles Killar
	Kevin M. Morley
Appendix A	Tim Page-Bottorff, CSP
Appendix B	Tim Page-Bottorff, CSP

Authors' and reviewers' efforts were supported by the following organizations:

AECOM

Black & Veatch Corporation, Kansas City, Missouri

Carollo Engineers, Broomfield, Colorado

CDM Constructors Inc., Atlanta, Georgia

CDM Smith, Edison, New Jersey; Nashville, Tennessee; and Tampa, Florida

Central Contra Costa Sanitary District, Vallejo, California

Central Marin Sanitation Agency, San Rafael, California

City of Kalamazoo, Michigan

City of London, Ontario, Canada

Clean Water Services, Hillsboro, Oregon

Cornell University–ILR/Workplace Health and Safety Program, Buffalo, New York

Delta Diablo Sanitation District, Antioch, California

Donohue & Associates, Chesterfield, Missouri

Eagle River Water & Sanitation District, Vail, Colorado

ehs International, Foothill Ranch, California

Freese and Nichols, Inc., Houston, Texas

Gannett Fleming, Woodbury, New York

Global Environmental Operations, Inc., Lilburn, Georgia

Haley and Ward, Inc., Waltham, Massachusetts

HDR Inc., Omaha, Nebraska

Kennedy/Jenks Consultants, San Francisco, California

Kent County Dept. of Public Works, Milford, Delaware

Louisville and Jefferson County MSD, Louisville, Kentucky

Macon Water Authority, Macon, Georgia

Malcolm Pirnie/ARCADIS, the Water Division of ARCADIS, White Plains, New York

Matt Wheeler Engineering, Inc., Sacramento, California

Orange County Sanitation District, California

Safestart, a Division of Electrolab Ltd., Belleville, Ontario, Canada

Safety Center, Sacramento, California

Savannah River National Laboratory, Aiken, South Carolina

Severn Trent Environmental Services, Inc., Ft. Washington, Pennsylvania

Total Safety Compliance, Mesa, Arizona

University of Pittsburgh, Pittsburgh, Pennsylvania

Upper Occoquan Service Authority, Centreville, Virginia

Utilities Authority, DeWitt, Michigan

Utilities Safety Services, Napa, California

Water Environment Federation, Alexandria, Virginia

Weston & Sampson, Peabody, Massachusetts

Woodard & Curran, Inc., Portland, Maine

SAFETY, HEALTH, AND SECURITY IN WASTEWATER SYSTEMS

Chapter 1

Introduction to Health and Safety

From the 1700s and the industrial revolution to passing of the Occupational Safety and Health Act in 1970, the safety and health of workers has been constantly evolving. During the 1990s, another period of evolution introduced security to safety and health professionals. There are disparities in how safety and health are enforced in the private and the public sectors. Indeed, the wastewater industry is faced with an almost equal number of employees in each sector. Organizations or factors that affect enforcement and guidance for both the private and public sectors are the Occupational Safety and Health Administration (OSHA), state or local department of labor offices, insurance carriers, and employer-driven policies and programs. The wastewater industry is unique in terms of safety because of the vast spectrum of work activities that must be performed in both operations and maintenance. This variety of tasks is the root cause of challenges faced by safety professionals and operations and maintenance personnel who are responsible for safety in their workplace. The question, "Where do I go to find out information on … ?," is often met with multiple responses and additional requests for information on a "what if" scenario basis. Unfortunately, there is no single definitive document or reference for all safety issues. In the wastewater industry, resolutions to these issues are not always clear and must be met with knowledge, decisions based on experience, and best work practices, as identified in this manual.

1.0   NEED FOR HEALTH, SAFETY, AND SECURITY

Regulatory compliance, reduction of liability, reduction of costs, and, finally, prevention of injury and illness are the core components necessary for optimum workplace health, safety, and security. The Occupational Safety and Health Administration publishes guidance for safety and health program management guidelines that can be referenced when establishing a health and safety program. These are non-mandatory standards and are used as examples of programs that address various components of programs that may be mandatory under other regulatory standards.

Requirements for security in wastewater facilities are constantly evolving and efforts must be in place to remain informed about the current regulatory environment, changing threats, and methods available to protect both physical and informational assets. In many organizations, security has been integrated into the role of the safety and health professional's duties. This new role is addressed in Chapter 12.

Despite the creation of regulatory standards, insurance carrier or litigation pressure, and best-in-class safety programs, the wastewater industry continues to maintain a high average workplace injury rate. This conclusion is backed by data based on the overall number of injuries or the severity of injuries, which are classified into what is called a *days away/restricted duty* (DART) classification. When injury/illness/fatality

(IIF) data are evaluated, the DART is the qualifying factor if an injury or illness is severe enough to be counted. Because injury data are qualified by an employer using guidance from OSHA, DART is the data standard for IIF reporting to the Bureau of Labor and Statistics (BLS). The *wastewater industry* refers to all the workers involved in wastewater treatment operations, maintenance of treatment facilities, lift stations, and associated conveyance systems and interrelated systems such as stormwater and pollution control. In 2009, the IIF rate in the nation was 3.6 cases per 100 workers, whereas the IIF incidence rate for the wastewater industry was 4.1 per 100 workers (BLS, 2009). The IIF rate for the wastewater industry has declined over the past few years and, for the first time in 2009, dipped below 5.0. Table 1.1 illustrates IIF rates for the wastewater industry compared to national averages and some similar industries. (The reader is referred to Section 1.1 to learn how to calculate the IIF for a given organization and to compare that rate to Table 1.1 to determine a baseline performance of the organization's safety.)

Table 1.1 shows classification as it relates to industry. The classification is a grouping of like industries or subindustries that, for statistical purposes, are grouped together. The BLS then uses these groups and subgroups to analyze trends in injury illness data. The lower the classification number, the more industries or subgroups that will be in a classification. The five-digit classification number contains

TABLE 1.1 Comparison of wastewater treatment industry IIF rates vs national averages and similar industries.

Industry	Classification	Total cases
National average (private sector)	All industries	3.6
National average (public sector)*	All industries	5.8
Wastewater/collection systems	221320	4.1
Water supply	221310	4.1
Water/sewer line construction	23711	4.9
Oil/gas line construction	23712	1.8
Mining	212	3.2
Electrical power generation and distribution	22111	2.3
Chemical manufacturing	325	2.3

*Forty-one states reporting IIF data to BLS (2009).

information that would be most specific to any matching industry. As an example, if one were in plant operations for wastewater 221320, he or she would not want to evaluate performance against water plant operations in classification 221310.

Information for public vs private sector national averages is based on the classification of the first two numbers. Public sector employees are classified under a separate category for statistical purposes because of the difference in OSHA federal jurisdiction and OSHA state plans. Additionally, not every state reports IIF data to BLS, which adds another margin of error to the BLS data tables.

The spectrum of activities in the wastewater industry exposes workers to a variety of hazards. These hazards must be addressed through awareness and application of various risk management techniques. Because of the variety, type, and complexity of safety issues facing the wastewater industry, there are multiple standards and guidelines that direct the need for health and safety in any specific safety challenge. It should be assumed that there will be multiple references, guidelines, and standards that need to be reviewed before addressing a safety issue in the wastewater industry.

1.1 Risk Management and Safety

The Insurance Institute of America defines *risk management* as "a managerial or an administrative process that includes the four functions of planning, organizing, leading and controlling the organization's activities to minimize the adverse effects of accidental and business losses at that organization to a reasonable cost." Applying this definition synonymously with *safety* is the same as saying injuries or fatalities are the cost of doing business. The business of safety is rooted in the management of risk. Indeed, the amount of risk that an organization's management, supervision, or field employees are willing to accept will directly affect the effectiveness of safety in the workplace. Some organizations will align the safety department under the risk management department, which is a way to address loss control of internal assets such as people and equipment. Safety is often seen as the reduction of internal risk through education, training, and use of proper work practices. Safer workers are more productive, produce higher quality work, and reduce the loss or damage of public or company property.

Much of the risk is assumed or implied based on certain levels of authority within an organization. While effective safety programs have direct oversight by all levels of supervision and management, there is a difference between responsibility and accountability for safety. The highest level of manager all the way up to a chief executive officer or a private utility has accountability for the safety program. Supervisors and managers in the field are both accountable for the actions or their employees and responsible for enforcing the policies and standards of safety. Employees also have a responsibility for safety in that they must be held accountable for their actions and be responsible for elements of a safety program that are either directly assigned to them or are implied in broad policy.

As Table 1.1 demonstrates, the wastewater industry has an IFF rate that is higher than the national average. In 2005, the industry injury rate was as high as 7.6; it declined to 5.2, 5.7, and 5.1 over the next 3 years, settling at 4.1 in 2009. To calculate an incident rate, the following information is needed: number of annual injuries or illnesses in a workplace and the total number of annual man hours worked. Therefore,

Incidence rate of recordable cases = Number of injuries/illness × 200 000/total hours worked by all full- and part-time employees (1.1)

For example,

Injury rate = 6 (OSHA recordable injuries) × 200 000/(200 employees × 2040 hours/ worker/year)

Injury rate = 2.9

An organization would calculate its injury rating, which is then compared against the national average or industry average to potentially gauge the overall safety performance in the organization. Incident and accident rates are lag indicators of safety program performance; it is recommended they not be used as the only measurement of safety performance.

Additional information regarding the types and severity of injuries can also be used to evaluate incident and accident rates. The DART-type situations provide another level of measurement for the number of incidents and also add the element of severity into consideration. While a fatality is the highest severity, the level below is any incident, which results in lost time

1.2 Regulatory Compliance Safety

Compliance with regulations and standards for safety is the minimal requirement for protecting workers from injury and illness. Many organizations rely solely on OSHA regulations and standards for their health and safety program management. The Occupational Safety and Health Administration has three main purposes: to set health and safety standards, enforce the standards through federal and state inspections, and provide employer and employee education and consultation. Often, there is confusion over the jurisdiction of OSHA. This approach is considered a compliance-driven approach because only minimum requirements are considered by employers. The following section defines the jurisdiction of OSHA directly from the Occupational Safety and Health Act.

1.2.1   Private Sector Workers

Most employees in the United States are under OSHA's jurisdiction. The Occupational Safety and Health Act applies to private sector employers and employees in all 50 states, the District of Columbia, and other U.S. jurisdictions, either directly through federal OSHA or through an OSHA-approved state program. State-run health and safety programs must be at least as effective as the federal OSHA program. To find contact information for the nearest OSHA federal or state program office, the reader is referred to the regional and area offices map on OSHA's Web site (http://www.osha.gov/).

1.2.2   State and Local Government Workers

Employees who work for state and local governments are not covered by federal OSHA, but have Occupational Safety and Health Act protections if they work in a state that has an OSHA-approved state program. Four additional states and one U.S. territory have OSHA-approved plans that cover public-sector employees only. These are Connecticut, Illinois, New Jersey, New York, and the Virgin Islands. Private sector workers in these four states and the Virgin Islands are covered by federal OSHA.

1.2.3   Federal Government Workers

Federal agencies must have a safety and health program that meets the same standards as private employers. Although OSHA does not fine federal agencies, it does monitor federal agencies and responds to workers' complaints. The U.S. Postal Service is covered by OSHA.

1.2.4   Not Covered by the Occupational Safety and Health Act

The following entities are not covered by the Occupational Safety and Health Act:

- Self-employed individuals;
- Immediate family members of farm employers that do not employ outside employees; and
- Workplace hazards regulated by another federal agency (e.g., the Mine Safety and Health Administration, the Federal Aviation Administration, the U.S. Coast Guard).

Compliance may encompass either following government standards or consensus standards. Government standards are developed and promulgated by federal, state, and local agencies to address safety through performance, as opposed to a technical specification that details how to accomplish a task. Consensus standards may be referenced by government standards, which may or may not have the same effect as being law. This distinction depends on how the government standard is written. An example of this is that OSHA directs monthly inspection and annual certification of fire extinguishers. The Occupational Safety and Health Administration does not direct how to inspect a fire extinguisher or how to determine if the device is serviceable. The National Fire Protection Association (NFPA) is an example of one agency that publishes consensus standards. Continuing with the fire extinguisher example, NFPA 10 (NFPA, 2010) addresses how to inspect a fire extinguisher and evaluate the condition, location of installation, signage, and determination of the proper type of extinguisher for expected use.

1.3 Best Management Practice Safety

There are numerous terms used to describe organizations that extend their practices in business and operations beyond minimal expectations. *Best in class* or *best management practice* have become terms used to describe organizations that set industry standards by practices put into place that exceed regulatory requirements. *Benchmarking* is a tool in which organizations can compare their performance, methods, or policies against other similar organizations.

Presently, only three wastewater plants in the United States have met the requirements of the OSHA Voluntary Protection Program (VPP) and have received a star rating. This accomplishment is a goal for management to strive for. The average VPP worksite has a DART case rate that is 52% below the average for its industry (OSHA, 2007).

International Organization for Standardization (ISO) 9001 is another set of guidelines that is available for reference if an organization sets a safety management system goal for best in class. The ISO sets the guidelines for a management system, but does not itself certify an agency. Certification of ISO 9001 is accomplished by a third-party auditing agency.

Both OSHA VPP and ISO certifications require a continued commitment of resources to maintain the safety program and the awarded status.

2.0 INTEGRATING SECURITY INTO HEALTH AND SAFETY

Integrating security into the duties of health and safety professionals creates unique challenges that are not unlike other challenges health and safety professionals have faced over the years. Many organizations struggle with incorporating health and safety into operations and, likewise, may struggle with security. Workplace health, safety, and security should not be thought of as programs outside of operations, but rather as integral to the everyday function of the organization and should be included within the management system in place. The overall organizational culture will affect the ability to successfully integrate security into the workplace. As with health and safety, management support must be present to allow for security programs and policies to be developed, implemented, and verified as effective in the field.

Security at wastewater treatment facilities has lagged behind the increase in security in the drinking water sector. This is attributed to a lack of regulatory guidance for wastewater facilities and a focus on the protection of drinking water treatment and distribution systems. While water systems were required by congressional mandate to conduct vulnerability assessments following the terrorist attacks in the United States in 2001, wastewater facilities have only recently been evaluated to be included in congressional security initiatives (Copeland, 2010).

3.0 SAFETY IN SMALL FACILITIES VERSUS LARGE FACILITIES

Classifying a facility as small, medium, or large operationally typically depends on flow, miles of pipeline, number of pumping or lift stations, and, potentially, the number of employees at an organization. Often, the classification of a facility is subjective in safety and not always related to the grading of classification of the system in relation to operations. For example, Grade A or Grade 4 facilities are the most complex wastewater treatment plants in some states based on the population they serve or technology used in the treatment process. However, regarding OSHA, the number of employees may determine the level of complexity or requirement of certain programs. In terms of health and safety, the challenges for small and large facilities are similar. While large facilities may have a greater frequency of certain activities that can increase their exposure to a specific hazard, that hazard should be no less of a concern for a small facility. Large facilities may have an advantage of multiple people with varied levels of experience identifying and addressing hazards, whereas a smaller plant could be limited in this factor. To address any safety issue, it must be identified and evaluated for appropriate mitigation. Chapter 3 of this manual ("Identifying and Predicting Hazards") illustrates methods that facilities can use to enhance their hazard identification and safety programs.

In addition to classifying an organization as large and small, there may be a difference if the agency belongs to the private or public sector. One of the largest differences in this area is not in the regulatory requirements of safety, but in the financial challenges each organization may face to comply with safety and health regulations. The same operational challenges for equipment in the facilities are often the same for safety and emergency response equipment. The life cycles of equipment in the public sector are typically prolonged. This increases maintenance and repair budgets as the requisition for new or replacement equipment is not submitted, which, in turn, creates situations where safety equipment is used past the operational life or manufacturer's recommendations. This situation is one that management must be prepared to face by putting proactive measures (such as policies and procedures) in place. The financial challenges of safety can be addressed with proper, frequent inspections to identify and project for future capital needs and equipment replacement. Many large organizations have asset management programs that project replacement of operations equipment. The same system can be applied to safety equipment and allow for planned expenses with regards to safety as opposed to reactionary purchases. Small organizations may face challenges with large capital purchases, but, again, with planning can avoid surprise expenditures related to safety equipment (Lotz and NyBlom, 2005).

4.0 EMERGING SAFETY CHALLENGES

Challenges facing the wastewater industry and safety will include the continued issues of lone worker safety, specialized or unique equipment, and a culture shift in the makeup of the workforce.

Even as BLS projections show an increase in employment in the wastewater industry, more and more workers are faced with working alone on a shift or at a location separated by miles from a main office or plant. Workers tasked with conducting maintenance activities in-house must use specialized equipment such as sewer cleaning machines, scissor lifts, boom trucks, and other pieces of heavy equipment. Finally, a generational change in culture is affecting worker demographics in the industry as more and more workers retire or transition from field to management positions. These are some examples of emerging challenges the wastewater industry is faced with today and will have to address in the next 10 to 20 years.

4.1 Lone Worker Safety and Geographically Separated Worksites

Working alone or with minimal co-workers present at the workplace presents unique challenges for safety. The following are some examples of events in which there would be only one or possibly two employees present in the workplace. Collecting samples from a waterway outside the facility fence line, checking operations of equipment at lift stations, or maintaining operations at a small package plant typically require no more than one operator to complete these tasks. A worker is called out at 1 a.m. to respond to a mechanical failure alarm at the treatment plant. The weekend shift requires a cursory observation of plant operations and some laboratory analysis. The absence of another worker available to notice an injured worker or summon emergency help is the primary concern for lone-worker situations.

Additionally, the presence of more than one worker can change the scope of a task to be conducted. A lifting operation that would be at the limits of a single worker and a potential back injury risk can be reduced by the presence of another worker and the use of team lifting. Environmental conditions such as weather can severely adversely affect the performance of a lone worker. For example, in cold climates lone workers are less likely to recognize the effects of hypothermia and the length of exposure to the elements may be greater because of the lack of a second set of hands to accomplish work in a shorter period of time. Lone workers are also more likely to be the subject of violence in the workplace.

The presence of additional workers also has a psychological effect on the behavior of an employee. Organizational culture will have an effect on the performance of lone workers in their decisions regarding safe work behaviors. Decisions made by individuals working alone should be no different than if another co-worker or supervisor were watching. A lone worker will be exposed to many situations in which their personal safety culture may dictate the safety and level of risk they are willing to work with while alone on the jobsite. This is known as a *safety value*. A person or organization that values safety will have more consistent safe work performance compared to an organization that prioritizes safe work practices. Safety must be integrated into management systems for it to be effective. For example, there is only one employee on shift from midnight to 6 a.m. and the company has a policy that requires wearing a hard hat at all times throughout the plant. Does that worker follow the policy even in the absence of direct supervision? Recognition of hazards is one of the single most important aspects of preventing workplace injuries. The presence of only one set of eyes to see, recognize, and identify hazards can increase the risks to lone workers.

Chapter 6 provides in-depth coverage of the safety challenges wastewater collection system operators and operators at facilities located in remote locations may encounter. Although the wastewater industry is not unique in having lone workers, the frequency with which operators must perform hazardous tasks during normal operations while alone creates a greater risk for injury.

4.2 Use of Special Purpose Vehicles

There are diverse mechanical and operational challenges in the wastewater industry. Indeed, workers in the wastewater industry are faced with unique safety challenges in the operation of sewer cleaning equipment, special purpose equipment such as high-reach lifts and mobile elevated work platforms or heavy equipment with attachments. Chapter 7 addresses commercial driver's licensing and powered industrial trucks and forklifts. These pieces of equipment pose a challenge to employee safety in terms of general operation of the equipment, competency training of workers, and, potentially, the inspection and recordkeeping requirements for special purpose vehicles.

Infrequency of equipment operation may also present a safety risk. If employees are not familiar with equipment operation, training may be required more frequently to maintain competency on special purpose equipment. There are few formal training programs and information regarding training on specialized equipment such as sewer cleaning equipment available from OSHA or other regulatory agencies. As such, organizations should rely on manufacturers' information, request training on equipment both during delivery and initial use, and inquire about the availability of recurring training. Recurring training will be needed for new employees and also for experienced employees who have demonstrated a lack of knowledge or skills on the job.

One safety challenge is the availability of specialized equipment through an equipment rental company. As an example, it may not be cost effective for an organization to own a scissors lift for a maintenance activity that occurs only twice a year so they rent the equipment on an as needed basis. The equipment rental typically does not come with an equipment operator and one of the organization's employees is assigned the task of operating the scissors lift. Has that employee been trained on the operation of the equipment and on any specific hazards that may be encountered during the operation of this aerial lift? Are there local or state certification requirements for the operation of this piece of equipment? These are questions that must be answered before an employee is allowed to operate a piece of rental equipment.

4.3   Adapting to Culture Changes

The makeup and diversity of the workforce in the wastewater industry is no different from the rest of the work force in the United States. Like other industries, the wastewater industry has experienced an increase in the number of women and Hispanic workers in the field. Communication between nationalities can be a challenge for safety. Indeed, communicating hazards and protective methods and, in the event of an emergency, alerting workers to imminent danger are key to employee safety. Additionally, outside of sex, race, or background, the wastewater industry is challenged with societal influences, such as peer pressure and lack of mentorship. There are also physiological challenges to performing a physically demanding job that are associated with worker age or obesity. These challenges constantly affect the industry's workforce and need to be considered when determining how to address health and safety in the workplace. Another of these challenges is that older workers have a lower injury frequency than younger workers, but the severity of injuries among older workers is higher.

The aging workforce in the wastewater industry forces health and safety professionals to address issues such as obesity, which can complicate workplace injuries through increased risk of permanent disability following a workplace accident or the requirement of additional treatments. Costs associated with worker's compensation are generally higher, as illustrated in a National Council on Compensation Insurance study. Workplace ergonomics is a key factor to consider when addressing the issues of older workers and, potentially, obese workers. Only through proper evaluation of the workplace and activities of workers can preventive controls be put into place.

Wastewater industry technicians working during the 1970s witnessed changes in workplace safety with the creation of OSHA and also operational changes as the U.S. Environmental Protection Agency increased enforcement of the Clean Water Act and provisions such as operator certification and facility construction standards crossed over from being strictly water standards to being applied to wastewater operations. Today, many of the engineers, operators, and laboratory technicians that endured the challenges that change brings are ready to retire. As this group retires, the experience level in the wastewater industry will decrease, leaving an opportunity for those who desire a career change and those that bring the enthusiasm of youth. The challenge will be to retain institutional knowledge of plant equipment and operations while adding new talent to the mix. Many workers joining the wastewater industry today are technologically savvy and come with a demand for learning methods and jobs that encourage use of these skills. This workforce shift will create challenges for health, safety, and security. The amount of risk that a worker is willing to accept is statistically higher in younger age groups and is illustrated by a higher injury rate among younger workers compared to older workers.

Methods for training health and safety subjects need to be relevant to not only the goals and objectives of training, but instruction techniques need to be applicable to the audience. For example, workers leaving the workplace may respond well to real life examples as they have years of experience to draw upon; a new hire with

TABLE 1.2   Safety, health, and security reference table.

Topic	Agency/organization	Web site
Federal safety regulations	OSHA	http://www.osha.gov/
State OSHA plans	OSHA Web page link to state plans	http://www.osha.gov/dcsp/osp/index.html
Injury and illness prevention	National Institute for Occupational Safety and Health	http://www.cdc.gov/niosh/
Traffic safety	National Highway Traffic Safety Administration	http://www.nhtsa.gov/
Chemical safety	U.S. Chemical Safety Board	http://www.csb.gov/
Public facility security	Department of Homeland Security	http://www.dhs.gov/index.shtm
Safety industry	American Society of Safety Engineers	http://www.asse.org/
Fire protection	National Fire Protection Association	http://www.nfpa.org/
First aid and emergency response	American Red Cross	http://www.redcross.org/
Work, home, and community safety	National Safety Council	http://www.nsc.org/Pages/Home.aspx
Injury and illness statistics	Department of Labor, Bureau of Labor and Statistics	http://www.bls.gov/iif/
Hazardous materials transportation safety	National Transportation Safety Board	http://www.ntsb.gov/

limited practical experience will still need to be taught the "why" and the "how" to perform a task safely.

In addition to issues directly facing the makeup of the workforce is a change in many organizational structures to include security in the risk management or safety area of responsibility. It is important that management recognize that the security of information, processes, and physical assets are integral to the safety and health of the workforce and the public. Both Chapters 11 and 12 will address this change in the culture of plant safety to include security as an aspect of daily operations. Chapter 11 outlines how to enhance coordination with outside agencies and the need to look beyond the fence line regarding support and interaction. Chapter 12 introduces security to the safety and health area and illustrates available risk evaluation methods and items that every facility should take into consideration regarding security. Table 1.2 provides a reference table of safety, health, and security issues and the organizations that address them.

5.0 REFERENCES

Copeland, C. (2010) *Terrorism and Security Issues Facing the Water Infrastructure Sector;* Congressional Research Service 7–5700; RL32189; Congressional Research Service: Washington, D.C.

Lotz, T.; NyBlom, S. (2005) *Conducting a Risk Management Needs Assessment.* American Society of Safety Engineers Annual Conference, Session No. 533 Abstract.

Morrison, K. (2011) Protecting the Public Worker. In *Safety & Health;* **183** (2), 44–48.

National Fire Protection Association (2010) Standard for Portable Fire Extinguishers, NFPA 10; National Fire Protection Association: Quincy, Massachusetts.

Occupational Safety and Health Administration (2007) Voluntary Protection Programs Web Site. http://www.osha.gov/dcsp/vpp/all_about_vpp.html (accessed April 2011).

Shuford, H.; Restrepo, T. (2010) *How Obesity Increases the Risk of Disabling Workplace Injuries.* http://www.ncci.com/documents/obesity_research_brief.pdf (accessed April 2011), National Council on Compensation Insurance, Inc.: Boca Raton, Florida.

United States Bureau of Labor and Statistics (2009) Home Page. http://www.bls.gov/ (accessed April 2011).

Chapter 2

Safety and Health Programs

15

1.0   DEVELOPING AND IMPLEMENTING SAFETY AND HEALTH PROGRAMS

Safety and health programs are established to create a structure for the management system of health and safety. Security programs may be an element of safety and health programs and will be discussed in detail in Chapter 12. A safety and health program should be implemented regardless of the size of an organization; the size of an organization will determine the requirements or elements of a program. Occupational Safety and Health Administration (OSHA) regulatory requirements for safety programs are specific to individual hazards or operations. Currently, comprehensive safety programs are mandatory only in some states, such as Nevada, if there are 10 or more employees and also in California, where the Injury Illness Prevention Program establishes the structure of a safety and health program.

1.1   Establishing a Program

The wastewater industry is categorically included in the utilities sector for safety classification. When establishing the goals and objectives for a safety program, it is possible to review other programs in similar industries such as an oil and gas refinery, an electrical utility, or an underground utility installation company. Many of the hazards will be similar in these industries; by reviewing established programs of these similar industries, an organization's management team can begin to formulate plans to address these hazards at their specific sites.

An organization's management team must develop a plan for their safety program with a vision of the desired end results in mind. This plan will help establish allocation of resources to accomplish the goals and objectives outlined in the plan. There are three levels into which a safety and health program most likely will fit. These will be discussed in-depth in the next section. Additionally, the following are some essential elements that management must consider when developing goals and objectives for a safety program (Roughton and Mercurio, 2002):

- Management commitment—more than just a statement of commitment to hang on the wall or to insert into an employee handbook. Management commitment is evident when employees observe supervisors and management following safety policies and leading by example in the field. Management commitment should be seen as evidence of leadership in an organization. This leadership demonstration is not only for employees, but for the public;

it shows shareholders in private utilities that there is a focus on protection of employees as a valuable resource. Showing management commitment can be as simple as attending tailgate safety meetings, recognizing employees in the field while working safely, or even accompanying an employee while they conduct a facility inspection.

- Employee participation—educating and training employees to not only follow safety policies and regulatory guidelines, but also involving them in conducting facility inspections, drafting standard operating procedures (SOPs), writing a job hazard analysis (JHA), and encouraging feedback on ways to improve safety in the workplace from both a physical standpoint and employee culture.

- Hazard identification—establishment of frequent and meaningful inspections, evaluations, and methods in which to identify existing and potential hazards in the workplace. Implementing a process or system to ensure reporting of hazards, correction of these hazards, and a method in which to follow up and ensure that the correct actions have been taken.

- Hazard prevention and control—empowered employees who know what to look for and how to correct an unsafe work environment or established policies that guide and direct employees will help control hazards in the workplace. Employees who are unsure of what or how to address a safety concern allow the hazard to potentially remain in place and not be addressed by any means. Saying safety is everyone's responsibility is a good start, but ensuring that employees understand they have the authority to correct safety issues is more important. In most instances, there are legal statutes that afford protection to workers who refuse to act in an imminent danger situation or who are directed to perform work in an unsafe manner.

- Training—training employees on regulatory standards will give them a baseline of information regarding the "do's" and "don'ts" of a particular standard such as ladders or fall protection, but training must be site-specific to the policies of that organization for it to be effective. In addition to site-specific policies, supervisors and management must communicate their expectations for safe work performance in a specific area. An example of this is use of personal protective equipment (PPE) or safety harnesses for fall protection. Supervisors should show the importance of these policies by wearing the correct PPE at all times; doing so will emphasize the importance of wearing PPE that employees may have learned in training.

Training comes in many formats. An organization must evaluate the type of training needed to complement the skills and knowledge that employees may already possess. Showing a 15-minute video to a group of veteran operators may not be effective training when the objective is to evaluate their competency on responding to a chlorine gas leak. Therefore, training should always be selected based on an evaluation of the goals for training. Management should define objectives for the training and then determine which method of training will suit their organization.

Verification of the effectiveness of training is extremely important to the success of a training program. Tests of an employee's knowledge and verification of their skills in the field are two methods by which verification can be completed. Management should ensure that detailed documentation is completed to show what the employees were instructed, when they were instructed and by whom, and how they were evaluated.

- Evaluation of the safety program—evaluation of the safety program needs to be more than the measurement of injuries or days away from work. Effective safety programs measure the proactive means by which the organization is addressing safety.

The *scope* of a health and safety program may be defined by asking and answering some simple questions. (1) Will we focus solely on regulatory compliance issues? The answer to this question will lead to development of what is considered a regulatory compliance driven program. This type of program will focus only on requirements outlined in OSHA standards or local regulatory requirements. (2) Are we willing to add additional elements to sections of the safety program to exceed compliance requirements? An organization choosing this strategy may be applying the same line of thinking between operations performance and safety performance. If an organization strives to follow best management practices in operations, then the same culture should be applied in the safety program. (3) Do we want our program to be aligned with a recognized safety standard such as International Organization for Standardization 9001? And will we eventually want to partner with OSHA in their Voluntary Protection Program (VPP)? An organization that identifies its goals with positive answers to question number three positions itself to be a best in class or industry benchmark for safety in the wastewater industry.

1.2 Roles and Responsibilities

1.2.1 Management

An effective safety program must have commitment from management. Additionally, resources will be needed to establish a safety program. Management most likely will control the financial resources and manpower needed for training, equipment, and hours necessary to implement a safety program. As discussed in Section 1.1, management will define the scope by identifying a level of commitment to safety. The larger the organization becomes, the more management may assign different roles and responsibilities to employees. Conversely, smaller agencies must maintain many of the same responsibilities with regard to establishing a safety program; they will also have to assign multiple roles to fewer people to accomplish the same goals as a large organization.

1.2.2 Supervision

While management may assume the largest burden of accountability for safety, the supervisor also bears a large portion of responsibility for safety. While all employees share in responsibility for safety, the supervisor's role often involves implementing the safety program at the field level and maintaining the effectiveness of the programs or policies the employer creates.

1.2.3 Field-Level Supervisors and Crew Leads

Field-level supervisors and crew leads are in the greatest position to influence the safety of the workplace. Supervision and management set the tone for compliance with policy and safety programs by endorsing and distributing these programs to the field. However, it is field level supervisors who must practice the organization's safety policies to effectively influence employees. Employees will watch closely how field-level supervisors endorse and practice the organization's safety policies. It is possible that the actions of field-level supervisors can create obstacles to the success of a safety program if they do not follow or embrace the program or only verbally endorse the initiative. Employees will observe their supervisor not complying with safety and, as a result, an attitude of, "Why do I need to?" can develop in the workplace. Conversely, a field supervisor that verbally and physically demonstrates commitment to the safety program is the strongest influence over the performance of their subordinates. Additionally, enforcement of safety policies will be initiated by field supervisors because they are the most direct and frequent observers of employees.

1.2.4   Employees

Potentially, the most critical link in an effective safety program is people. Indeed, employees in the workplace are faced with final decisions that may result in working safely or acts that result in an injury or incident in which property or equipment are damaged. Commitment letters can be drafted and signed by an upper level of management; programs that address regulatory requirements can be written and distributed to employees. Equipment can be purchased to protect workers or make tasks safer, but the employee still must make conscious decisions to work safely. Employees must not only be informed of present or potential hazards in the workplace, but they must also be educated, trained, and empowered to mitigate these hazards if necessary. Employees should be confident in having the authority to stop work if an unsafe work environment is present by being given the responsibility of stopping work and working safely.

1.2.5   Accountability

All levels of an organization bear both responsibility and accountability. Responsibilities have been outlined in the preceding sections, but accountability is both moral and legal. As an employee's position within a company advances, his or her accountability and responsibilities will increase. Indeed, the only responsibility for employees is to follow standards; accountability is limited to their own decisions and actions as they relate to safe work practices. Supervisors and managers, then, assume more accountability as they must ensure that their subordinates follow standards; they also have the responsibility of overseeing implementation and execution of company policies and programs.

1.3   Effective Safety Program Management

Evaluation of a safety program and measurement of performance typically focus on either lead or lag indicators. Lead indicators are factors that can be measured before an injury or accident. Lag indicators happen after an incident has occurred. The hierarchy of injuries is an important factor to understand (it is explained in more detail in Chapter 1). A near miss is the least significant injury followed by a minor first aid incident, an OSHA recordable injury that can then progress to a restricted duty or modified duty, a lost-time incident (LTI) in which an employee is too severely injured to be able to be in the workplace, and, finally, catastrophic events such as hospitalization of a member of the public, three or more employees being injured in the same event, and fatalities. Tracking the number of days between lost-time incidents is a lag indicator and is not a positive indicator of safe work performance; it does not indicate a measurement of proactive efforts within an organization.

1.3.1   Lead versus Lag Indicators

A common measurement of safety program effectiveness is the counting of injuries and accidents in the workplace. These are examples of lag indicators as an unsafe act or behavior that has already occurred. Once these incidents have been counted, they may be compared against the industry average, the national average for injuries, or number of similar injuries. Chapter 1 shows an example of this by illustrating the injury rate of the wastewater industry compared to other similar industries. Organizations can evaluate the entire organization or even an individual department against both the industry and/or national average. This can be done for total injuries in the workplace or a specific injury such as a back injury. Back injuries and strains or sprains caused by improper lifting and material handling are examples of injuries that are higher than average in the wastewater industry.

An example of how this may be used is in an organization that has had employees with numerous hand lacerations. The number of hand lacerations can be researched from the National Institute for Occupational Safety and Health and then a comparison against the organization can be made. It should be emphasized that this is a lag indicator comparison and is not an effective measurement to predict the future performance of an organization's safety program.

Additional common lag safety program measurements are the counting of days between incidents. This may be done for LTIs or OSHA-recordable incidents.

One of the most popular lead indicators, and a proactive activity for safety, is reporting of near misses. Organizations throughout different industries use a variety of terms similar to *near miss*. Other terms that are commonly used are *near hit* or *close call*. A near miss is an event that had the potential to cause an injury or damage to property, but did not. Documentation and reporting of near misses can help to identify trends of behavior that eventually could result in an injury or property damage. Documentation of near misses is a means for management to establish goals and objectives on a proactive safety activity that they can then evaluate in performance reports to quantitatively measure an employee's safety performance. These reports should be shared and discussed with all employees to encourage safe work performance.

The following are some examples of near miss reporting: (1) the chain link gate at the entrance to a plant was blown closed by wind, almost hitting a service truck as it was entering the plant; (2) an employee was stepping down from an extension ladder and missed stepping on the last step and stumbled as he or she came down; and (3) when taking a box down from the storage closet, a second box fell to the floor. The second box contained toilet paper and nothing was damaged nor were there any injuries.

1.3.2   Identifying and Predicting Hazards

A common sense approach to safety is the assumption that all employees will see or identify a hazard and then correct the hazard so that it does not cause harm to themselves or any coworkers. Unfortunately, each person has a different baseline level of knowledge when it comes to safety and a level of risk they may be willing to accept as part of the job. Organizations must identify acceptable levels of risk and methods in which to identify and address those risks. The best method to accomplish this is through comprehensive hazard analysis. Hazard analyses should be conducted at multiple times. A baseline hazard analysis needs to be conducted if there has never been a thorough audit; an evaluation of hazards is performed when a process changes or new facilities come online. Routine job hazard analysis should also be performed periodically as part of the duties of management, supervisors, and even field-level employees. Conducting regular facility or site inspections is a means by which to identify hazards and should be conducted at least once a month. A system should be implemented to not only identify these hazards, but to develop a method in which the identified hazards are corrected and these corrections communicated to employees. Communicating the entire process of hazard identification and mitigation to employees shows follow-through on the part of management when a reliable system is used to remove hazards from the workplace and prevent injuries from occurring.

Job hazard analysis (JHA) is used as a routine method to help predict or identify potential hazards when performing a task in the workplace. A JHA is a step-by-step evaluation of a task or process to evaluate potential hazards. Once each hazard has been identified, JHA outlines how each hazard will be addressed through engineered controls, administrative controls such as safe work practices, or the use of PPE. The JHA is best used at the field level by individuals or groups that perform the task and have the most working knowledge of the task to be evaluated. This knowledge assists in completion of the JHA because these employees are most familiar with the steps involved in the task, the specific tools available at the facility to conduct the task, and the method that is currently in use at the facility. The JHA can then be communicated to employees or incorporated into a larger document like a standard operating procedure (SOP) that could include multiple JHAs. Job hazard analyses are often used to drive the creation of an SOP. A well-written JHA will have all the essential elements or steps of a procedure outlined. The SOP is typically a conversion into a more user friendly, readable document for use in everyday operations. The JHA may be seen as the "what to do" and the SOP becomes the "how to do it." Chapter 3 will discuss how to complete a JHA in greater detail.

1.3.3 *Facility Inspections*

Facility inspections are useful in a safety program for two reasons. The first is to satisfy regulatory requirements for either mandated inspection cycles of items or frequent inspection intervals of items as determined by company or manufacturer policy. Secondly, facility inspections are used to gain a "snapshot" of the facility condition at a given time.

Frequent inspections are required for fire protection and emergency response equipment and many PPE items. If possible, facility inspections should be conducted by a group rather than one individual. The concept is that if a member of supervision, a member of the maintenance team, and a member of operations conducts the inspection together, there is a greater opportunity for identification of hazards and a potential for immediate corrective actions to be evaluated and determined. This team concept applies to larger facilities, as in medium or smaller organizations, and the roles discussed previously are typically filled by fewer people. In a small organization, the benefit of different people evaluating the plant can potentially be addressed by not allowing the same person to conduct the inspection month after month. Rather, the assignment should be alternated between employees.

In addition to creating an inspection team or rotating the assignment of conducting plant inspection, it is important that anyone conducting the inspection be properly trained. While most employees can recognize many obvious hazards in the plant such as hoses not rolled up or extension cords left out after maintenance, not all of them may be familiar enough with OSHA regulatory requirements or consensus standards to identify or mitigate all hazards during a facility inspection. Training can fix this information gap with anyone assigned to perform a facility inspection. First, management should identify the type of inspection and then train the employee(s) to a competent level regarding the type of inspection. By addressing different topics over time, employees will become more and more proficient conducting inspections.

Examples of different categories of inspections are as follows: general housekeeping, fall protection, fire prevention and emergency equipment, chemical storage, electrical, and tools and equipment.

The final component of facility inspections is documentation and follow-up. Identifying hazards only to be documented and not addressed undermines the safety program and creates an attitude of complacency in the workplace. The form and style of documentation is up to the employer in most instances. While OSHA may direct frequency of documentation, there is little guidance on the specific format required to collect and retain information. The employer can create inspection checklists and forms or search the Internet for a variety of forms that are available to use as templates.

1.3.4   Safety Program Audits

Many people use the terms *audit* and *inspection* interchangeably; in the safety profession, however, there is a distinction between the two. As discussed in the previous section, an inspection focuses on the condition of the work environment such as the buildings, walkways, and work centers at a facility. Although an audit may include a facility inspection, it will typically focus on the safety management system and the effectiveness of the safety program at the field level. Evaluation of written programs, safety documentation, training, and, finally, the condition of safety in the field, are all elements of an audit.

Any audit that is conducted should follow an established evaluation and review process. Elements of the program should be graded, which allows for quantitative evidence of the status of the safety program to be communicated back to the organization. Grading can be as simple as assigning a numerical value to established criteria such as 5 points for "exceeds" requirements, 3 points for "meets" requirements, and 0 points for areas needing improvements. The following is an example of how this grading can be applied to an audit of the hazard reporting system at a facility:

1. Is a system established for employees to document and report hazards found throughout the plant?
2. Is evidence of corrective actions available for any hazards identified under the hazard reporting program?
3. Are employees encouraged to report hazards they find at the facility?
4. Is there evidence of application of interim measures to address identified hazards in between identification and final correction of the hazards?

5. Are changes in plant processes or operations evaluated before implementation to determine if they will increase hazards or expose employees to hazards not previously present at the facility?

Total score received = _____ (out of total possible 25 points)

The scale for evaluating the effectiveness of the area being audited may vary. What is important is that management and the auditor agree upon the scale and understand the results of the scale as it applies to the facility. The graded results from the audit can then be used to prioritize corrective action items. Some organizations may emphasize an aggregate score to show progression over time or to be able to compare facilities within an organization.

Action plans should be suggested that define personnel accountable for correcting any deficiencies and establish timelines for completion of the deficient items. Conducting a safety audit is only useful if the results will generate improvement in the overall program or provide an efficient means to identify, track, and correct deficient areas of the safety program. If these three things are not done, then collecting information during the audit serves no purpose.

1.3.5   Recordkeeping and Documentation

Recordkeeping and documentation for safety come in many different formats. Some records document the completion of tasks and others are used for communication of information to employees about the condition of a hazard. Many standards address what needs to be documented, but each organization must determine how to document the items and identify or design the specific form or method to record any information required by the regulatory standards. Chapter 4 expands on the specific requirements of many recordkeeping items needed for safety in wastewater treatment plant operations.

All organizations are required to record injuries or illnesses that occur in the workplace. Every year, incidents that occurred during the previous year are required to be communicated to all employees. The Occupational Safety and Health Administration designates form 300A for posting from February 1 to April 30 each year. If there are fewer than 10 employees in the workplace, information does not need to be posted but must still be communicated to all employees. It is recommended that no matter how many employees an organization has, form 300A should be posted in an area common to all employees. If there is a state OSHA plan in place there may be a variation of form 300A; however, the purpose and information will be the same because the state form must be as effective as the federal OSHA form.

1.3.6   Training

There are many different approaches to safety training. Regulatory requirements for training are not defined in many OSHA standards and must be interpreted by the employer. This is where safety programs may outline requirements as a combination of OSHA regulatory requirements, employee skill evaluations, and safety industry best practices. Within the safety program, types of training methods to be used such as traditional classroom, video, computer-based, or on-the-job training can be identified for specific safety topics. Identification of training goals and objectives can be defined. An employee's level of competency with safe work practices can be established. Training may be conducted completely in-house through use of competent employees who can communicate the requirements and objectives of the topic or may be outsourced to consultants and professional training organizations. Additionally, many professional safety organizations and state agencies offer safety training at little or no cost to employers.

Training may be as simple as communicating the hazards of a task and the methods in which to protect the employee during this process or it may be as complex as multiple hours in a classroom followed by written examinations and practical exercises designed to evaluate an employee's competency. The employer is responsible for evaluating employees and hazards and then determining the level of training appropriate for the organization's needs. Occupational Safety and Health Administration requirements and employee exposure to hazards should be the primary guidelines for determining training needs. Using audits and inspection tracking programs will allow for evaluation and reporting of hazards so that utilities may evaluate training needs against frequently cited hazards.

1.4   Incident Analysis

1.4.1   Importance of Training Before Incident Occurrence

Incident investigation training is important because learning to effectively investigate accidents should never come from frequent experience in performing this task. While the term *investigation* implies finding fault, it should be noted that *accident investigation* and *incident analysis* are interchangeable terms. Safety professionals prefer the term *incident analysis* to more accurately reflect the process that is used to determine incident causes. Investigating accidents identifies the failure in the safety management system and outlines preventive actions going forward. Any employee who may be conducting an accident investigation or incident analysis should receive some level of formal training. Elements such as interviewing witnesses, documenting the scene, and determining the cause are all essential elements for accident investigation. There are many models available to determine causes and organizations should evaluate which model works best for the facility and the type of operations and potential incidents they may be encountered. Supervisors must be familiar with how people, equipment, environmental conditions, and management interact to create conditions in which an accident occurs. An incident investigation may be conducted for incidents that result in damaged equipment or injured employees; additionally, near misses can also reveal useful information to prevent future reoccurring events. The primary focus of any investigation or analysis should never be to assess blame; rather the focus should be to identify deficiencies in the safety management system so they can be corrected. A final note to remember is that even though root cause is the goal of any incident, this does not imply that there is only *one* factor that may need to be corrected at the conclusion of an incident analysis, which will be discussed further in Section 1.4.3 (Ferry, 1988).

1.4.2 Importance of Medical Case Management Following an Incident

Medical case management can be divided into two equally important sections. The first is the employer playing an active role in monitoring the treatment of an injured employee. Secondly, case management is the completion of any applicable worker's compensation paperwork and OSHA reporting requirements. Occupational Safety and Health Administration reporting requirements are addressed in Section 1.3.5 and, in greater detail, in Chapter 4.

Supervisors and employers have rights and access to certain information regarding the care of an injured worker. Some employers choose to establish healthcare provider networks (HPNs) or medical provider networks (MPNs) to establish an open line of communication with occupational clinics, urgent care facilities, doctors, and specialists who may be used in the event of a workplace injury. The purpose for employers qualifying HPNs or MPNs before sending an injured worker to a medical center is to prevent delays in care because of insurance issues and then to streamline the process involved in getting all necessary medical paperwork from the medical facilities back to the employer. Additionally, an employer can discuss return-to-work policies that outline the availability of light-duty positions within a company to help return an employee to the workplace as soon as is medically possible. Additionally, an employer can build a relationship with doctors and care centers that will assist in the long-term management of serious medical events.

1.4.3   Root Cause Analysis

The object of analysis is to prevent similar events from reoccurring. By identifying the root cause, or all causes, organizations can reduce the frequency of events, minimize exposure to employees, and potentially lessen the consequences if the event were to repeat itself (Roughton and Mercurio, 2002). Chapter 3 provides an in-depth discussion of analysis methods such as "what if," failure mode and effects, and fault tree. Other available analysis models that can be used are sequence models, five "whys," hazard scenario, management oversight and "risk tree," and technic of operations review. Each of these methods can be used as tools to investigate an incident.

Typically, one type of method should be chosen for use in an organization. Analysis of different specific events may require use of a different technique for that event. Fire and vehicle accidents are two specific examples for which a specialized method may be identified for use.

2.0   WRITTEN PROGRAMS

2.1   Description of the Purpose of Written Programs

The term, *written program,* may refer to varied documentation within a safety program. The Occupational Safety and Health Administration requires different documentation throughout the different regulatory standards. Some standards require documentation of training with verification of effectiveness in the field. Other OSHA standards require structured written programs, scheduled inspections, audits, and reviews of documentation. Finally, some written programs are created to outline an employer's specific methods in addressing the requirements of an OSHA standard.

2.1.1   Written Programs Required by Regulation

The primary purpose of OSHA requiring employers to have written programs in the areas outlined in this section is because of the complexity of requirements of the programs. Additionally, the term, *written program,* may refer to the need for recordkeeping and documentation. The Occupational Safety and Health Administration directs *what* an employer must do regarding a specific hazard and then asks the employer to create a written program documenting *how* they will accomplish the requirements they outline in the standard. All of these elements may be stand-alone policies or programs or may be incorporated into one safety management system within an organization. The programs are as follows:

- Emergency action plan—required to have a written plan when an organization has greater than 10 employees in the workplace. Six critical elements required by OSHA standards are (1) procedures for reporting fire or other emergencies, (2) procedures for emergency evacuation, (3) procedures for employees to follow who must remain to operate critical plant operations, (4) procedures to account for all employees after an evacuation, (5) procedures for employees performing rescue or medical duties, and (6) name or contact information of the employee who may be contacted if employees need more information on the plan (29 CFR 1910.38).

- Fire prevention/protection plan—required to have a written plan when more than 10 employees are in the workplace. Five critical elements required by OSHA standards are (1) a list of all significant fire hazards, (2) procedures to control accumulations of flammable or combustible materials, (3) procedures for regular maintenance of safeguards on heat-producing equipment to prevent accidental ignition of combustible materials, (4) the name or position of the employee responsible for maintaining equipment to prevent or control sources of ignition on fires, and (5) the name or title of the employee responsible for control of fuel source hazards (29 CFR 1910.39).

- Bloodborne pathogens exposure control plan—organizations that have determined they have an occupational exposure must establish a written exposure control plan with a minimum of the following three elements: (1) the exposure determination, (2) the schedule and method of implementation, and (3) the procedure for the evaluation of circumstances surrounding exposure (29 CFR 1910.1030).

- Hazard communication program (HAZCOM)—there are three broad components to the written HAZCOM program. Each of the following elements has detailed requirements listed in the OSHA standard that outline specific requirements for employers to follow: (1) labels and other forms of warning for chemicals in the workplace, (2) material safety data sheets, and (3) employee information and training (29 CFR 1910.1200).

- Respiratory protection program—when a determination to use respirators is made or when employees have voluntarily selected to wear respirators in the workplace, a written program with work-site specific procedures is required. The following are nine elements that must be addressed in the program: (1) procedures used for selection of respirators; (2) medical evaluations of employees; (3) fit-testing procedures for tight-fitting respirators; (4) procedures for proper use of respirators in routine and reasonably foreseeable emergency situations; (5) procedures and schedules for cleaning, disinfecting, and maintenance of respirators; (6) procedures to ensure adequate air quality, quantity, and flow testing of breathing air for atmosphere-supplying respirators; (7) training of employees in respiratory hazards; (8) training of employees in the proper use of respirators; and (9) procedures for regular evaluation of the effectiveness of the program (29 CFR 1910.134).

- Hearing conservation program—there are recordkeeping requirements regarding employee audiometric testing and the measurement of noise levels in the workplace. Although there are no requirements for a written program, establishment of a program that outlines site-specific training requirements, audiometric testing procedures, available hearing protective devices, and the purpose of the program is recommended (29 CFR 1910.95).

- Permit required confined space entry program—an organization must first determine if employees will be allowed to enter and work in confined spaces. If employers determine that their employees will not enter and work in confined spaces, all they are required to do is implement effective measures to prevent employees from entering or others from inadvertently entering permit-required confined spaces by means of warning signs or securing access to these locations. If an organization determines they will enter and work in confined spaces, a written program is required. There are 14 elements to a confined space program that are discussed in-depth in Chapters 4 and 5 (29 CFR 1910.146).

- Fall protection program—most fall protection written programs encompass documentation and recordkeeping by regulations. Best management practice is to establish a written fall protection program in the workplace because of the numerous different locations in which regulatory guidance for fall protection is noted. By creating a written program, employees will have a worksite-specific reference to guide safe work behaviors in the following areas: walking working surfaces, fixed ladders, portable ladders, scaffolds, vehicle-mounted elevating platforms, and lifts. Additionally, a written program will provide knowledge of what inspections are required for equipment such as fall-arrest or fall-restraint harnesses and lifelines. The duty to protect employees from falls crosses over into confined space entry operations, trench and excavations, and general maintenance duties throughout the facility.

- Personal protective equipment—the written program element of PPE is OSHA's requirement to evaluate the hazard to determine the appropriate type of PPE for the workplace and task. A written certification that hazards in the workplace have been evaluated is required and is discussed in detail in Chapter 10 (29 CFR 1910.132).

2.1.2   *Written Programs Used to Establish Consistency of Safe Work Practices*

As discussed in the previous section, not all regulatory standards outline specific requirements for the elements of a written program. As a best management practice, organizations may use written programs to establish consistency throughout the workplace and to create continuity in the event of personnel or management system changes. Establishment of written programs outside of OSHA regulatory requirements can also be used to direct safety training requirements, integrate safety in operations, or meet the requirements of OSHA's VPP or Star Program. Insurance companies and worker's compensation funds may also direct the requirements for employers to create specific written programs to address issues identified in the workplace.

3.0   BEHAVIOR-BASED SAFETY

Of the four elements discussed previously that can contribute to an incident (i.e., man, environment, equipment, or management), the focus of behavior-based safety is on the "human" element. In some ways, this is the psychological "why" we do what we do and the factors that influence people at work to conduct what is known as "at risk behaviors." Employees who conduct more frequent at risk behaviors may sustain more injuries or contribute to more damaged equipment in the workplace. It is also the theory behind repetition of these behaviors despite policies or procedures that are in place that direct employee behavior to be counter to what it currently is. Behavior-based programs look at elements that encourage employees to move from knowing what the safe work behavior is to employees doing and performing the safe work behaviors to reduce at risk activities.

The interaction of employees and the interaction of management with employees are focal points of behavior-based safety. Understanding why employees conduct at risk behaviors is as important as knowing why employees work safely. Understanding why employees work the way they do also helps identify at risk behaviors that may be outside of the control of the employee. An employee's behavior may be the result of poor equipment design or a faulty process. Identification of at risk behaviors is the root of being able to make changes in the workplace that affect safety. Employees must believe that they personally have control over safety in the workplace that affects the overall safety of an organization in a behavior-based safety culture.

3.1 Employee Involvement and Importance of Feedback

A company that has open lines of communication between not only management and subordinates, but throughout company divisions and departments will have fewer obstacles when establishing an effective safety program. Training, inspections, audits, and JHAs are all elements of the safety program that will require effective communication to fully achieve substantial implementation of a safety program. Whether the organization selects a "top-down" or "bottom-up" approach to safety, management must acknowledge that both will require their employees to be engaged and involved in the safety program. Even using the term, *program*, with the term, *safety*, may require caution as some people view programs as having distinct create, start, implement, and review phases; therefore, an employee may unconsciously think "temporary" when hearing the term, *safety program*. Indeed, however, safety should be ongoing at an organization and, as such, should be labeled as another continual improvement process or system without a defined ending.

Management and supervisors should carefully address the comments and concerns of employees. Employees should be given the opportunity to share their ideas about the safety program and any elements within the program. Supervisors should have conversations with employees following training sessions to determine the effectiveness of training. New employees should be asked about the quality of on-the-job instruction and supervisors and employees alike should be asked about the safe work practices of other employees. Additionally, management and supervisors should strive to create an atmosphere of non-retribution at the worksite because everyone should have the same goal of a safe workplace in mind.

3.2 Incentive Programs

There are pros and cons to establishing employee incentive programs based on safety and safe work performance. The argument against establishing these programs is that if they are not implemented where a strong, positive safety culture already exists, they could lead to under-reporting or nonreporting of workplace injuries because an employee does not want to be the individual that causes a group to miss a bonus. However, in an organization where there is an established, effective safety management system in place, use of incentive programs can enhance the programs far beyond minimal compliance and into best in class or benchmarks—for safety performance.

In a traditional incentive program, management will establish rewards for predetermined goals. With safety programs, this often leads to incentives for reduction of the number of injuries, reduction of the numbers of days lost, or restricted duty assignments. The negative outcome of these types of programs is that the individual employee or department "feels" punished when there is an injury in the workplace. Good incentive programs will highlight and reward safe work performance without negatively affecting any aspect of the safety management system. Safe work performance goals should already be integrated into the performance goals of all employees for their regular reviews. Supervisors should frequently communicate their expectations for production, quality, and safety to all employees. When this is being routinely done, establishment of an incentive program is beneficial to enhance and drive the safety program forward. As an example, if a supervisor is already required to perform three safety inspections on the facility and one on a piece of equipment in a quarter, then the incentive should be based on a performance factor above the standard objectives. Employees may be rewarded for performing duties above their level, but not out of their knowledge or abilities. In organization A, JHAs are reviewed monthly as part of the supervisors' duties, but an employee steps up to volunteer to conduct one as well, and the department doubles the expectations of JHA review for that department. These are examples of positive, proactive engagement of employees within a safety program and can be used to define safety incentive programs. Some additional proactive methods that can be measured and used for incentive programs include giving a safety meeting, conducting training, submitting corrective work orders to fix a hazard, safety committee membership, attending safety classes outside of primary duty scope, safety team membership, and volunteering for additional duties on a design review committee specific to identify potential safety deficiencies.

Many of the aforementioned examples that are used as incentives in some organizations become standard in organizations that have set a goal for safety at best in class. The Occupational Safety and Health Administration has voluntary programs that organizations can join such as VPP and the Star Program, which is a component of VPP. Organizations that commit to these program levels are considered best in class and set industry standards for safety.

4.0 REFERENCES

Ferry, T. S. (1988) *Modern Accident Investigation and Analysis*, 2nd ed.; Wiley & Sons: Hoboken, New Jersey.

Roughton, J. E.; Mercurio, J. J. (2002) *Developing an Effective Safety Culture*; Butterworth-Heinemann: Burlington, Massachusetts.

Chapter 3

Identifying and Predicting Hazards

(continued)

1.0 ACCIDENT PREVENTION SYSTEM

The traditional approach (Krieger, 2008) to preventing occupational illness involves recognizing, evaluating, and controlling hazards. This is also a useful way to approach controlling work conditions that cause physical injuries.

1.1 Recognition of Hazards

1.1.1 Hazard Definition

Hazard is the capacity to cause harm. It is an inherent quality of a material or a condition. It is not the same as *risk*, which will be defined shortly. For example, a rotating saw blade has a capability (hazard) to slice through flesh. A toxic chemical has the capability (hazard) to cause illness.

The most favored techniques in the "hierarchy of control," discussed in Section 1.3.2 of this chapter, consist of removing the hazard (Rochester Institute, http://www.rit.edu/~w-outrea/training/Module3/M3_HierarchyControls.pdf). Buying precut wood, as mentioned in our example, or casting a moldable material in place would remove the hazard of the saw blade by removing the saw blade altogether.

1.1.2 Sources of Information

Many sources of information exist for chemical hazards such as explosivity, flammability, and toxicity. These sources are fairly easy to use because the information in them is arranged alphabetically by chemical or material name. Several of them are listed in Section 8.0 of this chapter.

Because physical equipment and physical situations are more difficult to organize in an alphabetic system, the sources of information on such topics are slightly more difficult to use. Chapter 4 lists many hazardous physical devices or situations. Several important sources are also listed in Section 8.0.

1.2 Evaluation of Hazards

1.2.1 Risk Definition

Risk is the chance or probability that a person will experience harm. Risk is not the same as hazard. Risk always involves both probability and severity elements. The hazard of a rotating saw blade is the same whether it's exposed to the workplace or enclosed in a proper guard. The probability of contacting the hazard is greatly reduced by the presence of a guard, which would change the risk of working with a saw tremendously. This relationship is often represented in the following pseudo-equation:

$$\text{Risk} = \text{Hazard} \times \text{Probability} \tag{3.1}$$

When people discuss the hazards of disease-causing agents, the term typically used more than probability is *exposure*. If a certain type of chemical has a toxicity hazard, the risk of illness rises with the degree to which that chemical contacts your body or enters your lungs. In that case, the equation becomes

$$\text{Risk} = \text{Hazard} \times \text{Exposure} \tag{3.2}$$

1.2.2   Sources of Information

Many of the information sources listed in Section 8.0 specifically focus on reducing the probability or exposure factors. Most safety publications that relate to hazards focus on reducing probability or exposure to hazardous agents.

1.3   Control of Hazards

Most people easily identify ways to get work done without undue exposure to hazards. Organizations document their methods in hazard control programs. These programs contain all the steps needed to protect workers from exposure to a substance or system and the procedures required to monitor worker exposure and their health to hazards such as chemicals, materials or substance, or other types such as noise and vibration. Successful implementation of a hazard control program requires dedication of time and resources to develop, implement, and maintain the program.

1.3.1   Safety Definition

Safety is the practical assurance that no harm will occur. Safety is the inverse of risk, a relationship summarized by the following equations:

$$\text{Safety} = 1/\text{Risk} \tag{3.3}$$

$$\text{Safety} = (1/\text{Hazard} \times \text{Exposure}) \tag{3.4}$$

Safety is, necessarily, comparative. There is no environment or condition that is completely safe for everybody all the time. Therefore, an organization may set a goal for employees at a treatment plant to be as safe as office workers or as safe as they would be in their homes or beds.

1.3.2   Hierarchy of Control

Health and safety professionals apply a "hierarchy of controls" to the selection of feasible and effective controls. This hierarchy, described in *Occupational Health and Safety Management Systems* (ANSI, 2005) establishes the following priority order for selecting controls:

- Elimination,
- Substitution,

- Engineering controls,

- Administrative controls, and

- Personal protective equipment (PPE).

Elimination is the most favored alternative in this hierarchy because it completely removes the hazard from the workplace. Substitution is the next most favored alternative because it removes the hazard and substitutes another material or procedure that potentially reduces the overall hazard potential. It is less favored than elimination because the substitute sometimes turns out to have its own hazards that were not foreseen at the time of selection.

Engineering controls consist of placing barriers on the hazardous condition or intervening in the pathway. Examples include (1) use of mechanical transport rather than manual means or (2) use of wet grinding methods rather than dry methods to reduce or eliminate dust. Engineering controls are lower in the hierarchy because the enclosures might be inadequate or not be used or they might fail because of lack of maintenance.

Administrative controls consist of reducing the hazard by changing the position of the employee or the duration of time the employee spends exposed to the hazards (Rochester Institute, http://www.rit.edu/~w-outrea/training/Module3/M3_HierarchyControls.pdf). The implementation of standard operating procedures or work rules is a good example. For exposure to toxic vapors, reducing the duration of time the employee spends in the contaminated area can be an effective administrative control. These controls are less favored because they often require employees to undertake inconvenient or uncomfortable steps to reduce the hazard.

Personal protective equipment consists of barriers on the body of the employee. It is the least favored alternative because some PPE in the American workplace is uncomfortable, easy to forget, or hard to work in. Employees may sometimes ignore the need for PPE because of these reasons.

2.0   JOB HAZARD ANALYSIS

Organizations evaluate hazards using several techniques.

2.1   Activity Hazard Analysis, Job Hazard Analysis, and Job Safety Analysis

Hazard analysis is known by many names including job safety analysis (JSA), activity hazard analysis (AHA), or job hazard analysis (JHA). This type of analysis helps integrate accepted safety and health principles and practices into a specific task. In a JSA, each basic step of the job is reviewed, potential hazards identified, and recommendations documented as to the safest way to do the job. The following discussion summarizes typical questions one should ask during a JSA.

2.2 When Can This Approach Work Well?

Job hazard analysis by whatever name can be powerful when used on a task that the analysts understand well. When the reviewer has no practical experience with that task, one of the techniques described in Section 3.0 might be useful.

2.3 What Tasks Will Be Performed?

The work team breaks the project or job into tasks for this review. They identify, in turn, each task needed to complete the procedure. After analysts evaluate the hazards of one stage in the process, they move on to the next, until the whole scope of work is complete.

2.4 What Could Go Wrong?

As shown in Figure 3.1, work teamslook for specific types of potential accidents and ask the following questions about each basic step:

- Can the employee strike against or otherwise make injurious contact with the object?
- Can the employee be caught in, on, or between objects?
- Can the employee strain muscles by pushing, pulling, or lifting?
- Is exposure to toxic gases, vapors, dust, heat, or radiation possible?

2.5 How Much Harm Would Be Caused?

The consequence or seriousness of any hazard can be identified by answers to a series of "what if" questions. What if analyses involve reviewing possible deviations from operating procedures or design intent such as the following: What if the (name of component) fails? Both short- and long-term effects should be considered in the assessment.

The consequence analyst should also assess the possibility of conceivable events or conditions. What if questions should be posed for malfunctions, explosions, performance failure, or wastewater blockages. As systems become larger and more

Activity hazard analysis				
Project name:	Sewer Surcharge Investigations		**Project no.:**	234-1515
Analyzed by:	Joe Worker	**Date:** 02/19/11	**Reviewed by:**	Guy Safety

Description of work activity

Observe sanitary sewer manholes via upper frame/cover opening (no entry!)

Potential hazards	Hazard controls
Sewer gases	No manhole entry permitted! City sewer department maintains and uses gas meter to check atmosphere during work.
Traffic	Employees to wear high-visibility vests and hard hats. Daylight-hour inspections only. Employees to confirm traffic controls in place. Conform to H&S Manual Section 16.22 (attached).
Slip and fall hazards	Plan your steps. Be aware of debris and objects in walking path. Two people on-site at all times.
Lifting and carrying drain grates or manhole covers	City sewer department personnel will remove grates or manhole covers if needed.

Training required	Equipment required
Team safety meeting	Steel-toe footwear, cut-resistant work gloves, safety glasses, hard hats, high-visibility vest
	Manhole hooks, crowbars, flashlight, spotlight

FIGURE 3.1 Activity hazard analysis form.

complex, other analytical methods, described in the following sections, are more appropriate.

2.6 How High Is the Risk?

Risk evaluation identifies the cause of undesirable consequences and the likelihood of occurrence so that proper controls can be selected. The challenge is to set a level of risk that is low enough for improvement, but not so low that it is unattainable. The definition of *acceptable risk* (see Section 2.6.3) will vary according to an individual's experience, knowledge, and perception of benefit.

This third step determines how the risk is created in the operation. What combination of events can lead to the hazard causing harm? Most accidents happen as a result of several things going wrong in sequence or at once (WEF, 1992). Once the combinations of events are found, the probability of those combinations occurring can be assessed.

2.6.1 Objective Evaluation

Some risks can be quantitatively estimated. If it is known how frequent the incidents are, just what will be harmed, and how often the incidents resulted in the harm of concern, the number of injuries or fatalities per a specific time period (i.e., million staff hours) can be quantified (through estimation). Insurance companies frequently perform this kind of analysis for construction projects.

2.6.2 Subjective Evaluation

Frequently, however, analysts do not have the aforementioned rate and linkage information and are forced to evaluate the risk using personal biases and prejudices. Such analysis relies on a reviewer's "gut feelings." When numbers cannot be put on the analysis it does not mean the analysis is useless; rather, it is an exercise to develop potential hazards that could be observed during the activity. Risk evaluations can still be produced that help create a safer workplace through subjective evaluations.

2.6.3 Acceptable Risk

Employers need to strive to achieve a level of "acceptable risk," although it is hard to agree on just what that is. Upon first reading, "acceptable risk" may sound like "permissible death." Risk is acceptable, or not, when a specific audience agrees that it is. Wastewater utilities, for example, would not accept the injury rates of the National Football League, but the football players union does.

Although some analysts believe that an organization can remove all risk from the workplace, there is probably some residual that can never be removed while work progresses. Even those who believe that every accident can be prevented by some combination of human efforts would hesitate to suggest that half of the budget of a working organization be devoted to such accident prevention.

2.6.3.1 Definitions of Acceptable Risk

If we intend to keep our workplaces reasonably safe but cannot remove all possible risk, we must strive for a level of risk that is "acceptable" to our organization and society. Some of the sources listed in Section 8.0 define *acceptable risk* for specific types of activity. In general, the following sources define which risks are acceptable in our society:

- Occupational Safety and Health Administration (OSHA) standards, including
  - Design and performance standards,
  - Work practice standards, and
  - Permissible exposure limits;
- Regulations from state OSHA programs (e.g., California OSHA [2011]);
- Safety regulations promulgated by other agencies (e.g., speed limits, U.S. Environmental Protection Agency [U.S. EPA] regulations, and hazardous materials transportation rules);
- Fire codes (municipal and consensus) (NFPA, http://www.nfpa.org/categoryList.asp?categoryID=124&URL=Codes%20&%20Standards);
- Building codes (municipal and consensus) (ICC, http://www.iccsafe.org);
- Consensus standards (such as those published by the American National Standards Institute, the American Society for Testing and Materials, and National Fire Prevention Association (http://www.nfpa.org/categoryList.asp?categoryID=124&URL=Codes%20&%20Standards); and
- The practical experience of everyday citizens, for example, expectations regarding slippery surfaces.

2.6.3.2 *Societal Expectations*

An employer or organization might have achieved an acceptable risk when they have

- Complied with every law and standard that applies to the activity they are conducting (this includes the OSHA standards, fire codes, and consensus standards discussed in Section 2.6.3.1);
- Made every effort that a reasonable person would have made to prevent such an accident (note that the scope of "reasonable efforts" is often determined after an accident occurs—it is a rather high standard);
- Communicated with those affected by the hazard to determine what steps they think would be appropriate for the control of the hazard; and
- Taken all of the steps that this process identifies.

2.7 How Can Harm Be Prevented?

When all known and foreseeable hazards associated with each job have been identified and their causes understood, the final step is to develop ways to eliminate the hazards. The reviewer should focus on the goal of the job and the ways the goal can be accomplished to see if one way is entirely safe. For each hazard recorded on the JSA, the reviewer should ask, "What should the employee do, or not do, to eliminate this particular hazard"? The answers must be specific and concrete to be worthwhile.

Consistent with the discussion in Section 1.3.2, prevention consists of removing the hazard, keeping the hazardous agent away from the exposed employee, adopting procedures that keep the employee at a distance, or use of PPE.

If the hazard cannot be removed, the safety effort can consist of interventions that reduce probability or exposure or those that reduce consequences. Purchasing a pump that is less likely to experience vapor lock reduces probability. Purchasing three pumps to reduce the facility's reliance on any one pump reduces consequence.

One way to minimize the exposure is to reduce the frequency with which the task needs completion. If a repair or service job has to be done frequently because a condition needs correction, the reviewer should ask, "Can we eliminate the condition that makes this repair necessary?" If the cause cannot be eliminated, he or she should ask, "What can be done to minimize the effect"?

3.0   OTHER METHODS OF ANALYSIS

3.1 Informal Analysis

3.1.1   Mental Job Hazard Analyses (Safe-Think Process)

Although most documentation about using JHA assumes that the team will record the analysis in writing, many of the benefits of JHA can be accomplished with a mental or verbal JHA. Some safety managers call this method the *safe-think process*. Although documenting an analysis in writing often improves its quality, the immediacy of the safe-think process provides a benefit that analyses done in the office trailer cannot achieve.

The safe-think process is simply a mental activity hazard analysis. Before the employee conducts any task, they should spend a few minutes asking the following:

- What am I going to do?
- What could go wrong?

- ○ How could I get hurt?

- ○ How might others get hurt?

- ○ What can make us safe?

- Do we have the right equipment?

- How will we control the work?

- Can I perform this task safely?

- Should I perform the task, not perform it, or find help?

- Should we change the place where we are working?

Employees should be encouraged to conduct a safe-think analysis whether there is a written health and safety plan, a written JHA, or nothing in place.

After identifying any potential hazards, employees must find a way to make the task safe. For example,

- Employees are expected to conduct work safely and take the necessary steps needed to do so;

- Any concern by any individual must be resolved before work begins; and

- If a hazard is identified that is not easily controlled, the activity should be paused and the facility's health and safety designate should be contacted.

3.1.2 Group Discussion

Halfway in effectiveness between a mental AHA and one committed to writing are those that occur verbally through group discussion. Because group members tend to remember things differently, and documentation is typically not completed for such discussions, this approach is typically limited to a simple task with four to six hazards. The process, however, is the same.

3.2 What If?

Another technique for evaluating hazards in the workplace is called the *what if process*. The process is just as it sounds. The team asks, "What if some disturbance of desirable conditions occurs and what consequences could result"?

If the consequences are insignificant, or acceptable, that scenario is satisfied. If the consequences are significant and unacceptable, the process proceeds to the question, "What safeguards are now in place to reduce the probability of this scenario or reduce the consequences"? After listing the safeguards, the team asks whether those safeguards adequately protect the assets (people, property, and reputation) that the organization cares about.

If the safeguards are adequate, that scenario is satisfied. If not, the team proceeds to brainstorm potential recommendations. (Some facilitators call these recommendations "other considerations.") After the potential recommendations are listed, the team selects among them until they agree that the combination of existing safeguards and recommendations they have chosen achieves an acceptable level of risk.

The purpose of this process is to identify a list of recommendations that would improve safety at the facility. Sometimes, a list of 100 scenarios will produce as few as 30 recommendations, some of which will require no significant effort or expense.

3.3   Checklist

The checklist process is typically based on a written set of questions like the ones shown in Figure 3.2. Such checklists are often available from regulatory agencies, commercial publishers, corporate health and safety groups, and so on. Most checklist questions at least imply the safest or best answer to each question.

The checklist process is most effective for situations that are well known to the author of the checklist. Completely new situations are rarely modeled this way because the authors may not fully understand the environment in which the work occurs, the nature of the task, or the hazards associated with both.

3.3.1   Self-Made

If a team will analyze the same type of process at many different locations, development of a written checklist will facilitate the analysis. The better the team understands the process, the better the checklist will be.

3.3.2   Commercially Published

Hazard checklists are available from industry associations, from commercial publishers like J. J. Keller (http://www.jjkeller.com/webapp/wcs/stores/servlet/category-Search_10151_-1_10551_Workplace%20Safety | 16660_OSHA%20/%20Workplace%20Safety_126_18523) or Business and Legal Reports (http://safety.blr.com/find.aspx?terms=checklist), or from government agencies like OSHA (http://www.osha.gov/

RMP Audit Form

Process Safety Management - Observation of Site Conditions

(Derived from OSHA CPL 2-2.45A)

40 CFR 68.65 & 1910.119(d): PROCESS SAFETY INFORMATION	
1. Do observations of a representative sample of process chemicals and equipment indicate that the process information is complete?	No
(Information that does not correspond to the actual conditions demonstrates incomplete information. Check critical equipment and components to see if they have been properly identified.	
2. Do observations of a representative sample of process components indicate that the process complies with recognized and generally accepted good engineering practice?	Yes
(Review a representative number of safety devices such as pressure relief devices or containers for proper sizing according to the maximum anticipated pressure.)	
3. Based on interviews with a representative number of operators, is MSDS information readily available to the operators who work with hazardous materials?	Yes
40 CFR 68.67 & 1910.119(e): PROCESS HAZARD ANALYSIS	
1. Do observations of a representative sample of process-related equipment indicate that obvious hazards have been identified, evaluated, and controlled?	Yes
(For example, hydrocarbon or toxic gas monitors and alarms are present; electrical classifications are consistent with flammability hazards; destruct systems such as flares are in place and operating; control room siting is adequate or provisions have been made for blast resistant construction, pressurization, alarms, etc.; pressure relief valves and rupture disks are properly designed and discharge to a safe area; pipe work is protected from impact; etc.)	
2. Do observations of a representative sample of process-related equipment indicate that PHA recommendations have been promptly resolved?	No

FIGURE 3.2 Checklist example (derived from OSHA CPL 2-2.45A).

dcsp/compliance_assistance/quickstarts/general_industry/gi_library. html#Publications). Some of these checklists show extensive understanding of specific situations or task scenarios. Many checklists, however, are developed by individuals without an understanding of either specific situations or actual work being performed.

3.3.3   Gap Analysis

Checklists can be effectively used for gap analysis. Gap analysis consists of using a checklist in which each item documents some action, program, or condition necessary to create a safe situation. By asking questions in a systematic way, the team conducting the analysis can quickly identify recommendations that would improve their operation.

Of course, the gap analysis approach, like the checklist analysis that it is part of, is most useful for situations that are well understood by the checklist author before the analysis begins. Figure 3.3 presents an example of gap analysis.

3.4   What If Checklist Process

The what if/checklist process provides the flexibility of the what if process with the efficiency of the checklist process. After an organization studies a specific type of task the first time, the resulting analysis table can be used as a checklist to make subsequent analytical efforts quicker. An example appears in Table 3.1.

Risk Management Gap Analysis Worksheet				Ozone				Hours
Applicability Analysis	40 CFR 68	Done?	Good?	Where?	Who?	Needs?		L of Effort
Covered Chemicals - O_3	115	No	No	a	Facilitator	okay		1
Threshold Quantities	115	No	No	Overview	Facilitator	Covered Chemicals - O_3		1
Covered Processes - O_3	12	No	No	a 1	Facilitator	Boundary issues		3
Previous Incidents - None?	42	No	No		Utility	Not provided		1
Program Group - 3	10	No	No		Facilitator	Covered Processes - O3		1
Work Plan	40 CFR 68	Done?	Good?	Where?	Who?	Needs?		L of Effort
Current Program Status	Proj mgmt	No	No	Here	Facilitator	Covered Processes - O_3		12
Incomplete Items	Proj mgmt	No	No	Here	Facilitator	Current Program Status		8
Completion Schedule	Proj mgmt	No	No	Here	Facilitator	Incomplete Items		8
Hire Consultant	Proj mgmt	No	No	CDM	Utility	Completion Schedule		14
Establish PHA Team	67 d)	No	No	PHA	Utility	Hire Consultant		6
Ozone	40 CFR 68	Done?	Good?	Where?	Who?	Needs?		L of Effort
Toxicity Information	65 b)	No	No	d 1	Design Team	Right MSDS		1
Safe Exposure Limits	65 b)	No	No	d 1	Design Team	Right MSDS		1
Physical Data	65 b)	No	No	d 1	Design Team	Right MSDS		1
Reactivity Data	65 b)	No	No	d 1	Design Team	Right MSDS		1
Corrosivity Data	65 b)	No	No	d 1	Design Team	Right MSDS		1
Stability Data	65 b)	No	No	d 1	Design Team	Right MSDS		1
Hazards of Mixtures	65 b)	No	No	d 1	Design Team	Right MSDS		1

FIGURE 3.3   Gap and analysis example.

TABLE 3.1 What if checklist example.

Activity hazard analysis			Water plant	
What if …	Consequences / hazard	Safeguards	Okay?	Recommendations
Effect of construction on emergency response capabilities				
Construction operations damage the roadway in such a manner that emergency response capabilities are diminished.	Injuries and discharges to community air are more likely.	Construction quality management process. Management of access is a key responsibility of the construction manager on the cover projects.	Yes	
People need to leave the site because of another emergency.	Loss of ability to account for all employees.	Contractors will be trained on emergency action plan (EAP), including the primary assembly area.	No	Authority will train contractors on EAP.
People need to assemble during a chlorine release.	Difficulty gaining control of large workforce	Contractors will be trained on EAP, including the primary assembly area.	Yes	None

(continued)

TABLE 3.1 Continued

Activity hazard analysis

What if ...	Consequences / hazard	Safeguards	Okay?	Water plant Recommendations
Construction operations block emergency evacuation.		Construction traffic is highly regulated by the contract. The site has multiple entrances, which can be used if one is blocked. Construction vehicles are prohibited from the treatment area, except when the vehicle is needed for a specific purpose in the immediate area. Manage road closures as a management of change item.	Yes	Contractor must maintain continuous access for evacuation and emergency vehicles. Contract must clearly state who has the power to interrupt or delay contractor operations.
Construction operations block site access by emergency responders	Reduction in emergency capability.		No	
Construction operations block emergency evacuation of plant employees.				
There is flooding, tornado, or heavy snowfall during construction?	Blockage of the roadway is much more likely. Site accidents are much more likely.	Emergency standard operating procedures. Contractor must "protect the work." Chlorine facilities are sheltered in strong buildings. Chlorine facility maintains enough chlorine to operate for 30 days.	Yes	Contract must establish which contractor repairs such damage. Contractor plows and clears its own work areas. Clear contract language on responsibilities, monitoring of plowing in restricted areas.

3.5 Hazard and Operability Study

The hazard and operability (HAZOP) study process uses analytical tools developed for use in the chemical industry to identify ways that an accident or an undesirable incident can occur. This analysis is most appropriately used for processes like chemical reactors or disinfection. Some have, however, used it for operations as mundane as fence construction or truck loading. An example of the HAZOP study process appears in Figure 3.4.

Before this analysis can begin, a facilitator breaks up the process into "nodes." These nodes should be small enough to facilitate a thorough technical analysis, but few enough in number to allow the process to proceed with reasonable speed.

The analysis assumes the process will create no undesirable consequence when it operates as designed. That is, accidents or undesirable incidents will occur only when disturbances in the process occur. Therefore, the team asks what happens if specific parameters (pressure, temperature, order, duration, etc.) vary in specific ways (none, more, less, instead of, early, late, etc.). As with what if analysis, the team brainstorms

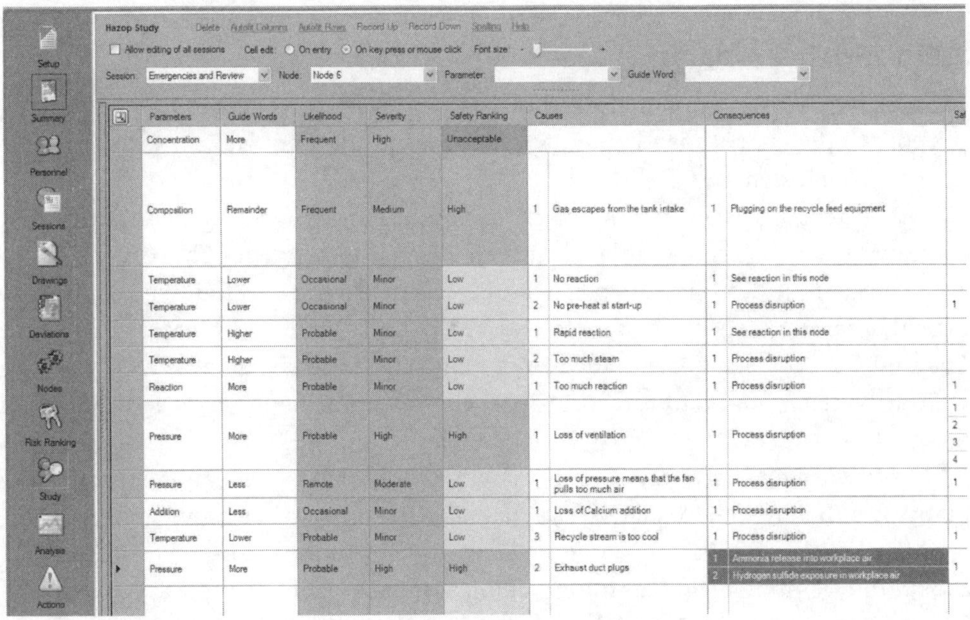

FIGURE 3.4 Hazard and operability study example (courtesy of Isograph Inc.).

ways in which these disturbances can affect the node under study upstream nodes and downstream nodes.

If any negative consequence is identified, the team brainstorms physical or procedural conditions that could lead to the disturbance (parameter and variation) type under study. If they find one or more of these, they evaluate safeguards and develop recommendations as described for the what if process in Section 3.2. As with the description of the what if analysis, the purpose is to develop a list of recommendations that will improve safety.

3.6   Failure Mode and Effects Analysis

Failure modes and effects analysis is closely related to the hazards and operability study described previously. As opposed to considering disturbances in a process, the team considers all of the possible ways in which the system's individual components can fail separately or together. The consequences and likelihood of each failure are determined in a semi-quantitative way. The team then considers the effects and likelihood of combinations of component failures. Figure 3.5 presents an example of this analysis.

3.7   Fault Tree Analysis

Fault tree analysis is common in aviation, military science, and computer design. The purpose of the analysis is to quantitatively predict the frequency or probability of undesirable incidents.

Fault tree analysis is similar to failure modes and effects analysis performed "backward" (from accident to cause instead of cause to accident). The team typically starts with an undesirable event or result and then works back down the process logic diagram to identify sequences with the potential to lead to that failure event. The undesired events become the top of a fault tree and the analyst works downward from these effects toward probable causes. Figure 3.6 presents an example of this analysis.

As stated previously, teams performing fault tree analyses attempt to work quantitatively. When failure frequencies are published (e.g., for a ball valve or a pressure-release valve [CCPS, http://www.aiche.org/CCPS/ActiveProjects/PERD/index.aspx]), the resulting estimates of probability can be reliably quantitative. When the failure frequencies are less well known (e.g., for the quality of operator training in a

Revision 6.0 2/11/98

Design FMEA

			Org. Date 2/11/98	Page 1 of 2
System ☐	Customer: Chrysler Motors Corporation	Customer Part No. DC-77323-XYZ		
Subsystem ☐			Key Date 2/11/98	FMEA No. DFMEA-001
Component ☑	Supplier: Any Company, Inc.	Code ACI-001	Dwg. Rev. 8	
		Supplier Part No. A-9514		

Part Name: Filter — Application/Model Year: Sedan/1998

Design Responsibility: Brad Anderson

Prepared By: Brad A. Anderson — Date 2/11/98

Core Team: Brad Anderson, Jerry Benware, Lisa Brown, Ken Caracci, Bill Cox, Fred Jordan, Ken Kratz

Item/ Function	Potential Failure Mode	Potential Effect(s) of Failure	Sev	Class	Potential Cause(s)/ Mechanisms of Failure	Occur	Current Design Controls	Det	R.P.N.	Recommended Action(s)	Responsibility & Target Completion Date	Actions Taken	Sev	Occ	Det	R.P.N.
Filter for assembly with B44 to firewall	Insufficient wax coverage over specified surface	Deteriorated life of door leading to: Unsatisfactory appearance due to rust through paint over time, Impaired function of interior door hardware	4	◇	Insufficient wax thickness specified	4	Supplier certification	1	16	None	N/A 2/11/98					
					Inappropriate wax specified	5	set up set up	4	80							
							Five piece setup, in-process, end of run study	2	40	None	N/A 2/11/98					
	Corroded interior lower door panels	Improper oxide coating	6	◇	Entrapped air prevents wax from entering corner/ edge access	6	Test spray pattern at startup and after idle periods, and ...	5	180	Add team evaluation using production spray equipment and specified wax	Engineering and Assembly Operations 2/18/98	Based on test results (Test #9989) spray head modified to ...	6	2	5	60
				◇	Spray heads clogged: Viscosity too high, Temperature too low, Pressure too low	4	Incomming audit per 200-16 certification, SPC Lot/Qtr	2	48	Add laboratory accelerated corrosion testing	ABC Labs 2/27/98	Test results show specified ...	6	3	3	54
							Laboratory test using "worst case" wax and application hole size	3	72	Conduct DOE on wax thickness	Engineering Associates 2/18/98	DOE shows 25% variation in specified thickness is acceptable	6	2	2	24
					Feeder not properly or	3										

Approved By: Brad A. Anderson — Date 2/11/98

FIGURE 3.5 Failure mode and effects analysis example (graphic courtesy of the FMEA Information Centre).

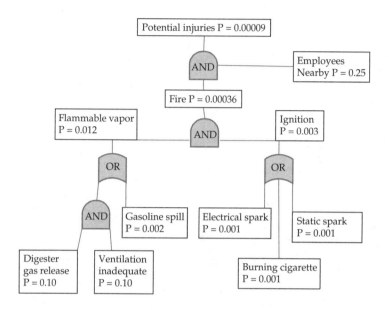

FIGURE 3.6   Fault tree analysis example (P is the probability of a condition being true in any single minute. These probabilities are strictly for illustration and do not represent any real location.).

specific organization), the estimates of probability can still be used for comparison within the analysis, even though they may not represent objective reality.

Fault tree analysis is most productive when the team objectively understands the component parts well, but does not subjectively understand the overall process. While it produces high-quality results, it demands an extensive investment on the part of the analytical team and its facilitators. For processes involving a lot of human input, particularly those that the analytical team understands well, the less formal analyses described previously may be more cost effective.

4.0   DOCUMENTATION OF HAZARD ANALYSIS
4.1   Formal

All of the formal hazard analysis procedures that have been discussed serve to make the workplace safer. If analyses are properly documented they can also comply with applicable regulation, demonstrate to managers and regulators that appropriate attention is being paid, and reduce liability after an accident occurs.

If an analysis needs to meet any of those goals, the analysis will need to be documented in writing. Documenting an analysis in writing can also increase the quality of that analysis because people pay more attention when their names appear on a document.

Records kept on paper are traditional and secure. However, records kept electronically organize the analysis in a manner that allows subsequent investigations to proceed quickly. They are also often easier to store and distribute. If these records are kept, it is important to make sure to produce backups such as storage on a CD-ROM or a secondary server. Off-site storage is a must.

4.2 Informal

Although formal documentation can improve the process, informal documentation, including hand-written notes and verbal agreements, should be used when teams analyze conditions in near real time.

4.3 Continuous Improvement

Some teams make the assumption that they should analyze a process or hazard just once and then implement the recommendations. It is important to realize that processes change over time and that later teams might discover a factor that the first team missed. Nearly every product of human effort can be improved at some later time.

Teams should re-analyze the process or hazard periodically. Frequency of analysis should depend on the following:

- Seriousness of the hazard (more frequent analyses for catastrophes than for minor disturbances);

- Prior experience of the analysis team (less frequent analyses if the team had a lot of experience before this analysis); and

- Frequency or intensity of the operation (more frequent analyses for processes that occur every day and for those that occur once a year).

5.0 HAZARD ANALYSIS FOR THE ENVIRONMENT

This volume is different from its predecessors in being an environmental health, safety, and security document. Previous volumes did not include procedures for analyzing environmental hazards. In this manual of practice, "Environmental" means, "effects on the community and the natural world, not related to the facility's waste-water permit."

5.1 Analysis of Continuous Releases

For decades, most U.S. EPA regulations focused on continuous or periodic releases from industrial and commercial activity. Releases into air and water or onto land were regulated by many federal statutes. Sudden or short-term releases are addressed in Section 5.2.

5.1.1 Materials Inventory

Many of the environmental regulations published by U.S. EPA regulate specific chemicals, but not others. Examples of lists are the hazardous air pollutants regulated by 40 CFR 63 (U.S. EPA, 2011a) or the extremely hazardous substances regulated by 40 CFR 68 (U.S. EPA, 2011b). There are also regulations that address a single compound, such as 40 CFR 76, which regulates polychlorinated biphenyls (U.S. EPA, 2011c).

One of the first steps a facility's environmental program must take is to identify any chemicals on-site that are regulated by such a special requirement. Facility managers should complete an inventory of the materials that they use and store on-site and compare them to the U.S. EPA Title III Consolidated List of Lists, which can be found at http://www.epa.gov/osweroe1/tools.htm. Facility managers at older wastewater plants, in particular, should note the potential for problem chemicals to remain on-site after they stop using them.

5.1.2 Emissions Inventory

Because environmental regulations, in general, exist to protect people and nature off a property, a good way to evaluate the comprehensive effect of the facility is to create a materials flow diagram that shows how materials arrive on-site, where they are stored, and how they leave. An emissions inventory (ARB, http://www.arb.ca.gov/ei/ei.htm) of all the materials that leave the site reveals how each of those materials affects off-site receptors. The inventory also shows conditions, concentration, and flow characteristics at the receptors.

Some of the emissions will be beneficial, such as water the facility recycles for reuse and irrigation, and some will have minor or longer-range effects, such as the carbon dioxide emitted by facility boilers. Other emissions will have more critical effects, such as paint waste or biosolids disposed on land. Once these effects are understood, they can be compared to environmental regulations or other definitions of socially acceptable risk.

5.1.3   Environmental Audits

Although the two procedures described previously can yield significant information about the environmental effect of the facility, a formal environmental audit can help place these effects in clearer perspective. There are two common types of environmental audits: an environmental management audit and the environmental compliance audit. Neither of these audits provides all the information the emissions inventory would provide, but both assume the information that would be generated by one.

5.1.3.1 Environmental Management Audits

An environmental management audit does not necessarily measure the effects of the facility on the community and the natural world. Rather, the management audit evaluates the degree to which the facility knows about that effect and takes responsibility for controlling those effects in accordance with their value system.

The most well known guidance for creating or auditing an environmental management system is International Organization for Standardization (ISO) 14000, the *International Standard for Environmental Management Systems* (ISO, http://www.iso14000-iso14001-environmental-management.com/), and its related standards. Environmental auditors frequently rely on ISO 14010, 14011, and 14012, which are guidelines for environmental audits(ISO, http://www.iso14000-iso14001-environmental-management.com/).

The environmental compliance auditor might review the facility's emissions inventory, but the auditor does not evaluate those emissions. Rather, he or she determines whether the facility has a good system for identifying these emissions and their effect on the community or natural receptors. These effects are called *aspects*.

5.1.3.2 Environmental Compliance Audits

An environmental compliance audit typically assumes an emissions inventory, but it often is conducted using a regulatory checklist. It is best if the environmental compliance auditor is a seasoned professional with practical experience in each of the regulations that might apply to the facility. Therefore, a seasoned auditor should be chosen with experience in the wastewater treatment field.

These compliance audits are limited to environmental effects that are subject to regulation. They do not provide a comprehensive view of every environmental effect of the facility. For example, compliance audits conducted prior to 2005 typically did not evaluate emissions of greenhouse gases.

5.2 Analysis of Sudden Releases

During the last 20 years, environmental regulations have focused more on preventing short-term accidental releases than they have in the past. There is also more focus on preventing chemical accidents from both fixed facilities and transportation. The methods described in Section 3.3 are commonly used to analyze and control such accidental releases.

6.0 HAZARD ANALYSIS FOR SECURITY

6.1 Vulnerability Analysis

Vulnerability assessments help identify appropriate security measures for wastewater systems. The assessment seeks gaps or problems in security procedures, software, internal system controls, transmission of data, or the lack of ability to recover from an attack. A vulnerability assessment helps identify

- Measures that can reduce the accessibility of critical assets to attack;
- Specific measures that can increase the reliability of critical assets after an attack; and
- Ways to protect staff, customers, and information.

Vulnerability assessments can be prepared by

- Wastewater treatment plant staff,
- Public works departments,
- Consulting engineering firms, and
- Combinations thereof.

Analysis of security measures for each facility is best done by teams of wastewater treatment plant staff, municipal administrators, law enforcement, fire department staff, and others.

The remaining sections describe the types of vulnerability assessment tools that are available.

6.1.1 Security Risk Assessment Methodology for Water Utilities

Sandia National Laboratories developed the Security Risk Assessment Methodology for Water Utilities (RAM-W) software in response to a challenge grant established by U.S. EPA (Sandia Corporation, 2011). The software was completed shortly after the attacks of September 11, 2001. The RAM-W software applies the principles and approaches that the U.S. Department of Energy uses to protect nuclear weapons facilities to the protection of water and wastewater utilities. Figures 3.7 and 3.8 present examples of this analysis.

This assessment tool uses a sophisticated approach. It works well for large wastewater treatment plants. Users identify malevolent threats and evaluate security measures to reduce those threats. Using the tool requires good computer skills, and methodology training is essential. For more information on RAM-W, the reader is referred to Sandia National Laboratories' Web site at http://www.sandia.gov/ram/.

6.1.2 Vulnerability Self-Assessment Tool

The Vulnerability Self-Assessment Tool (VSAT) was produced by the North American Clean Water Association with funding from U.S. EPA. The Vulnerability

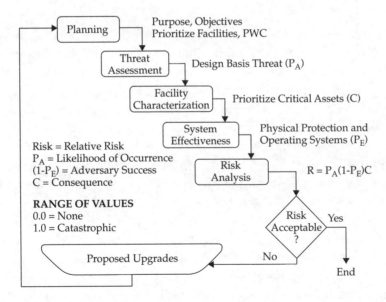

Figure 3.7 Security risk assessment methodology for water utilities example (courtesy of © Sandia Corporation [2011]).

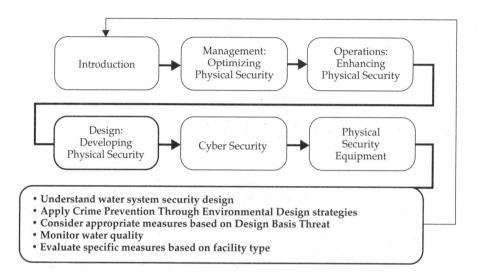

The figure contains boxes with text:

Introduction → Management: Optimizing Physical Security → Operations: Enhancing Physical Security

Design: Developing Physical Security → Cyber Security → Physical Security Equipment

- Understand water system security design
- Apply Crime Prevention Through Environmental Design strategies
- Consider appropriate measures based on Design Basis Threat
- Monitor water quality
- Evaluate specific measures based on facility type

FIGURE 3.8 Security risk assessment methodology for water utilities example (courtesy of American Water Works Association, http://www.awwa.org/awwa/science/wise/report/AWWA_Securities/Section4.htm).

Self-Assessment Tool provides a comprehensive, intuitive system for wastewater utilities seeking to analyze their vulnerability to both intentional threats and natural disasters. It differs from RAM-W mainly in requiring less training and support. Using the tool, however, requires good computer skills.

The assessment team works stepwise through a formal series of questions to identify security measures that can reduce the effects of man-made and natural disaster threats to the wastewater system. The software helps utilities determine critical wastewater system assets, assign possible threats, assess how security measures will reduce vulnerabilities, and identify the most cost-effective security measures. Figure 3.9 presents an example of this analysis.

Water and wastewater utilities can download a free copy of VSAT™ software by registering with the VSAT Web site at http://yosemite.epa.gov/ow/SReg.nsf/description/VSAT. This assessment method is recommended for most wastewater treatment plants, and those with supervisory control and data acquisition systems. Intermediate computer skills are required to use this software tool. Training on VSAT™ usage is recommended, although U.S. EPA does not currently offer it.

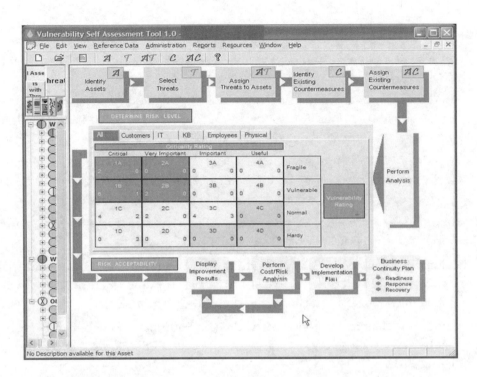

FIGURE 3.9   Vulnerability self-assessment tool example (courtesy of NACWA [2002]).

6.1.3 Text-Based Assessment Tools

The National Environmental Services Center (NESC) developed *Protecting Your Community's Assets: A Guide for Small Wastewater Systems*. The guide uses a simple evaluation checklist and does not require the use of a computer to complete. It is recommended for use with small-sized (serving less than 10,000 people) wastewater systems. The document can be downloaded free from the NESC Web site at http://www.nesc.wvu.edu/netcsc/netcsc_index.htm.

The National Rural Water Association developed the *Security Vulnerability Self-Assessment Guide for Wastewater Systems*. The guide can be downloaded free from the Wisconsin Rural Water Association Web site at http://www.wrwa.org. This vulnerability assessment method, which uses a simple evaluation checklist, does not require a computer to complete, and is recommended for use with small- to medium-sized wastewater treatment plants.

7.0   REFERENCES

Air Resources Board, ARB's Emissions Inventory Web Site. http://www.arb.ca.gov/ei/ei.htm (accessed Aug 2011).

American National Standards Institute (2005) *American National Standard for Occupational Health and Safety Management Systems*; ANSI Z100–2005; American National Standards Institute: Fairfax, Virginia.

American Water Works Association, Design Considerations for Developing Physical Security at New Facilities. http://www.awwa.org/awwa/science/wise/report/AWWA_Securities/Section4.htm (accessed Nov 2011).

Business and Legal Reports Web Site. http://safety.blr.com/find.aspx?terms=checklist (accessed Aug 2011).

California Occupational Safety and Health Administration, Division of Industrial Safety (2011)Titles 3 to 11; California Occupational Safety and Health Administration: Sacramento, California.

Center for Chemical Process Safety, Process Equipment Reliability Database. http://www.aiche.org/CCPS/ActiveProjects/PERD/index.aspx (accessed Aug 2011).

International Code Council Web Site. http://www.iccsafe.org (accessed Aug 2011).

International Organization for Standardization, ISO 14000/ISO 14001 Environmental Management Web Site. http://www.iso14000-iso14001-environmental-management.com/ (accessed Aug 2011).

Isograph Inc., Reliability Workbench 11 Web Site. http://www.isograph-software.com/ (accessed Nov 2011).

J. J. Keller Web Site. http://www.jjkeller.com/webapp/wcs/stores/servlet/categorySearch_10151_-1_10551_Workplace%20Safety I 16660_OSHA%20/%20 Workplace%20Safety_126_18523 (accessed Aug 2011).

Krieger, G. (2008) *Accident Prevention Manual, Security Management*; National Safety Council: Itasca, Illinois.

National Association of Clean Water Agencies (2002) *The Vulnerability Self-Assessment Software Tool* (*VSAT*™) [CD-ROM]; National Association of Clean Water Agencies: Washington, D.C.

National Environmental Services Center Web Site. http://www.nesc.wvu.edu/ netcsc/netcsc_index.htm (accessed Aug 2011).

National Fire Prevention Association, Codes and Standards Web Site. http:// www.nfpa.org/categoryList.asp?categoryID=124&URL=Codes%20&%20 Standards (accessed Aug 2011).

Occupational Safety and Health Administration, Compliance Assistance Web Site. http://www.osha.gov/dcsp/compliance_assistance/quickstarts/general_industry/gi_library.html#Publications (accessed Aug 2011).

Rochester Institute, Hierarchy of Control Web Site. http://www.rit.edu/~w-outrea/training/Module3/M3_HierarchyControls.pdf (accessed Feb 2012).

Sandia Corporation (2011) Security Risk Assessment Methodologies for Critical Infrastructures ™, Sandia National Laboratories Security Risk Assessment Methodologies. http://www.sandia.gov/ram/ (accessed Aug 2011).

U.S. Environmental Protection Agency (2011a) National Emission Standards for Hazardous Air Pollutants for Source Categories; U.S. EPA 40 CFR 63–2011; U.S. Environmental Protection Agency: Washington, D.C.; http://ecfr.gpoaccess.gov/cgi/t/text/text-idx?c=ecfr&sid=ec522f54af4b26a44b4c4f8d8469ed5b &rgn=div5&view=text&node=40:9.0.1.1.1&idno=40 (accessed Feb 2012).

U.S. Environmental Protection Agency (2011b) *Chemical Accident Prevention Provisions;* U.S. EPA 40 CFR 68–2011; U.S. Environmental Protection Agency: Washington, D.C.; http://ecfr.gpoaccess.gov/cgi/t/text/text-idx?c=ecfr&sid =ec522f54af4b26a44b4c4f8d8469ed5b&rgn=div5&view=text&node=40:15.0.1.1 .5&idno=40 (accessed Feb 2012).

U.S. Environmental Protection Agency (2011c) *Polychlorinated Biphenyls;* U.S. EPA 40 CFR 761–2011; U.S. Environmental Protection Agency: Washington, D.C.; http://ecfr.gpoaccess.gov/cgi/t/text/text-idx?c=ecfr&sid=ec522f54af4b26 a44b4c4f8d8469ed5b&rgn=div5&view=text&node=40:31.0.1.1.18&idno=40 (accessed Feb 2012).

U.S. Environmental Protection Agency, Databases and Tools Web Site. http:// www.epa.gov/osweroe1/tools.htm (accessed Aug 2011).

U.S. Environmental Protection Agency, VSAT Web Site. http://yosemite.epa. gov/ow/SReg.nsf/description/VSAT (accessed Aug 2011).

Water Environment Federation (1992) *Supervisor's Guide to Safety and Health Programs*; Special Publication; Water Environment Federation: Alexandria, Virginia.

Wisconsin Rural Water Association Web Site. http://www.wrwa.org (accessed Aug 2011).

8.0 SUGGESTED READINGS

Canadian Centre for Occupational Health and Safety, Hazard and Risk Web Site. http://www.ccohs.ca/oshanswers/hsprograms/hazard_risk.html (accessed Jan 2011).

Cascio, J. (1996) *The ISO 14000 Handbook*; CEEM Information Services: Fairfax, Virginia; p 163.

Channing, J.; Ridley, J. (1999) *Workplace Safety—Safety at Work Series*, Volume 4; Elsevier: New York.

Cox, S.; Tait, R. (1998) *Safety, Reliability, & Risk Management—An Integrated Approach*, 2nd ed.; Elsevier: New York.

Department of Defense, Standard Practice for Safety, Appendix H, MIL STD-882D. http://www.faa.gov/library/manuals/aviation/risk_management/ss_handbook/media/app_h_1200.pdf (accessed Jan 2011).

Federal Aviation Administration, System Safety Handbook. http://www.faa.gov/library/manuals/aviation/risk_management/ss_handbook/ (accessed Jan 2011).

Hagan, P.; Montgomery, J.; O'Reilly, J. (2008) Administration and Programs; In *Accident Prevention Manual*, 13th ed.; National Safety Council: Itasca, Illinois.

Hagan, P.; Montgomery, J.; O'Reilly, J. (2008) Engineering and Technology; In *Accident Prevention Manual*, 13th ed.; National Safety Council: Itasca, Illinois.

Kent, J. (2007) *Kent and Riegel's Handbook of Industrial Chemistry and Biotechnology*, Volume 1, 11th ed.; Springer-Verlag: Heidelberg, Germany.

Krieger, G. (2008) *Environmental Management*; National Safety Council: Itasca, Illinois.

Maine Department of Labor, Job Hazard Analysis, Safety Works! Web Site. http://www.safetyworksmaine.com/safe_workplace/safety_management/hazard_analysis.html (accessed Jan 2011).

Mobley, R. K. (1999) *Root Cause Failure Analysis;* Elsevier: New York.

National Environmental Services Center, Training Division. http://www.nesc.wvu.edu/training.cfm (accessed Aug 2011).

Occupational Safety and Health Administration, Hazard Analysis Methodologies Web Site. http://www.osha.gov/SLTC/etools/safetyhealth/mod4_tools_methodologies.html (accessed Jan 2011).

Occupational Safety and Health Administration (2011) *General Industry Standards;* OSHA 1910 standards; Occupational Safety and Health Administration: Washington, D.C.

Occupational Safety and Health Administration (2002) Job and Hazard Analysis Web Site. http://www.osha.gov/Publications/osha3071.pdf (accessed Feb 2012).

Occupational Safety and Health Administration, Safety and Health Management Systems E-Tool Web Site. http://www.osha.gov/SLTC/etools/safetyhealth/mod4_tools_methodologies.html (accessed Aug 2011).

Rosaler, R. (2002) *Standard Handbook of Plant Engineering;* McGraw-Hill: New York.

Smith, D. (2005) *Reliability, Maintainability, and Risk—Practical Methods for Engineers,* 7th ed.; Elsevier: New York.

States, S. (2010) Security and Emergency Planning for Water and Wastewater Utilities; American Water Works Association: Denver, Colorado.

U.S. Environmental Protection Agency, Response Protocol Toolbox Web Site: Planning for and Responding to Drinking Water Contamination Threats and Incidents. http://www.epa.gov/safewater/watersecurity/pubs/rptb_response_guidelines.pdf (accessed Jan 2011).

Wikipedia, Hazard Analysis Web Site. http://en.wikipedia.org/wiki/Hazard_analysis (accessed June 2011).

Chapter 4

Safety and Health in Wastewater Treatment Plant Operation

(continued)

1.0 COMMON WASTEWATER TREATMENT PLANT HAZARDS

Safely working around or near hazards of wastewater treatment facilities requires continuous observation, training, use of safety equipment, and safe practices to avoid injury and illness. This chapter presents an overview of common wastewater treatment hazards that operators, consultants, engineers, and other personnel may be exposed to while working in and around treatment plants. Table 4.1 provides an overview of typical hazards that wastewater employees should be aware of. Table 4.1

TABLE 4.1   Common wastewater treatment plant hazards.

Common waste-water plant exposures	Typical exposure sources/activities	Risks	Prevention guidelines	Other resources
Asbestos Asbestos-cement pipe (ACP) Thermal insulation systems	Renovation, demolition, or other activities that damage or disturb asbestos-containing products such as insulation, fireproofing, acoustical materials, floor tiles, and asbestos-cement (transite) pipe.	When disturbed, microscopic asbestos fibers can become airborne and can be inhaled into the lungs, where they can cause serious lung diseases.	Maintain asbestos-containing materials (ACMs) in good condition through a well-run building maintenance program; undisturbed asbestos materials do not pose a health risk. When removing ACP, conduct an initial exposure assessment to demonstrate that employees' exposures are below the OSHA 8-hour time-weighted average PEL of <0.1 fibers/cubic centimeter and follow OSHA abatement guidelines for removal. Contact an asbestos professional for consultation and removal if exposures will exceed the OSHA PEL.	See 29 CFR 1926.1101 for regulatory details.

Chemicals (liquid) Sodium hypochlorite, sodium bisulfite, sodium hydroxide, ferric chloride, polymers, anhydrous ammonia, hydrogen peroxide, and methanol	Unloading, connecting, and disconnecting activities; transferring bulk chemicals to secondary containers; and emergency response to accidental spills.	Acute respiratory hazards from inhalation of toxic offgases or vapors; potential acute or chronic injuries/illness to unprotected eyes and skin; slip hazards from wet, slippery surfaces; and potential thermo-dynamic reactions from mixing incompatible materials.	Employees must be trained on proper chemical handling procedures and wear the proper level of PPE (refer to the chemical's SDS for PPE recommendations); employees who will respond to a spill must be trained in emergency response procedures and be equipped with the proper level of PPE; clean up all spills immediately, no matter how small; and properly label bulk chemicals including tanks, associated pipes, pumps, and valves.	Refer to 4.2.6, 4.3.3, 4.4, 4.4.3.8, and Chapter 10 for additional information.
Chlorine (gas)	Loading/unloading, connect and disconnect activities, and emergency response to accidental releases.	Acute respiratory hazards from inhalation of chlorine gas. At 40 to 60 ppm, chlorine gas causes toxic pneumonitis and pulmonary edema; at 430 ppm, an	Employees must be trained on chlorine handling procedures and must wear the proper level of PPE when working with chlorine. During loading/unloading, either a full-face air-purifying	Refer to 4.2.6.1 and Chapter 10 for additional information.

(continued)

TABLE 4.1 Continued

Common waste-water plant exposures	Typical exposure sources/activities	Risks	Prevention guidelines	Other resources
		Local chemical or thermal (frostbite) burns to the skin from contact with liquid chlorine. Gaseous chlorine in contact with the skin can dissolve in body moisture to form hypochlorous and hydrochloric acids. Eye irritation from low concentration of chlorine gas to serious thermal and/or chemical burns from liquid chlorine.	exposure is lethal; and, in 30 minutes and at 1000 ppm, it is fatal within minutes. respirator or SCBA should be worn depending on the expected exposure concentrations. Emergency response to a release will require a higher level of protection. In addition to gloves (thermal protection) and a SCBA; the Chlorine Institute recommends the following: level B PPE when liquid chlorine is not involved and enhanced Level B PPE when liquid chlorine is involved.	

| Compressed gases | Storing and using compressed gas and air cylinders. | Projectile hazards from sudden release of pressures; fire and explosions from flammable or reactive gases; oxygen-deficient atmospheres from leaks of inert gases; and poisonous atmospheres from leaks of toxic gases. | Properly secure cylinders in a well-ventilated area away from heat, flames, and the sun; when not in use, store upright and leave cap on and valve closed; when stored inside, store compressed gases at least 6.1 m (20 ft) from highly combustible materials; separate oxygen cylinders from fuel gas cylinders at a minimum of 6.1 m (20 ft) or by a non-combustible barrier at least 1.5 m (5 ft) high; and SCBA breathing air cylinders must be tested and maintained as prescribed in the Shipping Container Specification Regulations of the U.S. Department of Transportation (49 CFR part 173 and part 178). | See 29 CFR, 1910 Subpart H for compressed gas regulatory details. See 29 CFR 1910.134 for breathing air regulatory details. |

(*continued*)

TABLE 4.1 Continued

Common wastewater plant exposures	Typical exposure sources/activities	Risks	Prevention guidelines	Other resources
Confined spaces	Entering (i.e., breaking the plane) into a confined space.	Toxic atmospheric conditions from hydrogen sulfide, carbon monoxide, and other contaminants; oxygen-deficient conditions; and flammable conditions.	No one may enter a confined space unless properly trained as an entrant; follow confined space entry procedures including ventilation, gas monitoring, lockout/blockout procedures, and using the proper level of PPE and rescue equipment.	Refer to Chapter 5.8 and Chapter 6.5 for additional information. See 29 CFR 1910.146 for regulatory details.
Cranes and hoists	Using a mobile crane or a hoist to lift and/or move materials.	Cranes: Fatalities and serious injuries from a crane tip-over; Electrocution from accidental contact with overhead lines; and Injuries and/or damages from accidental contact with people, equipment, or buildings	Only employees who are authorized by the employer and trained in safe operations of cranes or hoisting equipment may operate such equipment. In certain states, mobile crane operators must have a valid certificate of competency (certificate) by an accredited certifying entity to operate mobile cranes meeting certain load capacity and other criteria.	See 29 CFR 1926.552 and 1910.179 for regulatory details.

		Hoists: Pinch/nip points and Injuries and/or damages from dropping the load.		
Elevated work	Working from unprotected elevated locations; elevating work platforms and aerial lifts, ladders, and scaffolds; and working near unprotected wall or floor openings.	Fatalities, broken bones, spinal cord injuries, concussions and other serious injuries as a result of falling off of an elevated work area or into a pit or other opening. According to the Bureau of Labor Statistics, in 2007, 15% of all fatalities were from falls.	Ensure all elevated work areas have standard guardrails if they expose employees to a fall of 1.2 m (4 ft) or more; only use ladders that are properly rated for the load and type of work being performed; inspect ladders before use for damages or wear; ensure scaffolding has been erected and dismantled by a qualified person; do no overload scaffolds and maintain them in a safe condition; employees who operate or drive an elevating work platform or aerial lift must be trained; use a personal fall protection system if standard guardrails are not provided; keep all floor and wall openings covered	Refer to Chapter 5.1 for additional information See 29 CFR 1910 Subpart D; 29 CFR 1910 Subpart F; 29 CFR 1926 Subparts L–N for regulatory details.

(continued)

TABLE 4.1 Continued

Common waste-water plant exposures	Typical exposure sources/activities	Risks	Prevention guidelines	Other resources
			or protected by a standard guardrail or other effective barrier; never leave an open manhole unattended or other pit unattended; and ensure skylight openings are guarded by a standard skylight screen or have a fixed standard railing on all exposed sides.	
Excavation and trenching	Cutting, trenching, or making depressions into the surface and removing earthen materials in order to lay or repair pipes, lines, cables, or other underground installations.	Suffocation from cave-ins; toxic or oxygen-deficient atmospheric conditions; explosions and fires from cutting live fuel lines; and electrocutions from cutting live electrical lines.	Daily inspections of excavations, the adjacent areas, and protective systems by a competent person; installing protective systems to protect employee from falling materials and cave-ins; marking the location of all known underground utility installations; providing safe access and egress; providing protection from vehicular traffic, falling loads and	Refer to Chapter 6.4 for additional information. See 29 CFR 1926 Subpart P for regulatory details.

		water accumulation; and testing the atmosphere if employees enter an excavation greater than 1.2 m (4 ft) if oxygen deficiency or hazardous atmospheres exist (or could reasonably be expected to exist).	
Fires and explosions	Fueling vehicles and equipment, storing and using flammable materials, and working on, or near, flammable fuel sources such as methane or natural gas supplies.	Turn off engine before refueling any internal combustion engine with a flammable liquid; keep open lights, flames, or sparking/arcing equipment away from flammable areas, including fuel tanks; ensure flammable containers are plainly marked as a flammable substance; keep flammable liquids in covered containers when not in use; store flammable substances in an approved flammable storage cabinet; provide portable fire extinguishment and control equipment in quantities	See 29 CFR 1910.1.6 for regulatory details.
	Fires and explosions		

(continued)

TABLE 4.1   Continued

Common waste-water plant exposures	Typical exposure sources/activities	Risks	Prevention guidelines	Other resources
			and types needed for the types of hazards presented; and use grounding and bonding techniques for all Class I liquids when dispensing into containers unless the nozzle and container are electrically interconnected.	
Flying particles	Performing activities such as grinding, chipping, landscaping and using a jackhammer or other equipment that cause flying particles to be emitted.	Eye and skin injuries	When feasible, use shields, screen, guards or enclosures and wear eye, face, and body protection.	Refer to Chapter 10 for additional information. See 29 CFR 1910.133.
Hazardous energy	Cleaning, repairing, servicing, setting-up, or adjusting prime movers or electrical systems.	Electrocutions, amputations, or other serious injuries from unexpected energization or startup of machines or	Only trained employees may work on equipment, machines, or electrical systems under lockout/tagout conditions and follow lockout/blockout/tagout procedures when cleaning, repairing,	Refer to Chapter 5.2 for additional information. See 29 CFR 1910.147 for regulatory details.

		equipment or from the release of stored or secondary energy (e.g., capacitors, springs, batteries, and uninterrupted power supplies).	servicing, setting up, or adjusting prime movers or electrical systems.	
Heat and cold	Working outdoors in extreme weather conditions for prolonged periods of time.	Heat illnesses including heat stroke, heat exhaustion, heat cramps, fainting, and heat rash and hypothermia and frostbite.	Provide adequate shade and water for employees who need to work in extreme hot weather conditions and train them on heat illness prevention and provide short exposures, warm clothing, and hot beverages to employees who need to work in extreme cold weather conditions and train them on cold weather illness/injury prevention.	For additional information, visit http://www.osha.gov/index.html for heat stress publications.
Hot surfaces	Working near pipes or other exposed surfaces that are within 2.1 m (7 ft) and have an external surface temperature of 60 °C (140 °F) or higher.	Burns	Guard against contact or cover with thermal insulating material.	California Code of Regulations; Title 8, §3308

(continued)

Table 4.1   Continued

Common wastewater plant exposures	Typical exposure sources/activities	Risks	Prevention guidelines	Other resources
Hot work	Welding, cutting, brazing, or performing any work activity that produces heat, flames, or sparks.	Fires and explosions.	Perform welding in an approved hot work area if possible; evaluate the surrounding work area for flammable or combustible products and implement safeguards to protect against accidental fires or explosions; do not perform hot work activities in oxygen-enriched conditions; test any area for oxygen if there is any opportunity for enriched oxygen atmospheric conditions (e.g., pure oxygen treatment systems); and complete a hot work permit when performing hot work inside a confined space.	Refer to Chapter 5.7 for additional information. See CFR 29 1910.146 for regulatory details when performing hot work in confined spaces.
Industrial trucks (forklifts)	Driving or operating an industrial truck (forklift)	Fatalities or serious injuries from tipping the forklift over; damages to equipment and	Employees may not drive or operate a forklift unless they have been trained and have shown competency in their ability	Refer to Chapter 7 for additional information See 29 CFR 1910.178 for regulatory details

		structures; and carbon monoxide poisoning.	to drive or operate the forklift; when operating internal combustion engine forklifts inside enclosed or semi-enclosed buildings or structures, ensure that natural or mechanical ventilation systems keeps toxic fumes and gases below the OSHA permissible limits; if unsure, wear a personal gas monitor while operating a forklift inside an enclosed work area.	Refer to Chapter 10 for additional information on respiratory protection. See 29 CFR 1926.62 and 29 CFR 1910.1025 for regulatory details.
Lead	Demolition or renovation activities that involve lead-based paints.	Lead poisoning	If lead is present, perform an exposure assessment to determine if any employee may be exposed to lead at concentrations greater than 50 ug/m^3 of air averaged over an 8-hour period. Wear the appropriate respiratory protection and other PPE to prevent exposure to lead.	

(continued)

TABLE 4.1   Continued

Common waste-water plant exposures	Typical exposure sources/activities	Risks	Prevention guidelines	Other resources
Line breaking	Opening closed-pressurized or gravity-fed pipes or systems containing hot, poisonous, corrosive, flammable, or other hazardous substances.	Burns and other injuries from exposures to chemicals, stream, and toxic or other hazardous products.	Identify what the pipe or systems contain before breaking any lines or pressurized systems; purge with water or other compatible substances to reduce the concentrations inside the pipe or system; and relieve the internal pressure to prevent the sudden release of pressure or spraying liquid.	See 29 CFR 1910.119, 29 CFR 1910.146 for regulatory details. California Code of Regulations; Title 8, §3329
Machine guarding	Operating or working near prime movers, machines, and machine parts that grind, shear, punch, squeeze, cut, roll, mix, rotate, or similar actions.	Amputations or other serious injuries to the hands, fingers, arms, or other body parts.	Provide machine guarding if employees come within the danger zone.	Refer to Chapter 5.3 for additional information. See 29 CFR 1910 Subpart 0.
Muscular skeletal disorders (ergonomics)	Manual material handling (MMH) work such as lifting, moving, pulling, and pushing and	Strains and sprains to the back, shoulders, and upper limbs and vibration	Manual material handling Improve the fit between the demands of the work tasks and the capabilities of the workforce	For additional information on manual material handling, go to http://www.cdc.gov/az/DHHS (NIOSH) Publication No. 2007–131 (April 2007) and

using hand-held and stationary vibrating tools.

syndrome, also know as *white finger* and as *Raynaud's phenomenon of occupational origin.*

through engineering improvements (i.e., modifying or redesigning equipment, processes, or workstations),administrative improvements (i.e., alternating heavy tasks with light tasks and rotating job activities), and modifying work practices so that workers perform work within their power zone (i.e., above the knees, below the shoulders, and close to the body).

Use alternatives to handling materials manually such as special tools and powered and nonpowered equipment

Vibration

Reduce the acceleration speed of the tool or equipment, keep tools and equipment well maintained, use energy-dampening tools to reduce transmission from the tool to the hand, and modify the process to reduce or eliminate the need for vibrating tools.

DHHS (NIOSH) Publication No. 89–106.

(continued)

TABLE 4.1   Continued

Common waste-water plant exposures	Typical exposure sources/activities	Risks	Prevention guidelines	Other resources
Noise exposures	Working in high-noise areas such as backup generator rooms, blower rooms, and compressor rooms and performing high-noise activities such as using landscaping tools and jackhammers and operating heavy equipment, vactor trucks, or portable pumps.	Loss of hearing	Perform a complete noise survey on all work areas and job tasks that are suspect of noises that are higher than OSHA allowable limits, post areas that require hearing protection to be worn, wear hearing protection when required, and participate in a hearing conservation. program if exposed to the OSHA action level of an 8-hour time-weighted average of 85 dB on the A scale (slow response) or, equivalently, a dose of 50%.	See 29 CFR 1910.95 for regulatory details
Powder-actuated tools	Driving fasteners into concrete or steel walls using powder-actuated tools (tools that use powder cartridges).	Fatality or other serious eye and body injuries from nails, fasteners, or studs.	Only trained and qualified persons may operate powder-actuated tools. Keep the tool in a locked container when not in use. Post warning signs when in	Refer to Chapter 5.5 for additional information. See CFR 1926.302 for regulatory details.

Power and hand tools	Operating electric, hydraulic, pneumatic, fuel-powered tools.	Electrical shock, effect from attachments accidentally being expelled; injuries from ricochets; injuries from high-pressure, high-velocity releases; and flammable or oxygen deficient conditions when using fuel-powered tools in enclosed work areas	use. Only use fasteners and power loads recommended by the tool manufacturer. Only electric power-operated tools that are double-insulated or grounded should be used. Never remove or deactivate safety clips, retainers, and other safety devices on pneumatic impact (percussion) tools. Shut off fuel-powered tools when refueling or servicing. Wear a personal gas monitor when using fuel-powered tools in enclosed, or semi-enclosed, work areas. Do not exceed the manufacturer's safe operating pressures for hoses, valves, pipes, filters, and other fittings when using hydraulic tools.	Refer to Chapter 5.5 for additional information. See CFR 1926.302 for regulatory details.
Radiological hazards	Natural and manmade radionuclides that are discharged into sanitary sewers; radiological	Studies have shown that natural and manmade radionuclides in wastewater sludge and ash	Being prepared for an RDE into the sewer system will require extensive studies and detailed plans. Among other things, procedures for detecting radioactive	Strom, 2005

(continued)

TABLE 4.1 Continued

Common waste-water plant exposures	Typical exposure sources/activities	Risks	Prevention guidelines	Other resources
	dispersion event (RDE) leading to significant quantities of radioactive material into the combined sanitary and storm sewer system. An RDE could come from a radiological dispersion device such as a "dirty bomb" contaminating the community at large or from the deliberate and malicious introduction or dispersion of radioactive material into the waterways and water supply systems.	do not indicate a widespread problem and that exposure doses are generally well below levels that would require radiation protection actions. Direct irradiation of wastewater workers is possible from a radiation dispersal event. Of particular concern is the malicious dispersal of radiation of materials into the wastewater system through a radiological dispersion device.	exposures, whether to treat or bypass the waste, how to segregate, store, and dispose of radioactive wastes, plus the duty (if any) of wastewater workers to protect the public by treating contaminated wastes will have to be considered.	

| Removing covers | Opening/removing a variety of covers such as manhole covers, tank covers, blind flanges, hatches, or grates. | Soft tissue injuries to back, shoulders, and arms.
• Fall hazards from open pits
• Toxic atmospheric conditions and/or flammable conditions from concentrated gases under the covers
• Pinch points
• Hazardous energy sources when opening pressurized systems
• Slip/trip hazards from loose or uneven covers and gratings | Use lifting devices designed for mechanical advantage to prevent soft tissue injuries when removing heavy covers. When covers are removed, provide an attendant or a physical barrier (e.g., portable guardrail) to prevent falls into floor openings or pits. Perform air sampling before opening a cover if there is a potential for buildup of flammable or toxic gases underneath the lid or inside the space. De-energize the system using standard lockout/blockout procedures when opening a cover to a pressurized system. Square covers (i.e., grates) can fall into the opening. Take precautions to avoid dropping them by using a lifting device or by using another worker, especially if the cover is heavy, large, or awkward to handle alone. | Refer to Chapter 4.2 and 4/3 for additional information See 29 CFR 1910.22 and 29 CFR 1910.23 for regulatory details. |

(continued)

TABLE 4.1   Continued

Common waste-water plant exposures	Typical exposure sources/activities	Risks	Prevention guidelines	Other resources
Respiratory hazards	Confined space entry; working with chemicals; biosolids dust, welding fumes, dry polymers, and other particulates; and emergency response to chemical releases.	Toxic and/or oxygen-deficient atmospheric conditions, acute or chronic respiratory hazards from inhalation of toxic chemical vapors or offgases, respiratory irritation from dry particulates, and high concentration of toxic gases when responding to a chemical release.	Test the air before entering any confined space. If the atmosphere is IDLH, a full-face pressure-demand SCBA with a minimum service life of 30 minutes or a combination full-face, pressure-demand, supplied-air respirator with an auxiliary self-contained air supply must be worn. When working with chemicals, review the label and/or SDS to determine if a respirator is required and/or recommended. Wear a particulate-type respirator if protection is needed when working with dusts or other dry, nonhazardous products. Wear a SCBA when responding to emergency chemical releases, especially if the concentration is unknown or if the chemical is offgassing.	Refer to Chapter 10 for additional information. See 29 CFR 1910.134 and CFR 1910.146 for regulatory details.

| Sampling and working over/near water | Sampling from basins, channels, and other treatment processes; sampling from streams, canals, and other moving bodies of water; sampling from lakes, ponds, lagoons, and other still waters; sampling from remote effluent structures; and sampling from watercraft. | Drowning exposures from falling into basins, standing in moving waters, or when sampling from watercraft; soft tissue injuries when carrying heavy sampling equipment; rashes and allergic reactions to poisonous vegetation, snakes, bees, and spiders when sampling from highly vegetated locations; and slip/trip hazards when carrying sampling equipment over rough terrain or when traversing up and down steeply sloped earthen or concrete embankments. | Do not climb on, climb over, or lean over guardrails or other protective barriers. If it is necessary to extend beyond a protective fall protection barrier, use personal fall arrest or positioning equipment. Wear a U.S. Coast Guard-approved personal floatation device (PFD) when working on or in water, especially if working over deep water, near/in fast-moving water, or if you cannot swim. Wear a U.S. Coast Guard-approved PFD if there is a chance you may be "pulled in" while performing grab sampling. Employees who will use watercraft to collect samples must be trained on boating safety and have a valid U.S. Coast Guard license for the class of watercraft and type of water being navigated. Use good lifting techniques when lifting automatic | Refer to Sections 2.2 through 2.4 for additional information See 20 CFR 1926.106 for regulatory details |

(continued)

TABLE 4.1   Continued

Common waste-water plant exposures	Typical exposure sources/activities	Risks	Prevention guidelines	Other resources
			samplers. If the sampler is full or too heavy, use a jib crane, mechanical hoist, or have another person help lift it. Practice good landscaping around remote sampling sites that are subject to overgrowth of vegetation to discourage poisonous plants and animals. Use a sturdy walking stick or have a secure anchor point when traversing up and down steep embankments.	
Slip/trip hazards	Wet surfaces; chemical spills; poor housekeeping; loose grates; covers; uneven surfaces; traversing down ramps; stairwells; and sloped surfaces,	Contusions, broken bones, and miscellaneous injuries.	Immediately clean up spills to floors or walkways or use a cone or other warning device to alert people to the hazards. Use nonskid paint, mats, or other materials in areas subject to slippery conditions. Clean up all chemical spills immediately. Secure all grates or covers	Refer to Sections 2.2 through 2.5 for additional information

			or replace them if not flush with the pavement or walkway to prevent trip hazards. Wear sturdy work boots with good tread. Use handrails or other holds when traversing down slopes or stairways.	
Traffic hazards	Setting up equipment, entering confined spaces, and cleaning or inspecting sewers or other activities performed on public roads.	Fatalities and serious injuries from vehicular incidents.	Set up work zones according to U.S. Department of Transportation's *Manual on Uniform Traffic Control Devices (MUTCD) for Streets and Highways.*	See CFR 23, Part 655, Subpart F for regulatory details.

is not all-inclusive and is intended only to provide a general understanding of identified hazards with some guidelines on prevention. For detailed instructions on safe practices, the reader is referred to the applicable regulatory standard as cited.

2.0 WASTEWATER TREATMENT PLANT HAZARDS: LIQUID PROCESSES

2.1 Wet and Dry Wells

Wet wells are a portion of the wastewater pumping station that receive and temporarily store wastewater for pumping purposes. Wet wells may incorporate screening as part of the process. Wet well areas are often the source of atmospheric hazards from combustible and toxic gases; they are also a potential source of asphyxiation (oxygen deficiency) as a result of wastewater decomposition and industrial discharges into the sewer. For protection against toxic and flammable atmospheric conditions, continuous ventilation must be used and air monitoring must be performed before entering these work areas. Additionally, proper confined space entry procedures must be strictly adhered to. Walkways in wet wells are subject to wet and slippery conditions and, as such, care must be taken to minimize slip hazards.

Dry wells are often used to house the pump station's electrical and mechanical equipment. Dry wells are designed to completely and permanently exclude wastewater or wastewater-derived atmospheres. However, dry wells can contain toxic gases, such as hydrogen sulfide, because of accidental leakage from shaft seals, leaking pumps, loose couplings, and spills. Therefore, if ventilation is not provided in a dry well, air monitoring should be performed before entering these work areas. Dry wells do not require any other special safety precautions unless they contain open electrical panels (live electrical), have restricted ingress and egress issues, present fall hazards, or have other unique hazards.

2.2 Headworks

The headworks of a wastewater treatment plant represent the initial stage of a complex process. The purpose of the headworks operation is to remove inorganic materials such as sticks, stones, grit, and sand from the influent wastewater stream to protect or reduce wear on downstream process equipment.

Treatment plant staff must understand the hazards of working in or near the headworks area, regardless of whether it is enclosed, semi-enclosed, or exposed to the atmosphere. It is important to be aware of the composition of the waste stream being treated, the ratio of domestic and commercial wastewater, and the type of industrial users within the plant's service area because these questions will provide an idea of the potential atmospheric hazards that may be encountered. Industrial and commercial wastewaters generally contain raw materials and intermediate byproducts and end products from various industries; as such, these wastewaters may contain higher concentrations of metals or organics than domestic wastewater. Although industrial discharges to the sewer system are regulated, some byproducts will enter the wastewater through regulated means, from accidental discharges, or from intentional illegal industrial discharges. High strength, organic food processing wastes can cause septic conditions in sewer systems, which, in turn, can create high levels of hydrogen sulfide, methane gas, and other wastewater byproducts. Manufacturing plants, dry cleaners, and other industries can introduce flammable substances and toxic chemicals into wastewater. Even chemicals used to remove roots or clean the collection system can introduce unhealthy chemicals to the wastewater stream. However, no matter how chemicals get into the sewer system, they all eventually end up at the wastewater plant and can affect both process control and the safety and health of employees.

For this reason, atmospheric monitoring for flammable and toxic atmospheric conditions should be standard practice regardless of the building configuration, although enclosed headworks require a higher level of atmospheric monitoring. Monitoring instrumentation (portable or installed air monitors) to test for flammable conditions (LEL), carbon monoxide, hydrogen sulfide, and oxygen should be used routinely to protect employees from hazardous atmospheric conditions.

Depending on their configuration, headworks often meet the definition of a permit-requiring confined space. If they are a confined space, special entry procedures such as ventilation, air monitoring, and completing a confined space entry permit will be required before entering these work areas. Like wet wells, walkways in these areas are often subject to wet, slippery conditions and care must be taken to avoid slip hazards.

2.2.1 Screens, Comminutors, and Other Screening Devices

Screens fall under two classifications: mechanical or manual screening devices. Mechanically or manually cleaned bar screens, perforated filter screens, comminutors, and other screening mechanisms are typically constructed within the headworks of the treatment plant. These devices are also used in other areas of the treatment plant such as screening equipment for process water (i.e., effluent) before reuse for meters or as more advanced equipment using plant water as part of its operation.

Mechanically cleaned screens have moving electromechanical devices such as motors, gears, augers, conveyance systems, and rakes with teeth. Comminutors incorporate a rotating blade that cuts and shreds the solid material. Under these operations, debris may wedge tightly between equipment bodies or surfaces, which may require manual cleaning to function properly. This exposes employees to amputation hazards and other injuries such as sprains, strains, lacerations, and infections. Extreme care must be taken to de-energize the equipment before cleaning, servicing, adjusting, or repairing. Equipment-specific lockout/tagout procedures must be strictly adhered to whenever preventive or corrective maintenance is being performed.

Manually cleaned screens often require rakes and other tools to remove screening materials from the screens. This places employees at risk of muscular skeletal injuries because of pulling, pushing, twisting, and working in awkward positions. The materials removed from headworks screens often contain razor blades, hypodermic needles, and other sharp objects. To avoid cuts, lacerations, and infections, rakes or other tools should be used while wearing heavy-duty leather gloves over disposable latex gloves.

2.2.2   Grit Separation Chambers

Aerated grit chambers generally receive untreated wastewater distributed into open channels or enclosed tanks. They are typically designed to reduce the velocity of wastewater to allow inorganic and organic solids to settle more easily. These basins are typically found within the headworks of the treatment plant immediately after the initial screening removal process.

Aerated grit chambers are deep (3 to 3.5 m [10 to 12 ft]) and generally have sloped floors and sediment removal sumps. Entry into these tanks is typically from an extension ladder, which presents the risk of fall hazards. Whenever an extension ladder is used to descend into an empty process tank, proper ladder safety needs to be conducted. This includes using the proper ladder ratio when setting up the ladder (4:1), ensuring that the feet are nonskid and that the ladder is in good condition, and making sure it is tied off and extends at least 0.9 m (3 ft) above the entry point so that three-point contact can be maintained at all times.

Atmospheric and drowning hazards are other examples of concerns for staff entering these tanks to perform routine or corrective maintenance. Underground tanks that have limited ingress (e.g., using a ladder to enter the tank) meet the definition of a confined space and, as such, confined space entry procedures must be strictly adhered to which include, among other things, gas monitoring and completing a confined space entry permit.

2.3 Biological Treatment Processes

Biological treatment processes are designed to substantially degrade the biological content of wastewater, which is derived from human waste, food waste, soaps, and detergents. Most municipal plants treat suspended solids using aerobic biological treatment processes such as trickling filters, aeration basins, pure oxygen systems, fixed film reactors, and oxidation ditches.

2.3.1 Trickling Filters

Trickling filters are similar to the natural purification process that occurs when pollutants enter a river or stream. As contaminated waters move over a rock bed or a rocky river bottom, naturally occurring bacteria in the rock bed remove soluble organic pollutants and purify the waters. Similarly, primary effluent through a trickling filter flows downward through a fixed bed of rocks, gravel, or plastic media. This causes a biofilm of predominately aerobic microorganisms to grow and cover the media. Oxygen is supplied by constant turbulent splashing action and from forced ventilation, which circulates air throughout the filter media using a series of fans and an air-distribution system.

The biofilm formed within these media beds is extremely slippery and caution should be taken when servicing the distribution system within the media beds. Performing maintenance on moving machinery requires proper isolation and de-energization (lockout/tagout) procedures whenever cleaning, servicing, adjusting, or making repairs to the trickling filters and associated equipment are being performed.

Odor-masking chemicals are sometimes used with trickling filters. Depending on the substance used, this may require workers to wear personal protective equipment (PPE); workers should refer to the substance's safety data sheet (SDS) for any recommended PPE.

2.3.2 Rotating Biological Contactors

Rotating biological contactors (RBCs) are similar to trickling filters because RBCs use a fixed-film media for the wastewater to come in contact with a biological medium to remove contaminants. However, in contrast to being stationary, the RBC media rotates into the wastewater. Rotating biological contact units are typically installed in a concrete tank so that the surface of the wastewater passing through the tank almost reaches the shaft. That means that about 40% of the total surface of the media disks are always submerged. The shaft continually rotates and a layer of biological growth is established on the wetted surface of the media disk. Aeration is provided by the rotating action, which exposes the biological growth on the disks to the air as the disks rotate out of the wastewater into the air. Failed filter media problems and constant troubleshooting are common occurrences with RBCs. This results in frequent inspections and repairs to the various moving mechanical parts such as the chain drives, belts, sprockets, and rotating shafts.

The constant troubleshooting and repairs required for RBCs mean that energy control procedures (lockout/tagout) must be routinely and consistently observed. Employees must always shut down the drive assembly, allow the shaft to come to a complete stop, isolate the unit, and lock out all primary and secondary energy sources. It is important to remember that gravity can be an energy source. Even when the primary energy source has been de-energized, the weight of the RBC biomass can cause back rotation when disconnecting the drive assembly from the shaft. This will require block-out methods to be used to keep the shaft from rotating. Additionally, the slow-moving parts of the RBC combined with the frequency with which these inspections and repairs are made can desensitize employees to the risks and cause employees to take unsafe shortcuts. An employee should never try to physically stop the rotation of the shaft with his or her body or any object and should never crawl under the shaft unless proper confined space and auxiliary support are provided.

Often, surfaces near the basin may have biological growth, which will result in slippery conditions. Therefore, care must be used when walking or working near these units.

2.3.3   Aeration Facilities and Diffused Air Systems

Unlike a fixed-media secondary treatment process, the activated sludge process is an aerobic, suspended-growth biological treatment method and is perhaps the most widely used process. Wastewater enters an aerated tank where previously developed biological floc particles are brought into contact with the organic matter of the wastewater (WEF, 2007). Diffused air or pure oxygen is used to mix the incoming wastewater with the biological floc (returned activated sludge) and provides the necessary oxygen for biological growth, which feeds upon the suspended and dissolved solids that remain after primary treatment. Although aeration tank sizes vary to provide the required aeration detention times, most basins are 3 to 3.5 m (10 to 12 ft) deep and are entered using a portable extension ladder. This classifies them as a confined space and, as such, proper confined space entry procedures must be followed when entering empty tanks to perform routine or corrective maintenance.

In addition to confined space entry concerns, employees are subject to fall hazards when entering empty basins to perform preventive or corrective maintenance activities. If using extension ladders to access these work areas, the ladders should be inspected to ensure they are in good condition. Ladders must also be properly set up and tied off to avoid slippage and subsequent falls.

Inservice basins are also extremely dangerous. A fall into a highly aerated basin presents a high risk of drowning because it would be difficult, if not impossible, to stay afloat in waters saturated with high concentrations of air. For this reason, an employee should never extend beyond the protection of guardrails unless another form of fall protection such as a fall-arrest, fall-restricting, or fall-positioning system is used. The Occupational Safety and Health Administration (OSHA) requires employees working over or near water where there is a risk of drowning be provided with a U.S. Coast Guard-approved life jacket or buoyant work vest and that ring buoys with at least 27.4 m (90 ft) of line be provided and readily available for emergency operations (20 CFR 1926.106). Because of potential drowning hazards, life rings (and life hooks) should be strategically located around all process tanks.

Enclosed blower rooms associated with aeration basins are a potential noise exposure that can, over time, affect hearing loss. A noise survey should be conducted to determine the decibel levels in all high-noise work areas such as enclosed blower control rooms. Hearing protection devices such as inserts, plugs, and hearing muffs should be strategically placed in these areas along with hearing signs to encourage and remind employees to wear hearing protection.

Care must also be taken to de-energize all associated equipment such as motor controls, blowers, gates, and valves before cleaning, servicing, adjusting, or making repairs to aeration basin equipment. Equipment-specific lockout/tagout procedures must be strictly adhered to whenever preventive or corrective maintenance is performed.

2.3.4   Pure Oxygen Systems

Pure oxygen wastewater treatment plants use pure oxygen purchased in liquid form or generated on-site to provide oxygen and mixing of the mixed liquor in the aeration basins. These types of facilities require all persons who work with the pure oxygen system, or who work in the general area of the system, to use extreme caution. It is paramount that the liquid and/or equipment supplier provide the necessary safety information and training for operation and maintenance staff.

Existing knowledge of common combustibles and non-combustibles does not apply to a lower than normal (19.0%) or higher than normal (20.9%) oxygen concentration in the atmosphere. Oxygen levels below 19.0% may yield false combustible gas readings, whereas, at high oxygen levels, combustion rates are accelerated to the point where dust and dirt burns. Normally flammable substances can explode with only a slight ignition source or upon impact. Therefore, an employee should use lubricants and cleaning agents on conveying valves, actuators, and pipelines in strict accordance with the oxygen supplier's or equipment manufacturer's recommendations to avoid potential fire hazards.

Immaculate housekeeping must be maintained in and around areas subject to high oxygen concentrations because all materials could be combustible. Absolutely no smoking is allowed near oxygen-enriched areas. Breathing pure oxygen can impair mental judgment and can burn the lungs. Heavier than air, oxygen can settle in pits and subsurface depressions. These areas must be purged to be safe.

Enclosed areas should be ventilated around oxygen storage and generation sites to prevent accumulation of high-purity oxygen. All unventilated areas should be purged before entry and the atmosphere tested until acceptable conditions are obtained. This may take six to 10 or more air changes per hour. Oxygen-related equipment should be repaired in accordance with manufacturer's guidelines, using only approved parts and replacement equipment. Liquid oxygen has an extremely low temperature of -183 °C (-297 °F), and can cause severe freeze-burn injuries upon contact. It is important to wear proper eye protection and full body protection whenever there is a possibility of being exposed to liquid oxygen. The supplier's recommendation for safe handling should be followed.

Oxygen can be trapped in fabric weave, making clothing an extreme fire hazard. If an employee is working on or near pure oxygen systems, it is important that he or she be aware that their clothing may be impregnated with pure oxygen. All ignition sources such as welding, grinding, cutting, or other hot work activities should be avoided. If clothing does become saturated with oxygen, the person affected should change his or her clothes immediately because a fire hazard will continue to exist until the oxygen has dissipated. Because this may take 30 minutes or longer, the person affected will continue to be at risk of ignition sources even if they are no longer working on or near the pure oxygen system. Clothing saturated with oxygen should be placed under a running shower to remove the oxygen.

2.3.5 Oxidation Ditches

An oxidation ditch is an extended aeration mode of an activation sludge process. It is typically an elongated loop with continuous flow through two channels separated by a wall. Partially immersed, a mechanical rotating brush is used to induce oxygen by agitating the mixed liquor and provides turbulence in the flow to prevent activated sludge from settling. Typical flow is maintained at about 0.3 m/s [1 ft/s]. Most oxidation ditches are designed to remove carbonaceous biochemical oxygen demand for denitrification. Safety issues associated with oxidation ditches include the possibility of drowning hazards from falling into the ditch. Therefore, wearing a U.S. Coast Guard-approved personal floatation device or using some type of fall-restraining system is recommended when working over or near an oxidation ditch.

2.4   Clarification Basins

Clarification basins are holding tanks that offer additional detention time to settle out suspended solids and organic materials. Materials that settle to the bottom of the clarifier are then removed by mechanical scrapers and are sent to further processing, whereas floaters like grease and oil are skimmed off the top. Clarification basins are used in both primary and secondary treatment processes.

Although clarification basins are typically open to the atmosphere, the basins are still considered confined spaces. Therefore, confined space assessments and entry precautions must be taken. Similar to other treatment basins, access into empty clarifiers for maintenance purposes typically requires an extension ladder. Care must be taken to use good ladder safety to avoid fall hazards. Care must also be taken to de-energize associated equipment such as motor controls, gates, and valves prior to cleaning, servicing, adjusting, or making repairs. Prior to working in empty clarifiers, it is important to ensure all associated gates and valves are closed and eliminate the likelihood of backflows into the basin.

If it is necessary to extend beyond protection of standard guardrails while the basin is in service to clean weirs, make adjustments to the sweep arms, or perform other operational and maintenance activities, care must be taken to avoid drowning hazards. As stated previously, OSHA requires that employees working over or near water where there is a risk of drowning be provided with a U.S. Coast Guard-approved life jacket or buoyant work vest and that ring buoys with at least 27.4 m (90 ft) of line be provided and readily available for emergency operations (20 CFR 1926.106).

When entering empty clarifiers by using an extension ladder, the risk of falls from the extension ladder must be considered and proper ladder use and safety must be used. This includes using the proper ladder ratio when setting up the ladder (4:1), ensuring that the feet are nonskid and that the ladder is in good condition, and making sure that the ladder is tied off and extends at least 0.9 m (3 ft) above the entry point so that three-point contact can be maintained at all times.

2.4.1   Primary Clarification

In primary sedimentation, influent flows into large tanks, commonly called *primary clarifiers* or *primary sedimentation basins*, where settleable and floatable solids are separated from liquid. These basins are used to settle sludge while grease and oils rise to the surface and are skimmed off. Primary settling tanks are typically equipped with mechanically driven rakes that continually drive the collected sludge toward a hopper in the base of the tank where it is pumped to sludge treatment facilities. Access, egress, engulfment, and energized equipment are the primary safety concerns, all of which must be addressed as part of confined space entry procedures.

To reduce odors, primay clarifiers are often covered. This creates an increased risk of hazardous atmospheric conditions such as high levels of hydrogen sulfide and/or oxygen deficiencies. If ingress and egress are limited, confined space procedures must be strictly adhered to. Even if a covered clarifier does not meet the definition of a confined space, respiratory hazards must still be considered and addressed through adequate ventilation and air monitoring prior to entry.

2.4.2 Secondary Clarification

Whether the secondary biological treatment process uses a fixed-film or suspended-growth treatment method, the biomass (e.g., mixed liquor suspended solids) must be allowed to separate and settle such that the cleaner wastewater can be further processed. Secondary clarifiers are used to slow the flow such that heavier solids can settle. Clarifiers come in several shapes and types such as circular, square, rectangular, and intrachannel. In some small package plants, hopper clarifiers are sometimes used. The secondary clarification physical process uses hydraulic suction, rotating plow sludge collectors, chains and flights, or traveling bridges to remove settled sludge. These concrete basins are anywhere from 3- to 6-m (10- to 20-ft) deep and, like most other basins in the wastewater plant, have similar fall and drowning hazards when they are being serviced and maintained.

Like other treatment basins, drowning hazards exist whenever a job activity requires an employee to work over or on a clarifier without the protection of guard-rails. For example, if it is necessary to extend beyond the protection of the guard-rails to perform an operational or maintenance activity such as adjusting draft tubes or cleaning weirs, an individual must take precautions against drowning hazards. Using a personal fall-restraint system to prevent falling into the basin or wearing a U.S. Coast Guard-approved personal floatation device is recommended.

Additionally, fall hazards, injuries from energized equipment, and confined space hazards must be addressed anytime it is necessary to enter an empty secondary clarifier to perform routine work or to perform preventive or corrective maintenance.

2.5 Tertiary Treatment

Tertiary treatment follows the secondary wastewater treatment process. This step further reduces contaminants from secondary treated wastewater through the use of more advanced treatment systems.

2.5.1 Membrane Bioreactors

A membrane bioreactor (MBR) is the combination of a membrane process like micro-filtration or ultrafiltration with a suspended-growth bioreactor. The membrane bioreactor system incorporates reinforced hollow-fiber membranes or flat plates (cartridges) specifically designed to meet the requirements of wastewater treatment. Membrane bioreactor systems replace conventional treatment and combine clarification, aeration, and filtration into a simple process. Operation of MBRs is generally safe. However, because membrane fouling often occurs during membrane filtration, care must be exercised if chemicals such as biocides are used when removing viable microorganisms that may have developed on the filter. Special precautions when handling or using biocides include wearing protective clothing and using proper handling equipment such as gloves and protective eye wear. Furthermore, used or excess biocides must be disposed of properly to avoid damage to the environment. Municipal, state, and federal regulations must be followed when disposing of any biocides needed for membrane fouling.

2.5.2 Filtration

Filtration is the process of removing one substance or material from another by mechanical means. There are many types of filtration processes used in wastewater treatment to remove impurities such as microbes and nutrients. Two common types are discussed in the following sections.

2.5.2.1 Reverse Osmosis

Reverse osmosis is a filtration method that removes many types of large molecules and ions from solutions by applying pressure to the solution when it is on one side of a selective membrane. The result is that the solute is retained on the pressurized side of the membrane and the pure solvent is allowed to pass to the other side.

Care must be taken to de-energize associated equipment such as motor controls and isolation valves before cleaning, servicing, adjusting or making repairs. Equipment-specific lockout/tagout procedures must be strictly adhered to whenever preventive or corrective maintenance is performed. Occasionally, reverse osmosis membranes need to be cleaned with a solution of citric acid, sulfuric acid, or sodium hydroxide, or sodium bisulfide is injected into the membranes to inhibit biological growth. Depending on the chemical being used and work activities being performed, this may require respiratory protection such as an air-purifying respirator using an acid-gas cartridge. It is important to refer to the product's SDS to determine the type of respiratory protection that is recommended and to determine what other PPE should be worn.

2.5.2.2 Rapid Sand Filtration

Rapid sand filters use relatively coarse sand and other granular media to remove particles and impurities that have been trapped in a floc through the use of flocculation chemicals, typically aluminum or iron salts. Water and flocs flow through the filter medium under gravity or under pumped pressure and the flocculated material is trapped in the sand matrix. In wastewater treatment, rapid sand filtration is used to further reduce microbes, nutrients, or other impurities when the receiving waters are reused for irrigation or as a raw water source of drinking water. Rapid sand filtration improves the quality of wastewater effluent, which enhances disinfection by UV irradiation or other methods.

When working with, or making repairs to, rapid sand filters, appropriate PPE should be worn. All associated motor controls, pumps, and valves should be isolated and de-energized using equipment-specific lockout/tagout procedures whenever performing repairs.

2.6 Disinfection

Disinfection is a process in which some type of disinfectant is used to kill a large portion of microorganisms (excluding bacterial spores) in or on a substance, with the probability that all pathogenic forms are killed, inactivated, or otherwise rendered nonvirulent. Wastewater effluent is often disinfected to decrease disease risks associated with discharging wastewaters containing human pathogens (disease-causing organisms) into receiving waters (WEF, 2007). The most common means to disinfect wastewater to acceptable standards is through the use of chemicals, ozone, or UV disinfection.

2.6.1 Gaseous Chlorine

Chlorine is the most widely used wastewater disinfectant in the United States; it kills most bacteria, viruses, and other microorganisms that cause disease. Chlorine in any form is corrosive and can be dangerous to workers if it comes into contact with skin or eyes; if inhaled, chlorine gas can be lethal. The Occupational Safety and Health Administration has established a permissible exposure limit (PEL) for chlorine at

0.5 ppm. The PEL is the maximum permitted 8-hour time-weighted average concentration to which a person can be exposed. At 10 ppm, chlorine is considered to be immediately dangerous to life and health (IDLH). This means that at the aforementioned concentration (or higher), it poses an immediate threat to life, would cause irreversible or delayed adverse health affects, or would interfere with an individual's abilities to escape from the area. At 30 ppm, chlorine exposure will result in immediate chest pain, vomiting, dyspnea, and coughing. Chlorine exposure is fatal within a few minutes at 1000 ppm or higher. In addition to immediate reactions to high levels of chlorine gas, pulmonary edema and chemical pneumonia may occur hours after exposure. Skin contact with chlorine can cause irritation, burns, and blisters.

The Chlorine Institute's (2008) *Personal Protection Equipment for Chlor-Alkali Chemicals* provides PPE recommendations for initial line breaking, material sampling, loading and unloading, and emergency response activities. The Chlorine Institute recommends a self-contained breathing apparatus (SCBA) or full-face air-supply respirator with an auxiliary self-contained air supply (with escape air provision) when performing loading or unloading (connecting or disconnecting) activities, unless industrial hygiene sampling demonstrates that the techniques being used will not result in chlorine concentrations that exceed the protection factor of the full-face air-purifying respirator (APR), if being worn. If employees are working with liquid chlorine, gloves for thermal (cold) protection are also recommended.

The Chlorine Institute has also determined that level B protection for chlorine gas and enhanced level B protection for liquid chlorine are appropriate protection for emergency responders when responding to chlorine releases. Enhanced level B protection requires a positive-pressure, full-face SCBA or air-supply respirator with an auxiliary self-contained air supply and a fully encapsulating protective suit that is not gas-tight. In addition to wearing specialized protective equipment, employees who will respond to a chlorine release must be specially trained in emergency response activities. Table 4.2 contains a summary of the Chlorine Institute's recommendations.

Although uncommon, leaks can happen. For this reason, chlorine storage and handling areas require ventilation systems, continuous leak monitoring, wind socks, alarms, and engineering devices such as neutralization systems (scrubbers) and self-closing valves to protect workers and the community at large. Small leaks can be detected by using aqueous ammonia vapors, which form a white ammonia chloride vapor in the presence of chlorine. The ammonia is used after connecting a new cylinder to look for small leaks. Small leaks can also be detected by the chlorine leak detector, which registers chlorine concentrations in the air as low as 0.5 ppm. The scrubber

TABLE 4.2   Summary of PPE recommendations for tasks involving potential exposure to gaseous or liquid chlorine (Chlorine Institute, 2008).

	Task previously sampled and within respiratory limitations	Tasks not previously sampled or sampled and above respirator limitations	
		Gas	Liquid
Initial line break	FFR G	SCBA	Enhanced Level B
Material sampling	FFR G	SCBA	SCBA G
Loading/unloading	FFT G	SCBA	SCBA G
Emergency response	When liquid is not involved – Level B When liquid is involved – Enhanced Level B		
FFR	- Full-face air-purifying respirator for protection against chlorine.		
G	- Gloves for thermal (cold) protection; recommendation is for liquid only.		
SBA	- SCBA or full-face air supply respirator with an auxiliary self-contained air supply (escape air provision).		

system's ventilation units should automatically engage whenever the chlorine detector detects a chlorine concentration greater than the alarm setpoint so that chlorine gas can be automatically neutralized. However, chlorine storage and handling areas without scrubbers should leave ventilation equipment in manual mode to prevent uncontrolled releases of chlorine gas to the outside, where unsuspecting workers or the public may be exposed. Repair kits, rated for the type of chlorine containers being used, should be immediately available in the area; however, the kits should not be stored in a location that is likely to be affected by a chlorine release.

2.6.2   Sodium Hypochlorite

Sodium hypochlorite solution, commonly known as *bleach*, is typically purchased in a 10 to 20% solution and is typically used as a disinfectant agent in the wastewater disinfection process. It is much safer to work with than chlorine gas. Sodium hypochlorite is a strong oxidizer and is very corrosive. It can cause irritation to the skin and irreversible damage to eyes, particularly when used in concentrated forms. Sodium hypochlorite solutions may react violently with strong acids, producing chlorine gas, and may react with metals to produce flammable hydrogen gas. Other materials that are incompatible with sodium hypochlorite and that may react violently if accidentally mixed include organic materials, oxidizable materials, ammonia, urea, nitrogen compounds, and alcohols. Therefore, when storing or using chemicals, steps must be taken to keep incompatible materials from accidentally mixing. Containers of incompatible chemicals must be stored in separate storage areas and chemical fill lines should be uniquely designed so that incompatible chemicals cannot be accidentally offloaded into the wrong tanks or containers. It is highly recommended that fill lines to all chemical tanks be kept locked so that "unsupervised" off-loading cannot occur and, instead, require that plant personnel approve all chemical deliveries.

The Chlorine Institute (2008) recommends chemical protection for the head, face, eyes, hands, body, and feet when manually unloading a container of sodium hypochlorite. The Chlorine Institute also recommends wearing a SCBA or full-face air-supply respirator with an auxiliary self-contained air supply when responding to severe instances where spraying of sodium hypochlorite is occurring. A SCBA or full-face air-supply respirator should also be worn if a spill results in fumes and offgasing. Table 4.3 contains a summary of the Chlorine Institute's recommendations. For additional information on respiratory protection, including air-purifying respirators and cartridges, the reader is referred to Chapter 10 "Personal Protective Equipment."

Storage areas are required to have emergency eyewash stations and showers in the immediate vicinity. Emergency eyewash stations and showers should be located in areas where workers may be accidentally splashed such as near chemical pumps and at the off-loading area in order to protect drivers and employees during preventive maintenance connect and disconnect activities. The American National Standards Institute Standard for Emergency Eyewash and Shower Equipment (ANSI, 1990) recommends that the unit be located as close to the hazard as possible, and on the same level. The maximum time required to reach the eyewash station or shower should be determined by the potential effects of the chemical. For strong acids or caustics, these units should be immediately adjacent to or within 3 m (10 ft) of the hazard. This includes remote locations throughout the plant where strong caustics or acids are being injected into process streams for process control purposes such as chlorine injection points into aeration basins for filamentous control or to the headworks for odor control. For all other chemicals, emergency eyewash stations and showers should be in accessible locations that require no more than 10 seconds to reach and should be within a travel distance no greater than 31 m (100 ft).

TABLE 4.3 Summary of PPE recommendations for tasks involving potential exposure to 3 to 20% sodium hypochlorite below 38°C (100°F) (Chlorine Institute, 2008).

	Chemical protective hat or hood	Face shield and chemical splash goggles	Chemical protective suit	Chemical protective gloves	Chemical protective boots or overshoes	Respiratory protection[b]
Initial line break	R	R	R	R	R	NA
Material sampling	N/A	R	N/A	R	N/A	NA
Unloading	R	R	R	R	R	NA
Emergency response[a]						
(1) Severe cases - spraying	R	R	R	R	R	SCBA
(2) All others	R	R	R	R	R	NA
R	- Recommended PPE for this task.					
NA	- This PPE is not believed necessary for this task.					
SCBA	- SCBA or full-face air-supply respirator with an auxiliary self-contained air supply (escape air provision).					

[a]Chemical protection of the neck (e.g., hood) is also recommended for emergency response

[b]Respiratory equipment may be needed in situations where there is a risk of sodium hypochlorite mixing with acidic or other incompatible materials resulting in the release of chlorine gas.

Note: When chemical protective equipment is worn to protect the feet and body and the garment has pant legs but does not have integral foot protection, the legs of the protective garment must be placed on the outside of the protective footwear.

2.6.3 Ozone

Ozone is a strong oxidant that reacts with unsaturated hydrocarbons effectively. Unsaturated hydrocarbons are organic compounds with double bond or triple carbon bond and, therefore, are more chemically reactive with oxygen, ozone, and potassium permanganate. Most wastewater treatment plants using ozone for disinfection generate it on-site by imposing a high-voltage alternating current (6 to 20 kV) across a dielectric discharge gap that contains an oxygen-bearing gas. Ozone is generated on-site because it is unstable and decomposes to elemental oxygen in a short amount of time after generation (U.S. EPA, 1999a).

Ozone has strongly oxidizing properties, is an irritant, is especially harmful to the eyes and respiratory systems, and can be hazardous at even low concentrations. To protect workers who are potentially exposed to ozone, OSHA established a PEL of 0.1 ppm (29 CFR 1910.1000, Table Z-1) that is calculated as an 8-hour time-weighted average. Higher ozone concentrations are especially hazardous; as such, National Institute for Occupational Safety and Health (NIOSH) established an IDLH limit of 5 ppm (CDC, 2007). Work environments where ozone is used, or where it is likely to be produced, should have adequate ventilation and should be continuously monitored for ozone concentrations.

2.6.4 Ultraviolet

A UV disinfection system transfers electromagnetic energy from a mercury arc lamp to an organism's genetic material (DNA and RNA). When UV radiation penetrates the cell wall of an organism, it destroys the cell's ability to reproduce. Ultraviolet radiation requires high-voltage and quartz lamps, and electrical safety procedures must be followed when working on or near this equipment. To be effective, all surfaces between the UV radiation and target organisms must be clean. This requires constant cleaning of the quartz sleeves or tubes by mechanical wipers, ultrasonic cleaners, or chemicals. Chemical cleaning is most commonly done using citric acid (U.S. EPA, 1999b). Workers servicing or cleaning UV equipment should wear PPE for eye, face, hand, and arm protection, including wraparound goggles or face shields that will absorb UV wavelengths.

2.6.5 Dechlorination

Chlorine residual is toxic to aquatic life and must be removed. Dechlorination is the process of removing residual chlorine from disinfected wastewater before discharging it into the environment. Sulfur dioxide is most commonly used for dechlorination by larger facilities, while sulfite salts such as sodium metabisulfite and sodium bisulfite are used by smaller facilities.

Sulfur dioxide is a colorless, corrosive, nonflammable gas with a characteristic pungent and irritating odor. Like chlorine gas, accidental exposure to sulfur dioxide can have severe and life-threatening consequences. The Occupational Safety and Health Administration has established a PEL for sulfur dioxide at 5 ppm (29 CFR 1010.1000, Table Z-1); however, short exposures to concentrations as low as 1 ppm may produce a reversible decrease in lung function. In higher concentrations, sulfur dioxide has the same effects on the respiratory system and skin as chlorine gas. Therefore, employees need to exercise the same precautions with sulfur dioxide as when working with chlorine gas; these precautions include using proper safety equipment, engineering controls, and PPE and following emergency response and training procedures. Table 4.4 presents a summary of recommended PPE when working with sulfur dioxide.

As an alternative to sulfur dioxide gas, many smaller facilities choose to use one of the sulfite salts because of the storage, handling, feeding, and safety problems associated with using gaseous sulfur dioxide on a large scale (U.S. EPA, 2000). Inhalation of sodium bisulfite will irritate the nose, throat, and respiratory tract, while direct skin or eye contact will cause irritation and discomfort. Accidental splashes in the eye may cause eye tissue damage if left untreated. Sulfiting agents, including sodium bisulfite, have been reported to cause reactions in sensitive individuals.

TABLE 4.4   Summary of recommended PPE when working with sulfur dioxide (NIOSH, 2007) (note: acid-resistant gloves, apron, protective suit, and boots should also be considered when working with this chemical).

Exposure levels	NIOSH recommendation
Up to 20 ppm	Chemical cartridge respirator with cartridge(s) to protect against sulfur dioxide or supplied-air respirator (SAR).
Up to 50 ppm	Powered air-purifying respirator with cartridge(s) to protect against sulfur dioxide or SAR in a continuous-flow mode.
Up to 100 ppm	Full-face chemical cartridge respirator with cartridge(s) to protect against sulfur dioxide; gas mask with canister to protect against sulfur dioxide; powered air-purifying respirator with a tight-fitting facepiece and cartridge(s) to protect against sulfur dioxide[a] or full-face SCBA; full-face SAR; or SAR with a tight-fitting facepiece operated in a continuous-flow mode[b].
Emergency response or planned entry into unknown concentration or IDLH conditions	Positive-pressure, full-facepiece SCBA or positive-pressure, full-facepiece SAR with an auxiliary positive-pressure SCBA.
Escape	Gas mask with canister to protect against sulfur dioxide or escape-type SCBA.

[a,b] Sulfur dioxide reported to cause eye irritation or damage and may require eye protection

3.0 WASTEWATER TREATMENT PLANT HAZARDS: SOLIDS HANDLING PROCESSES

3.1 Introduction

Sludge handling and processing can involve a number of potential safety hazards. Potential safety hazards can include the risk of falling into tanks of digesting solids; being exposed to combustible gases; working with or near ruptured pumps, pipes, and enclosed tanks; working with or near the release of toxic wastes; being exposed to the accumulation of toxic wastes and heavy metals in sludge; operating certain machinery; and using hazardous chemicals for solids treatment. Identifying these potential safety hazards and preventing them from occurring can be accomplished by following standard operating procedures and National Fire Protection Association and local regulatory restrictions, and by exercising common sense. Tasks specific to sludge processing, including sludge handling, treatment, and disposal and the relevant components for each, are explained in this section.

3.2 Sludge Handling and Processing

Sludge is typically transported by pumps, ejectors, augers, bucket elevators, or conveyor belts. In buildings where hazardous gases can accumulate, adequate natural or mechanical ventilation should be provided. Where appropriate, monitors with alarms should be installed to detect oxygen deficiency, toxic gases, and accumulations in combustible gas. At a minimum, it is important to install one primary and one secondary backup nonclogging submersible pump and sump downgrade to pump sludge leaks, floor washing, and pipe-cleaning operations. Additionally, precautions should be taken against trip and electrical hazards.

Conveyor belts are typically used in instances where sludge is too thick to pump. In instances where belts are used, trough rollers and splash guards should be installed to prevent spillage. Emergency stops should also be included.

Dried sludge may release dust and cause a nuisance. At a minimum, employees should wear goggles, a NIOSH-approved filtering face-piece respirator (dust masks), and gloves when handling dried sludge. If a cartridge respirator is being worn for protection against sludge particulates, it is important to ensure the cartridge contains a particulate filter. Particulate filters will be listed according to the type of protection provided. They will be either "N" (not oil-proof), "R" (oil-restricted), or "P" (oil-proof), and will contain a numerical rating of 95, 99, or 100, which is the percent efficiency of the filter. This efficiency rating is based on NIOSH testing procedures that determine the filter's ability to capture particles that are 0.3 μ in size.

Digested sludge can emit methane, hydrogen sulfide, and other flammable or toxic gases. The release of these gases is a concern for indoor sludge operating facilities and areas nearby digested sludge tanks. Because excessive pressure may build up within pipes, pumps, and tanks when sludge is isolated by valves, pressure indicators should be installed along pipe lines. Additionally, pressure and vacuum relief valves should be installed on digested tank covers. Operators should be mindful that pump seals can fail because of pressure or grit-induced wear.

3.3 Chemical Use

Sludge is treated or conditioned with specific chemicals that stabilize sludge, improve dewatering, reduce pathogens, or kill nematodes. Commonly used chemicals include polymers, lime, acids, caustic, and metal salts.

Chemical spills can pose a slip hazard. Therefore, caution should be exercised when handling slippery chemical agents such as polymer, as discussed in Section 3.3.2. Dry chemicals can also be hazardous. The release of dust from dry chemicals can irritate the eyes, nose, throat, and lungs. Chemical dust may be present in bag handling, unloading, and feeder areas. At a minimum, workers in these areas should wear filtering face-piece respirators (dust masks) and tight-fitting safety glasses with side shields. Additional protective equipment may be necessary and workers should refer to the chemical's SDS for detailed information on the type and level of PPE that should be worn. Workers that are exposed to dangerous chemicals should complete appropriate safety reports and seek immediate medical attention.

3.3.1 Chemical Stabilization

Sludge is sometimes stabilized using lime or chlorine. Lime slurry is mixed with sludge to increase the pH to 12 or more. The reader is referred to Section 3.3.3, "Lime," for lime-handling safety considerations and precautions; the same precautions apply to lime–sludge mixtures.

Chlorine sludge stabilization has been developed in which chlorine is mixed with sludge to obtain a low pH. Human contact with the mixture should be avoided because of the acidic conditions and high concentrations of chlorine present in the oxidized sludge. Chlorinated hydrocarbons can also be generated, which is dangerous because they are toxic and soluble in tissues and fats. The reader is referred to Section 2.6.1, "Gaseous Chlorine," for chlorine-handling safety considerations and precautions; the same precautions apply for chlorine–sludge mixtures.

3.3.2 Polymers

Polymers are manufactured in liquid and dry powder forms. Both forms are slippery and can irritate eyes, nose, and skin. Chemical burns may result if polymers are splashed into eyes or come in contact with skin. Personal protection equipment should be worn to prevent contact with skin and eyes and filter masks or respirators should be used to prevent inhalation of dust or vapors.

Dry and liquid polymer spills can irritate eyes and create a fall hazard. If dry polymer is spilled, the dry polymer should be left dry, swept up, and properly disposed of according to municipal, state, and federal regulations. If liquid polymer is spilled, an absorbent material should be applied to the spill and then the spill should be swept up and properly disposed of according to municipal, state, and federal regulations. It is important to keep in mind that slippery conditions can be aggravated when flushing with water. Therefore, a worker should adequately flush with enough water until the area is entirely clean and free of polymer.

3.3.3 Lime

Lime is available in powdered form. Workers should adhere to precautions for dust hazards. Ventilation and efficient dust collection and removal systems should be installed in lime handling areas. Any spilled material should be vacuumed with industrial vacuum cleaners and the bags disposed of afterward.

When working around lime off-loading, storage, slaker, and feeder facilities, workers should wear gloves, eye protection, respirators, long-sleeved shirts with sleeves and collars buttoned, and trousers with the legs down over the tops of shoes or boots. Clothing should not bind too tightly around the neck, wrists, or ankles.

If lime gets in a worker's eyes, they should immediately be flushed with large amounts of water for at least 20 minutes; medical attention should be sought immediately. Rubbing eyes irritated with lime dust will only add to discomfort and can cause further injuries.

Because lime mixed with water becomes very hot, perspiring workers may be burned if their skin comes in contact with lime. Lime burns should be treated like caustic burns. The burn area should be washed thoroughly with soap and water and then vinegar to remove all lime. To prevent infection, burn ointment such as boric acid salve should be applied and the burn area covered with a sterile bandage. Medical attention should be sought immediately.

Freshly slaked lime is not as dangerous after it cools; however, contact with skin will remove natural skin oils. Protective cream should be applied to exposed parts of the body to reduce chapping and the danger of burns or infection.

Lime should be stored in dry areas to avoid moisture absorption. Contact with small amounts of water may cause fires. It is important to not store flammable materials, acids, or other chemicals near lime.

Alternately handling quicklime and metal salts on the same conveyor should be avoided, unless it is thoroughly cleaned between uses. Alum and ferric and ferrous sulfates are commonly used in coagulant aids and contain water of crystallization that quicklime readily absorbs. This will result in an intense reaction (i.e., heat) as hydrogen is released from the water, creating a potentially explosive atmosphere.

3.3.4   Acids

Acids, such as hydrochloric, nitric, phosphoric, and sulfuric, are used to adjust pH and to clean equipment. They are dangerous to handle even in dilute concentrations. Acids should not be mixed with alkaline substances, unless under extremely controlled conditions. Acid should always be added slowly to water; water should never be added to concentrated acid solutions. This prevents rapid chemical reactions that produce high temperatures, rapid gas releases, and potential "splash back" onto the face, arms, and hands.

Although acids are commonly supplied in liquid form, mixing certain metal salts (i.e., ferric and ferrous chlorides, ferric and ferrous sulfates, and aluminum sulfates) with water provides an acidic solution. When acids come in contact with moist parts of the body, a severe burn can result.

A worker should never handle acids unless he or she is wearing gloves that are approved for handling the acid in question. Additionally, adequate clothing and body protection should be worn. Acid fumes and vapors should not be inhaled or nose, throat, and lungs may be damaged. Eye protection should also be worn to prevent splashes, fumes, and vapors from getting into eyes. If a worker is exposed to acids, the emergency shower or eyewash station should be used to flush the body with large amounts of running water.

3.3.5   Caustic

Caustic chemicals include any chemical with a pH higher than 9. Examples of commonly used caustic chemicals are calcium hydroxide (hydrated lime), sodium hydroxide (caustic soda), and calcium oxide (quicklime, unslaked lime, and burnt lime). These types of chemicals are used to aid coagulation, adjust pH, clean filters, and neutralize acid spills.

When the dry form of these chemicals or concentrated liquid forms are mixed with water, the chemical reaction creates heat and rapidly liberates hydrogen gas, which creates a potentially explosive atmosphere. If mixed in enclosed areas, rapid expansion of gas may rupture the vessel in which the reaction takes place. A worker should not inhale vapors and fumes and should wear eye protection to avoid contact with splashes, fumes, and vapors. If exposed to dry caustic materials, it is important that a worker not flush with water until he or she first brushes off as much dry chemical as possible; then, the emergency shower or eyewash station should be used to flush the body with large amounts of running water.

3.3.6 Metal Salts

Metal salts are commonly used at a wastewater treatment plant for sludge conditioning, filter aids, coagulant aids, settling aids, biological nutrients, and neutralization. Metal salts commonly used are ferric chloride, ferrous chloride, ferric sulfate, ferrous sulfate, and aluminum sulfate (alum).

Ferric chloride comes in solution or granular forms. In the presence of light, it decomposes to yield hydrochloric acid, making it an extremely corrosive chemical. Consequently, all tanks, piping, and valves should be either rubber-lined or made from acid-resistant plastic. Storage facilities should be well ventilated. Floors, walls, and equipment subject to splashing should be protected with corrosion-resistant paint or rubber mats. Workers handling ferric chloride solution and granules should be equipped with full-face cartridge respirators, acid-resistant goggles, face shields, rubber gloves, rubber suits or aprons, and rubber boots. At least one emergency eyewash station and safety shower should be located in the immediate area where ferric chloride is stored or used because contact with skin, mouth, or eyes may cause severe burns. If ferric chloride does touch the skin, it should be removed by first wiping the residual off with a cloth, then slowly flushing the area with small amounts of water, followed by rapidly flushing with large amounts of water to prevent skin burns.

The same precautions should be used for handling ferrous chloride and ferrous sulfate as those used for handling ferric chloride. Mixing ferrous sulfate with quicklime should be avoided or a violent chemical reaction may cause a fire. Metal salts are also extremely corrosive chemicals and should not be allowed to come into contact with aluminum or steel.

Aluminum sulfate, commonly known as *alum*, is available in liquid or hydrated granular form. The granular form presents a dust hazard when handled and is extremely corrosive. The liquid form is corrosive and its fumes should not be inhaled.

If either form is splashed in the eye, it can be seriously damaging unless the area is immediately flushed with large amounts of water for at least 20 minutes. Alum should be handled using the same precautions as those for ferric chloride. Mixing aluminum sulfate with quicklime should be avoided or a violent chemical reaction may cause a fire.

3.3.7   Hydrocarbons

Hydrocarbons found around treatment plants include lubricating oils, greases, aerosol sprays, pesticides, herbicides, insecticides, chemical reagents used in the laboratory, gasoline, diesel fuel, butane, propane, methanol, and methane. Hydrocarbons may be aqueous, liquid, or gaseous compounds with fumes and vapors. Many hydrocarbons are flammable, combustible, or otherwise harmful and, therefore, should be considered dangerous. Hydrocarbons should not be inhaled, allowed to touch the skin or other body parts, or stored near acids, caustics, or chlorine compounds. It is important to ensure that hydrocarbons are properly labeled and that an SDS is immediately available. Hydrocarbons should be used only in strict accordance with a manufacturer's instructions; additionally, spent or used containers should be disposed of in an environmentally safe manner.

3.3.8   Methanol

Methanol is used in wastewater treatment plants as an inexpensive, but effective carbon source for denitrifying bacteria (i.e., bacteria that converts nitrates to nitrogen for biological nitrogen removal). Methanol, however, is extremely toxic and can cause heart and liver damage. Methanol is also highly flammable, with its flame virtually invisible and producing little heat and virtually no smoke, thus making it difficult to see. This creates a potential for accidental contact and fire hazards if proper precautions are not used.

Storage of methanol is subject to the same requirements as those used for gasoline storage. Tanks must be grounded to protect methanol from accidental ignition resulting from static discharge, and bonding techniques should be used to dissipate static electricity generated during fluid transfer. Employees should never use mobile phones around materials that generate flammable or explosive fumes such as methanol, gasoline, and propane as they can become an ignition source. The same precautions apply for laptop computers, flashlights, battery lanterns, and other battery-operated devices that are not rated as explosion-proof. As a general rule, electronic devices should not be used within 7 m (20 ft) of a potentially explosive atmosphere. This distance is sufficient to provide a buffer distance between the potential source of ignitable fumes and the device. This distance should be increased to 17 m (50 ft) for pressurized liquid gases such as propane (Methanol Institute, 2011). Welding, cutting, grinding, or other hot work activities on or near methanol storage tanks or associated equipment will require hot work procedures to be strictly adhered to.

Exposure to methanol can occur from inhalation, skin absorption, contact with eyes, or ingestion; as such, PPE should be worn when handling or working with methanol. At a minimum, safety glasses with side shields or safety goggles and gloves are recommended. If airborne exposures are greater than the OSHA PEL, respiratory protection will be required. According to the Methanol Institute, air-purifying respirators with organic vapor (OVA) cartridges are not appropriate protection against methanol vapors because of the short service life of the OVA cartridge. Instead, use of a supplied air respirator with a full face piece operated in a pressure demand or other positive-pressure mode is the recommended respiratory protection (Methanol Institute, 2011).

All workers handling, storing, or using methanol should go through proper training in accordance with the Methanol Institute's (2011) *Methanol Safe Handling Manual*. The *Methanol Safe Handling Manual* also indicates that methanol equal to or greater than 24%, by weight, meets the U.S. Environmental Protection Agency's definition of an ignitable hazardous waste (Methanol Institute, 2011). When disposed, product-grade methanol is listed as a hazardous waste and, therefore, should never be discharged directly into sewers or surface waters. Waste methanol may only be disposed of at a licensed facility permitted to handle the waste as a hazardous waste as defined in the U.S. Resource Conservation and Recovery Act.

3.4   Anaerobic and Aerobic Digestion

Sludge can be digested aerobically in the presence of oxygen. Sludge can be digested anaerobically without the presence of oxygen. Aerobic digestion processes typically involve open tanks and aeration equipment. Because anaerobic digestion processes generally involve confined spaces, aerobic digestion processes tend to be a safer alternative than anaerobic digestion processes.

When used properly and in accordance with proper safety regulations, anaerobic digestion can be a powerful tool for solids stabilization. One benefit of anaerobic digestion is the production of digester gas as an energy-rich byproduct. Digester gas is generally composed of 70% methane, 30% carbon dioxide, and trace amounts of nitrogen, hydrogen, hydrogen sulfide, and oxygen. Because of possible combustibility and the potential for explosions, extreme caution must be used when working in the vicinity of anaerobic digesters, associated control buildings, and associated equipment.

Primary safety precautions at anaerobic digestion facilities include providing adequate ventilation, maintaining an explosion-proof environment, and performing frequent inspection and preventive maintenance of all digester system safety and monitoring devices.

To prevent atmospheric air from leaking into the system, sludge gas handling systems must be maintained under positive pressure. The explosive ratio of air to sludge gas ranges from approximately 20:1 to 5:1. Therefore, mixing sludge gas with air should be avoided at all times. All personnel either directly or indirectly involved in digester operation and maintenance activities should thoroughly understand how operations and mechanisms work because accidentally draining a digester below the operating range of a floating or fixed cover can introduce air into the digester. Tank pressure with a floating cover is generally constant because the cover will rise and fall according to sludge levels. In contrast, tank pressure within a fixed cover can be variable because there is a fixed volume within the tank. Therefore, adding sludge can increase internal tank pressure. In contrast, drawing out sludge can decrease internal tank pressure.

If sludge is added or drawn out too quickly from a fixed cover system, the connection between the digester cover and digester tank might become damaged. If damaged, atmospheric air can enter the digester tank or cause operational issues with a damaged dome.

Because of the sensitivity in gas pressure and sludge levels, liquid levels should be closely monitored and corrective action should be taken if the level drops and air is drawn into the digester. For information on completely emptying and purging digesters, *Purging Principles and Practices* (AGA, 2001) or other related safety publications can be used as a guide.

Gas leaks from the gas collection and storage system may also cause an explosive environment. Gas leaks can be detected with gas detection equipment and, sometimes, by smell. However, it is important to not rely solely on smell; indeed, the gas main and appurtenances should periodically be checked with portable gas detectors. Only nonsparking tools and equipment should be used and smoking, sparks, or open flames should not be allowed in the area (generally, within a 15.24-m [50-ft] radius). All electrical installations should be explosion-proof and maintained as such. An installation is not considered explosion-proof if even one light switch is improperly installed.

The most important precaution against gas buildup is positive ventilation throughout the digester facility. Positive ventilation also removes carbon monoxide and unburned hydrocarbons that could be produced in boilers, gas engines, or other equipment powered by sludge gas or natural gas. Equipment stacks should be designed, located, and extended to avoid exhaust gases from short-circuiting back through the ventilation system.

Safety equipment on sludge gas systems requires frequent inspections and immediate corrective maintenance. This includes flame arresters, pressure-relief valves, pressure-regulating valves, automatic control valves, automatic pilot valves, waste gas burners and controls, gas compressors and controls, and gas condensate traps. Flame arresters protect against flashback from waste gas burners, gas engines, and gas-fired boilers. Biogas equipment should be checked and cleaned regularly to prevent possible blockage. Pressure-relief devices provide relief from excessive pressure buildup in sludge gas systems and should be vented to the outside. Checks on relief valves and pressure-regulating valves should be inspected regularly to ensure that they work at the designated pressures. Automatic gas and pilot valves preceding gas burners and gas engines should be checked to ensure that they open and shut properly on demand of the gas-burning unit. Gas burners should be cleaned regularly and their controls adjusted as necessary. Gas compressors should be inspected and overhauled regularly, eliminating all elements that produce or add to overheating. Gas condensate traps should be drained frequently and the seals replaced as necessary.

The dangers associated with anaerobic digesters cannot be overemphasized. The following are safety procedures for shutdown operations:

- Plan the operation carefully to avoid dangerous situations;
- Relieve pressures gradually;
- Vent gases to the atmosphere, away from ventilator intakes;
- Isolate the digester for 30 days as recommended by a certified marine chemist;
- Purge the gas system and digester;
- Ventilate the digester thoroughly; and
- Follow all confined space entry procedures before, during, and after entry.

The reader is referred to *Design of Municipal Wastewater Treatment Plants* (WEF and ASCE, 2009) and *Operation of Municipal Wastewater Treatment Plants* (WEF, 2007) for additional safety precautions and considerations for anaerobic sludge digestion.

Before entering a digester, the following procedures are recommended. Additional procedures may be appropriate, such as diluting and pumping, and should be determined on a case-by-case basis.

- Shut down the digester. Stop feed, but continue to heat and mix for at least 30 days or until digester gas is no longer being produced. This should eliminate further methane production during dewatering.

- On floating covers, withdraw enough supernatant or sludge until the floating cover is firmly resting on support brackets or corbels. On fixed covers, raise the liquid level to the highest level as designed for the wastewater treatment plant.

- Close all sludge valves and gas valves to the digester. Chain, lock, and tag these valves.

- Post a checklist at entrances to the confined space. Be sure emergency telephone numbers are readily accessible.

- Post "no smoking" or "no open flames" signs near noticeable areas.

- Inject an inert gas such as carbon dioxide or nitrogen into the gas area and vent until a reading of below 2.0% combustible gas is detected throughout. Only purge areas with air once all sources of ignition are excluded and the site is carefully monitored.

- Lock out and tag all electrical disconnects for mixing, pumps, and other equipment. Blank off, valve out, and tag all sludge and gas piping leading to the digester.

- If entry into the digester is necessary, follow confined space entry procedures.

- Ensure all lighting and electrical equipment are explosion-proof.

- Whenever there is a potential for falling objects or head injuries, ensure personnel wear hard hats. The use of chin straps may help prevent hard hats from falling off accidentally.

- Check the condition of built-in rungs every time an employee ascends or descends. Do not trust these rungs. Ladders are preferable, but should be safely positioned and secured at all times.

- Train all personnel involved in the cleaning operation on the hazards of digester gas and on performing first aid, including cardiopulmonary resuscitation and artificial respiration. Automated external defibrillator training is highly recommended.

- Do not use compressed air to increase water pressure for wash down as there is a potential for trapped gas to be released.

- Be careful when working on top of digester covers. Ensure proper guardrails and handrails are installed. Install safety tie-off points, where appropriate. Note that some floating covers may not be secured to the digester tank. Be mindful the floating covers may possibly tip and capsize.

- Use proper fall protection, where appropriate.

A successful and safe digester cleaning operation involves proper planning, development of appropriate safety procedures, and regular use of daily equipment checklists. Failure to develop and enforce proper and safe procedures can result in injury or fatalities. It is important that margin of error not be assumed and that risks not be taken. It is also important to ensure that employees are thoroughly briefed and familiar with digester entry and exit and proper cleaning procedures before entering the digester.

3.5 Dewatering

Sludge is typically dewatered before disposal or before being used as fertilizer. Common dewatering equipment include drying beds, centrifuges, screw presses, vacuum filters, and presses. Most of these processes include electrical and mechanical equipment and have associated lockout/tagout hazards.

3.5.1 Drying Beds

Drying beds are composed of sand or other porous material on which sludge is applied and dried through drainage and evaporation. Aerobically, anaerobically, or partially digested sludge can be applied to drying beds. The application of partially digested sludge may release combustible gases. Once dried, residual sludge is removed manually or by mechanical equipment.

Employees handling or working near wet or dried sludge should wear rubber boots and gloves. If exposed to sludge, workers should immediately wash wet or dried sludge off their skin with disinfecting soap and water. Sludge can either be pumped or delivered by gravity flow to the drying beds. Filtrate is collected by gravity flow. Where appropriate, it is important to be aware of applicable mechanical and electrical hazards. Workers should be trained to operate equipment properly and to follow recommended and required safety precautions for disabling, locking out, and tagging equipment before servicing, repairing, adjusting, or maintaining the equipment. Workers should not smoke or use open flames in these areas, particularly when handling or applying partially digested sludge.

3.5.2   Centrifuges

Centrifuges are high-speed rotating machines designed to dewater sludge to a drier cake. Protective guards and devices for belts, gears, and other exposed moving parts should be used whenever equipment is operating.

Safety precautions should be used for rotating machines. Workers should avoid wearing loose clothing and lock out and tag electrical and mechanical equipment for maintenance and repairs. Improper bowl flushing may cause the centrifuge to vibrate; therefore, excessive vibration should be avoided and vibration shutdown controls should be checked frequently for proper operation. Often, chemicals such as polymers are used as coagulant aids. Chemical hazard safety precautions should be used and positive ventilation in the centrifuge area should be maintained because sludge gases are separated during the process.

Centrifuges may also splash sludge. Therefore, all personnel in the vicinity should wear gloves, boots, and eye protection. Sludge should immediately be washed off of exposed skin with disinfecting soap and water. Work areas and walkways should be kept as clean as possible and free from grease, sludge, oil, and chemical deposits.

3.5.3   Filter and Belt Presses

Filter presses operate by pumping sludge under pressure through feed holes onto a series of movable plates that close against a fixed end. The pressure, sometimes in excess of 1400 kPa (203 psi), forces filtrate through the filter cloth over each plate. The filter cloth is typically precoated with a material that aids in solids retention and release of the sludge cake. Sometimes, acid wash systems are provided by inplace washing of the cloth or fabric. Filter presses often are equipped with an automatic safety device, that is, light curtains that register if someone reaches or falls across the curtain and automatically shut down the plate-shifting cycle.

Belt presses operate by placing sludge on a porous belt or screen material that moves through a series of rollers, squeezing the water out.

Because sludge is being handled, positive ventilation should be maintained in the press area as strong odors are often generated. Presses may splash water and/or sludge and personnel should wear appropriate PPE and clean up spills and splashes immediately. Sludge should be washed off of skin with disinfecting soap and water. Work areas and walkways should be kept as clean as possible and free of grease, sludge, oil, and chemical deposits.

Protective guards and devices for belts, gears, and other exposed moving parts should be used whenever equipment is operating. Workers should avoid wearing loose clothing. Lockout, block-out, and/or tagout procedures should be used on all electrical and mechanical equipment whenever the equipment is being serviced, repaired, adjusted, or maintained.

3.6   Heat Drying

Heat drying digested and dewatered sludge reduces the volume of material for transport and disposal. The heating process may release carbon monoxide, sulfur dioxide, nitrous oxide, and other gases, which could cause oxygen-deficient and/or explosive atmospheres. High temperatures and pressures may be reached during the process and it is important to check temperatures and pressures and to make visual inspections of the machinery often. If the system temperature becomes higher than the manufacturers' recommendations, air compressors and sludge flow should be shut down and water should be used until the temperature falls to the desired level.

The system should be treated as a confined space. Maintenance should not be performed until the appropriate part of the system is depressurized. Vessels should be ventilated and completely isolated before entering.

It is important to watch for excessive carbon coatings on air-compressor discharge valves, which indicate too much oil is being used to lubricate the cylinders. Excessive buildup can cause fires at the discharge of these cylinders.

All precautions for electrical and mechanical hazards should be observed when working near these units. Legible signs warning persons of hot surfaces should be prominently displayed. Sensors, automatic shutdown controls, and warning devices that engage when a potentially dangerous situation is developing should be an integral part of this process.

The product of heat drying is a hot, combustible organic material. If the drying is incomplete, the material may continue decomposing in the storage vessels. This can generate additional heat and, under the right circumstances, can cause spontaneous ignition. Although adequate cooling should be incorporated into storage facilities, care needs to be taken because adding water to this material will produce noxious and dangerous off-gases.

3.7   Composting

Raw and digested sludge can be composted and stabilized through biological degradation. There are two types of composting operations commonly used: windrow and forced-air static pile. Both processes produce heat of up to 50 to 60 °C (122 to 140 °F) or higher. Blowers and composting machines are used for forced-air static pile composting. Special windrow turners are used for windrowing. Motorized equipment commonly used for both types of composting operations include drum screens, dump trucks, and rubber-tired front loaders.

Standard safety precautions should be used when working with motorized equipment. To prevent accidents involving trucks or loaders, devices should be used that warn when a vehicle is backing up; worker access to traffic areas should also be limited. Workers who operate heavy equipment must be trained and authorized on the equipment before driving or operating it. Workers should practice good personal hygiene after working around the area. Additionally, they should be aware that snakes, flies, mosquitoes, spiders, burrowing animals, and other types of animals may be in the area.

Smoking and the presence of other ignition sources should be prohibited from composting and storage areas. Dried, composted sludge may be flammable and composting may release enough combustible gases to cause an explosion.

Unauthorized entry and access should be prevented by enclosing the area with intruder-resistant fencing and posting legible signs warning against trespassing. The fence should be inspected daily and repairs made promptly.

3.8   Incineration

Occasionally, dewatered sludge is incinerated to reduce the volume of sludge material and to stabilize it for transport and disposal. Heat and combustion may release carbon monoxide, sulfur dioxide, nitrous oxides, and other gases, which can cause oxygen deficiency and other dangerous atmospheres.

Refractory walls and steel casings should be inspected frequently to identify hot spot burn and rust damage. Scheduled preventive maintenance should be performed on burners and control systems. Workers should wear dark protective glasses during internal inspections of the furnace. High temperatures near incinerators may cause fatigue because of body fluids lost through perspiration. Therefore, it is important to drink plenty of water and to wear heat-resistant clothing, boots, and gloves.

Incinerator fuel, such as coal, oil, or natural gas, may be stored on-site and, as such, presents a fire and explosion hazard. Smoking and other ignition sources should be prohibited in the area, especially when checking for fuel leaks. In addition, because coal and dried sludge dust may harm lungs and skin, proper dust-control measures should be used, PPE should be worn, and the area kept clean.

All precautions for electrical and mechanical hazards should be taken when working around these types of units. Legible signs should be prominently displayed in areas to warn persons of hot surfaces. Sensors, automatic shutdown controls, and warning devices should be used that actuate when a potentially dangerous situation develops.

Ash is the residual product of sludge incineration. Handling ash safely requires proper dust control measures and protective equipment. Poor ventilation may lead to explosions. Respiratory barriers and equipment should be used to avoid inhaling ash dust.

4.0 MISCELLANEOUS CHEMICALS

In addition to the common treatment chemicals already discussed in this chapter, there are other chemicals that are often used to stabilize and optimize wastewater treatment. Like most chemicals, these present safety and health hazards to employees who are working with or near them. These other chemicals are summarized in Table 4.5 along with brief descriptions of the potential hazards, recommended exposure controls, and PPE.

5.0 LABORATORY SAFETY

5.1 Physical Hazards

5.1.1 Working with Hot Equipment and Liquids

Laboratory activities often involve tasks that expose workers to hot equipment and hot liquids. Common hot equipment exposures include placing items inside or removing items from muffle furnaces and drying ovens and using autoclaves and handling hot glassware. Hot liquid exposures can occur when using hot or boiling liquids or when performing tests that result in heat-producing chemical reactions. Overheating liquids can result in "super heating" which, when disturbed, will suddenly release heat and steam and spew hot liquids onto unsuspecting workers. Using boiling chips will reduce this potential.

Laboratory workers need to wear face, eye, and hand protection when working with hot equipment or when performing laboratory procedures that produce heat or steam.

TABLE 4.5 Other chemicals used in wastewater treatment to stabilize and optimize treatment.

Chemical name	Use	Hazards	Exposure controls and PPE
Hydrogen peroxide	Bulking control, odor control, and sludge odor control.	Strong oxidizer: contact with combustible materials may cause immediate spontaneous ignition or combustion. Mixed with organic materials such as alcohols, acetone, and other ketones, aldehydes and their anhydrides, and glycerol can cause violent explosions. Spontaneous ignition may occur when hydrogen peroxide is added to cotton (cellulose). Contact with metals including iron, copper, chromium, lead, silver, manganese, sodium, potassium, magnesium, nickel, gold, platinum; metal alloys such as brass or bronze; metal oxides such as lead oxides, mercury oxides, or manganese dioxide; and many metal salts like potassium permanganate or sodium iodate could result in violent explosions. Tremendous explosions can also be caused by unstable mixtures with concentrated mineral acids. Health effects: vapors or spray can cause eye damage, impaired sight, or blindness; causes skin burns; vapors irritate the respiratory system and may cause coughing and difficulty breathing.	Store in cool, dry area in closed container away from combustibles, clothing, and incompatible materials. Refer to the product SDS for recommended PPE. In general, wear chemical respirator with an acid gas cartridge if engineering controls do not maintain airborne contaminants to acceptable levels; wear safety glasses with side shields, goggles and a face shield for eye and face protection, and appropriate chemical-resistant clothing and gloves for skin protection.
Potassium permanganate	Sludge and odor control.	Strong oxidizer: contact with combustible materials may cause fire. Incompatible materials include acids, peroxides; antifreeze, hydraulic fluids, and readily oxidizable inorganic materials including metal powers. Chlorine gas is liberated when mixed with hydrochloric acid.	Store in cool, dry area in closed container away from combustibles and incompatible materials. Refer to the product SDs for recommended PPE. In general, use respiratory protection in cases of overexposure to dust.

	Health effects: damages to eye on contact; irritating to skin; airborne concentrations of potassium permanganate dust or mist may cause damage to the respiratory tract.	or mist; face shields, goggles or safety glasses with side shields to protect eyes, gloves, and chemical suit or other form of body protection to protect skin.
Disinfection		
Anhydrous ammonia	Extremely hazardous liquid and vapor stored under pressure. Containers may rupture or explode if exposed to heat. Health effects: toxic and severe irritant of the respiratory tract and may cause cessation of respiration and death. Possible freeze-burns to mucous membranes and blistering from skin contact; exposures to the eyes may cause temporary or permanent blindness.	Store container in a cool, well ventilated area. Refer to OSHA 1910.111 "Storage and handling of anhydrous ammonia" for proper storage and handling procedures. NIOSH recommends that, at a minimum, an air-purifying half-mask respirator equipped with a cartridge approved for ammonia or a supplied-air respirator be worn for levels at 250 ppm. Refer to the *NIOSH Pocket Guide to Chemical Hazards* for and/or the product's SDS for respiratory protection recommendations for higher or unknown exposure levels; Skin protection required for exposures to liquid or mist >1000 ppm; wear chemical goggles (indirectly vented) and full-face shield for eye and face protection.

Special oven mitts or insulating gloves should be worn when handling hot equipment, transferring hot liquids, or when using glass containers that may become heated from chemical reactions. Open-flame Bunsen burners are often used in laboratories to sterilize metal inoculation loops and other laboratory equipment. This presents an opportunity for serious burns and for accidental laboratory fires. When using a Bunsen burner, the flame should be kept as low as possible and the apparatus should not be left unattended.

5.1.2   Compressed Gases

Some laboratories store and use compressed gases such as helium, argon, and nitrogen to perform certain laboratory tests such as metal analyses. Compressed gas cylinders need to be stored in well-protected, well-ventilated, dry locations that are at least 6 m (20 ft) from highly combustible materials. When not in use, valves must be closed with the valve protective cap in place. All compressed gas cylinders need to be properly labeled and secured to prevent them from falling over.

5.1.3   Ergonomics

Laboratory technicians sometimes need to perform repetitive job tasks such as performing grease and oils analyses and frequent titrations. Other tasks such as standing for long periods of time and bending over countertops to perform certain procedures often place laboratory technicians in poor or awkward postures for extended periods of time. All of these conditions can contribute to repetitive motion and soft tissue injuries such as carpal tunnel syndrome and lower back fatigue. Lifting heavy loads such as racks of full BOD bottles, water bottles, sample jugs, automatic samplers, and other heavy items can cause back, neck, and/or shoulder injuries. When performing repetitive job tasks, job rotations or ergonomic equipment should be used to prevent repetitive motion injuries. Whenever it is necessary to lift heavy or awkward items, using a "buddy" system involving two people lifting or using some type of material handling device such as a handcart or an elevating cart can reduce the risk of back and other soft tissue injuries.

5.1.4   Working with Glassware

Working with glass poses special hazards. Glass should be handled with care and used only for its designated purpose. All broken glass must be properly disposed of into a container designed for that purpose and never placed into a common trash receptacle. Glassware should be routinely inspected for cracks, damages, and imperfections before being used. This is especially important if it will be used for any procedure that involves extreme temperatures such as heat or cold as the glassware will likely break, potentially resulting in chemical contamination to the work area and to workers.

5.2   Hazardous Chemicals

5.2.1   Health Effects

Although the laboratory typically contains only small amounts of hazardous materials (chemicals), workers are at risk of serious chemical-related injuries and illnesses because of the concentrations of chemicals being used. When working with chemicals, health effects can be chronic and may not be apparent for many years. Or, health effects can be acute and cause immediate and serious damages to the body upon exposure. There are various ways to be exposed and adversely affected by chemicals; however, the most common chemical exposures in laboratories are those to hands, arms, and eyes. Because of this, laboratory workers should always wear PPE such as safety glasses, goggles, gloves, and laboratory coats when working with or near chemicals. The use and type of PPE will depend on the type and concentration of chemicals being used and on the type of analytical tests being performed.

5.2.2   Handling

When handling chemicals, even in small quantities, it is vital to know the chemical's hazardous properties and the safest means of handling the chemical. This includes understanding and using proper engineering controls and wearing the required PPE. Employees also need to be aware of incompatibility issues, proper spill response measures, and which chemicals may react and emit off-gases (i.e., fumes) when heated or mixed. To become more familiar with chemicals used in a laboratory, employees should consult with their supervisor or coworkers or review the chemical's SDS. The SDS provides detailed information on the chemical's hazardous properties and provides preventive measures such as first aid, engineering controls, and PPE that should be worn when working with the chemical.

5.2.3   Storage

Proper chemical storage is important not only for safety, but for quality control. Chemicals need to be dated, properly labeled, and inventoried regularly. Care must be taken to not store chemicals with other incompatible chemicals as they might react with each other and cause toxic off-gassing (i.e., fuming) and/or fires and explosions. Therefore, it is important to be sure that only containers marked for that chemical be used. For example, potassium permanganate placed into a bucket that contains organic substances can explode. Chemical storage must also provide secondary containment to keep spills, no matter how small, from contaminating surrounding surfaces, which could cause an injury to an unsuspecting worker. If secondary containment is not designed into chemical storage cabinets, a rubber tub or polypropylene tray can be used as long as it is compatible with the materials being stored.

5.2.4   Chemical Spills

Spilled chemicals represent an injury waiting to happen. This is especially true if they are not cleaned up right away. Small amounts of chemicals should be immediately neutralized and cleaned up using spill kit materials that are designed for that purpose. Common wastewater laboratory spill kits are available for neutralizing and cleaning up acid and base spills, mercury spills, and flammable liquids. Employees should never attempt to clean up a spill or release that is beyond their training and if the proper resources are not available. If a spill or release occurs, it may be necessary to evacuate and workers must be instructed on the site's emergency response procedures, including evacuation routes and assembly areas.

5.2.5   Transporting

Dropping even a gallon container of an acutely toxic chemical such as a concentrated acid can result in devastating injuries and/or cause serious health issues. When carrying containers of acutely hazardous chemicals, extreme care must be taken to not drop or damage the container. To avoid dropping or damaging containers, workers should limit the number of containers they carry; keep walkways and floors clear of

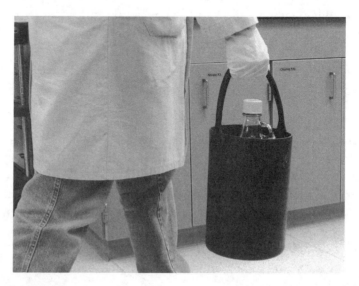

FIGURE 4.1   Bottle carrier.

debris, water, obstructions and other slip/trip hazards; and pay careful attention to where they are walking. When carrying acutely hazardous chemicals, workers need to keep focused and not allow themselves to become distracted.

If transporting or carrying a single bottle of an acutely hazardous chemical such as concentrated acids, a bottle carrier (see Figure 4.1) is ideal. The bottle carrier will protect glass containers from breakage while the chemicals are transported through hallways. The bottle carrier will contain the chemical if the original container fails. If carrying more than one chemical, a simple polypropylene tray on a utility cart can be used as long as the chemicals placed into the tray are compatible.

6.0 REFERENCES

American Gas Association (2001) *Purging Principles and Practices*, 3rd ed.; AGA XK0101; American Gas Association: Washington, D.C.

American National Standards Institute (1990) *Emergency Eyewash and Shower Equipment;* ANSI Z358.1–1990; American National Standards Institute: New York.

Centers for Disease Control and Prevention (2007) *NIOSH Pocket Guide to Chemical Hazards*, 3rd ed.; DHHS (NIOSH) Publication No. 2005–149; National Institute for Occupational Safety and Health: Cincinnati, Ohio.

Chlorine Institute, Inc. (2008) *Personal Protective Equipment for Chlor-Alkali Chemicals*, 5th ed.; Pamphlet 65; Chlorine Institute, Inc.: Arlington, Virginia.

Methanol Institute (2011) *Methanol Safe Handling Manual.* http://www.methanol. org/Health-And-Safety/Safety-Resources/Health—Safety/Methanol-Safe-Handling-Manual-English.aspx (accessed Aug 2011).

National Institute for Occupational Safety and Health (2007) *Ergonomic Guidelines for Manual Material Handling;* DHHS (NIOSH) Publication No. 2007–131; National Institute for Occupational Safety and Health: Cincinnati, Ohio.

Occupational Safety and Health Administration, *Code of Federal Regulations* Title 29, Part 1910, General Industry. http://www.osha.gov/**law-regs.html** (accessed July 2011).

Occupational Safety and Health Administration, *Code of Federal Regulations* Part 1926, Construction. http://www.osha.gov/**law-regs.html** (accessed July 2011).

Strom, D. J. (2005) *Radiological Risk Assessment for King County Wastewater Division;* PNNL 15163 Vol 1. http://www.pnl.gov/main/publications/external/

technical ... /PNNL-15163vol1.pdf (accessed March 2011), Pacific Northwest National Laboratory: Richland, Washington.

U.S. Environmental Protection Agency (1999a) *Wastewater Technology Fact Sheet Ozone Disinfection.* http://www.epa.gov/owm/mtb/ozon.pdf (accessed July 2011).

U.S. Environmental Protection Agency (1999b) *Wastewater Technology Fact Sheet UV Disinfection.* www.epa.gov/owm/mtb/uv.pdf (accessed July 2011).

U.S. Environmental Protection Agency (2000) *Wastewater Technology Fact Sheet Dechlorination.* http://water.epa.gov/scitech/wastetech/upload/2002_06work _28_mtb_dechlorination.pdf (accessed July 2011).

Water Environment Federation (2007) *Operation of Municipal Wastewater Treatment Plants,* 6th ed.; WEF Manual of Practice No. 11; McGraw-Hill: New York.

Water Environment Federation; American Society of Civil Engineers; Environmental & Water Resources Institue (2009) *Design of Municipal Wastewater Treatment Plants,* 5th ed.; WEF Manual of Practice No. 8/ASCE Manuals and Reports on Engineering Practice No. 76; McGraw-Hill: New York.

7.0 SUGGESTED READINGS

Centers for Disease Control and Prevention (1989) *Criteria for a Recommended Standard, Occupational Exposure to Hand-Arm Vibration;* National Institute for Occupational Safety and Health: Cincinnati, Ohio.

Metcalf and Eddy, Inc. (2003) *Wastewater Engineering—Treatment and Reuse,* 4th ed.; McGraw-Hill: New York.

State of California (1990) *Title 8, Barclays Official California Code of Regulations;* California Office of Administration Law: San Francisco, California.

U.S. Environmental Protection Agency (2003) *Managing Asbestos in Place—A Building Owner's Guide to Operations and Maintenance Programs for Asbestos-Containing Materials;* TS-799 (Green Book); U.S. Environmental Protection Agency, Office of Pesticides and Toxic Substances: Washington, D.C.

Chapter 5

Safety and Health in Wastewater Treatment Plant Maintenance

(continued)

1.0   WORKING SAFELY

1.1   Managing Safety Within a Maintenance Department

Maintenance involves activities as diverse as lubricating a bearing or running diagnostics on a complete system. To keep facilities operating at design standards, workers troubleshoot, diagnose, and test equipment, which often requires them to remove guards, override safety circuits, and work close to potential hazards. Maintenance personnel often perform field repairs in locations that may be remote, exposed to extreme weather conditions, or have demanding physical hindrances. Tasks may follow regular, predictable schedules or may be the unexpected result of emergencies. Compounded by operational demands, the need to return equipment to service may require temporary repairs and substitutions.

The following sections discuss many of the options, considerations, and practices used to decrease hazards and risks associated with wastewater industry maintenance. This material is not intended to be all-inclusive. Indeed, maintenance also requires skilled individuals, professional judgment, and an appreciation of hazards and potential solutions. This chapter will provide direction for some of these solutions.

1.2   Developing a Culture of Safety

Working safely is one of the greatest responsibilities of both employees and managers of municipal facilities. Every worker has the right to return from his or her workplace uninjured.

An effective safety program has to be practiced daily, and must be foremost in a worker's thoughts for the day. An effective safety program includes daily practice, a call to meeting, and a strong central leader. The central leader can be the head of a group or the safety director of the entire operation at an organizational level or even down to the supervisor of a work party. Safety briefings must be conducted daily with a focus on hazards that are prevalent at the worksite.

Safety briefings must be delivered in a positive way. The supervisor must emphasize the need for safety, making sure that workers are instructed about the hazards and proper precautions. The purpose of the briefings is to provide positive reinforcement, an awareness and recognition of hazards, and preventive measures. A culture of fear should be avoided. Alertness to duty and adequate provisions of safety equipment are keys to any successful safety program.

1.2.1   Safety Inspections

Safety inspections are part of safety briefings. The supervisor, no matter how long he or she has worked on the job, must be trained to perform safety inspections with a fresh eye at each worksite. Hazards have a way of changing; unfortunately, some of our routines do not. Even if the task has been performed a hundred or a thousand times before, a safety inspection that includes thorough inspection of safety equipment is necessary.

One of the best ways to provide a safety inspection is by checklist. Even pilots, who make hundreds of flights a year, performing the same actions over and over again, use a checklist to prevent omission of critical things required for safe operation of their aircraft. So it should be with safety programs. An inspection checklist does not need be overly long, but it should be specific enough to be effective. A generic checklist may be quick and easy to prepare and satisfy a basic intent to get people looking for safety hazards. A specific checklist does more to target remedies already in place to ensure they are well maintained. The goal or purpose of the inspection should be defined and inspectors trained to do the job right.

1.2.2   Safety Briefings

A prejob safety briefing is an excellent way to remind the supervisor and the workforce to look at the jobsite, to analyze hazards, and then to design a program to deal with the hazards. Jobs performed routinely can be analyzed through a job safety analysis (JSA) and written up for repeated use.

A critical part of a safety program is thorough examination of safety equipment to be used on the job. Are the ropes and harnesses used in good shape? Do workers need life preservers? Do they have the necessary personal protective equipment (PPE), including hard hats, gloves, boots, and so on? If there is a confined space, are rescue provisions required? All of these items are part of a safety prejob briefing and can easily be put into a JSA for supervisors and workers to prepare to work safely.

1.2.3   Recognizing Hazards

Everyone needs proficiency in hazard recognition as it takes training and repetition. The problem is that we often underrate hazards because we see many commonplace hazards nearly every day. We become accustomed to the uneven sidewalk-tripping hazard and eventually ignore it. We get comfortable with that old aluminum ladder; it is light and just the right height. So what if it is missing one rubber foot and the labels are unreadable? All of us probably have some little hazard that we've become tolerant of and have accepted as normal or just part of the job. We believe that we can manage these hazards readily because our past experience tells us that we have successfully done so before. But what about that new employee or a visitor; are they accustomed to those hazards?

Hazard recognition on the job involves brainpower and analysis. An employee who cannot or will not think on his or her feet has the potential to get himself or herself or others injured or even killed on the job. Carelessness, lack of situational awareness, and inattentiveness are the three primary contributors to accidents. Taking safety shortcuts just to speed the job along must be avoided. These habits need to be trained out of persons in the work force.

1.3 Fall Protection

Falls are one of the leading causes of injuries and deaths on the job. They can be caused by slips and trips, impacts from other moving equipment, environmental conditions caused by cold or moisture, medical reasons, or simply a loss of balance. Occupational falls can be complex events; they often involve faulty or missing equipment and almost always are associated with improper preventive work procedures. Many injuries and deaths could be prevented with the appropriate equipment and procedures in place.

Fall protection is a combination of methods and devices used to protect workers from falling off, onto, or through working levels. Fall protection methods and devices are typically divided into two categories: those that prevent falls and those that arrest falls. Fall protection also includes methods and devices that protect workers from being struck by tools, debris, or other objects falling from repair activities overhead. Examples of fall protection methods and devices include rails, guards, guardrails, barriers, fall-arrest systems, positioning device or fall-restraint systems, safety nets, hole covers, and various work practices and procedures. For more information on fall protection and fall-restraint equipment, the reader is referred to Chapter 10, "Personal Protective Equipment."

1.3.1 Fall Protection Training

The Occupational Safety and Health Administration (OSHA) requires employers to provide training for each employee in recognizing and minimizing the hazards of stairways and ladders. The training program needs to include hazards associated with ladders and the procedures that need to be followed to minimize those hazards. Each worker exposed to a fall hazard should be trained by a competent person in identifying fall hazards and safe work practices to avoid or eliminate fall hazards.

Specific training topics should include

- The nature of fall hazards;

- Proper construction, use, placement, and care in handling of all stairways and ladders;

- How to inspect all fall protection equipment prior to use;

- The maximum intended load carrying capabilities of any ladder used; and

- Occupational Safety and Health Administration standards covering stairways and ladders.

Workers bear the responsibility to learn the information and to follow the procedures.

With federal regulations, it is important to remember the 1.83-m (6-ft) rule. If a worker has the potential for a fall of 1.8 m (6 ft) or more, his or her work is likely to require fall protection. For some general industry or electrical industry work, the trigger height for fall protection is 1.2 m (4 ft). It is important to always ensure that any fall protection system meets or exceeds the required strength tolerances for the equipment and the anchorage points as defined in the applicable standard.

1.3.2 Ladder Safety Guidelines

Ladder users should read and follow all manufacturers' data regarding proper ladder selection, placement, use, and care. Only ladders that comply with OSHA design standards should be used.

For added safety while stepping off or onto a ladder, portable ladders should be positioned so that the side rails extend at least 0.9 m (3 ft) above the landing. Some ladders can accommodate side rail extensions (without the ladder rungs), making it much easier and safer to step through the side rails rather than swinging around the ladder, while still providing the required side rail support. Additional ladder recommended best practices include the following:

- Regularly inspect ladders for cracked or broken parts such as rungs, steps, side rails, and free and locking components as part of a preventive maintenance program;

- Any equipment found with defects and deemed unusable shall be immediately destroyed or removed from service and tagged as "dangerous" (i.e., "do not use");

- Do not apply more weight on the ladder than it is designed to support;
- Make sure that the weight on the ladder will not cause it to slip off its support;
- Step ladders should not exceed 6 m (20 ft) in height;
- Ladders should be maintained in good condition at all times;
- Ladder users should perform a pre-use inspection before use;
- Portable ladders should not be placed in front of doors opening toward the ladder, unless the door is blocked, locked, or guarded;
- Ladders should not be placed on boxes, barrels, or other unstable bases to obtain additional height;
- The ladder base section must be placed with a secure footing;
- Tops of ordinary step ladders should not be used as a step;
- The length of single ladders or individual sections of ladders should not exceed 9.14 m (30 ft);
- On multiple-section extension ladders, the minimum overlap for each section should be maintained following the manufacturer's recommendations and applicable regulations;
- Position portable extension ladders so the side rails extend at least 0.9 m (3 ft) above the landing or leading edge; and
- Bracing on the back legs of step ladders is designed for increasing stability and is not intended for climbing.

For ladder work practices when work is performed on or near electrical circuits, the reader is referred to 29 CFR 1910.333(c) (OSHA, 2011a). Ladders used around, on, or near electrical systems should be rated for electrical service. Additional standards specific to portable wood ladders can be found in 29 CFR 1910.25 (OSHA, 2011h); for portable metal ladders, in 29 CFR 1910.26 (OSHA, 2011h); and, for standards for ladder safety in the construction industry, in 29 CFR 1926.1053 (OSHA, 2011g).

1.3.3   Scaffolding

Scaffolds are temporary elevated work platforms used to hold workers and materials. There are three basic types of scaffolds: supported scaffolds, suspension scaffolds, and aerial lifts. A qualified person must train all employees who perform work on scaffolding to recognize the hazards associated with the type of scaffold used and to understand hazard control procedures. Training must include the following, as applicable:

- Any electrical hazards,
- Fall hazards and prevention measures,
- Falling objects,
- Fall-protection and falling object protection,
- Proper use of scaffold,
- Proper handling of materials, and
- Maximum intended load and capacity of scaffolds used.

The following are some best practices to protect maintenance workers from hazards while working on or around scaffolds:

- Do not allow tools, materials, or debris to collect on the scaffold;
- Never throw or drop tools, materials, or equipment off the scaffold;
- Make sure all connections are in place and completely tight;
- Do not stand on ties, guardrails, or plank extensions;
- Do not overreach outside of the guardrails;
- Stay off the scaffold during material loading and unloading;
- Use three points of contact when climbing a scaffold;
- Never leave partially dismantled scaffolds unguarded or unlabeled;
- Securely fasten the working platform to the scaffolding so that it cannot slip; and
- Ensure that the scaffold has adequate support on a solid foundation.

For further information, the reader is referred to 29 CFR 1926.451 and 29 CFR 1926.500 (OSHA, 2011f).

1.3.4   Fall Restraint

Fall-restraint equipment consists of a safety belt or harness and a rope that is tethered to a substantial anchor point. These body belt or body harness systems are intended to be set up so that a worker can free fall no farther than 0.6 m (2 ft); they should be secured to an anchorage capable of supporting at least twice the potential impact load of an employee's fall or 13.3 kN (3000 lb), whichever is greater. It is important to recognize that fall restraint is different from fall arrest in that the worker is restrained from falling more than 0.6 m (2 ft), which greatly reduces the fall-arresting force. Requirements for snap hooks, D-rings, and other connectors used with positioning device systems must meet the same criteria as those for personal fall-arrest systems. Whenever practical, guide rails or hand rails should be installed as added protection for workers.

1.4 Ergonomics

The three basic elements of an ergonomic program are specific task and worksite evaluations, training, and effective implementation of ergonomic control strategies. Ergonomics are not a one-time, fix-all procedure, rather, a continuous, ongoing process approach used to optimize the working environment.

There are several methods used to identify jobs that are most likely to result in ergonomic disorders. Managers and supervisors should monitor injury and illness records and worker's compensation data to identify patterns of ergonomic-related injuries and illnesses.

Providing employees with the appropriate tools and equipment is a necessary component of an ergonomic program. Therefore, ergonomics should always be considered when replacing equipment or designing new workstations.

Hands and wrists are most susceptible to the risk of developing a musculoskeletal disorder. Common work conditions that intensify stress on wrist joints include repetitive hand motions, poor keyboard or mouse technique, incorrect work surface heights, and forceful writing for an extended period of time. Periodic stretching will help reduce the stress.

Work methods and environmental issues can influence the efficiency and safety of the task. Maintenance department personnel routinely perform tasks that require bending, pushing, pulling, twisting, and lifting. Training employees to improve general body mechanics can greatly reduce the chance of injury. Control strategies should be developed and implemented to reduce or eliminate ergonomic risk factors in the workplace whenever feasible.

1.4.1 Musculoskeletal Disorders

Musculoskeletal disorders are typically a result of everyday use developed over a long period of time. Exposure to risk factors at work and at home, compounded by insufficient recovery time, can contribute to injury.

Musculoskeletal disorders can affect muscles, tendons, nerves, joints, and spinal discs. The severity of musculoskeletal disorders can range from mild to intermediate pain or discomfort to complete debilitating injuries. An ergonomic program cannot control disorders that have already developed, but it can assist in identifying possible risk factors and, therefore, prevent the worsening of the disorder. Early identification of the signs and symptoms followed by prompt intervention is the best method to prevent more serious or chronic musculoskeletal disorders.

Musculoskeletal disorders are generally hard to diagnose in early stages and typically take a long time to develop. Musculoskeletal disorders share common characteristics in that they all are a result of exposure to risk factors and are difficult to treat in later stages of development.

1.4.2   Risk Factors

Risk factors are conditions or circumstances influenced by the frequency and duration of an activity that increase the chances of developing a musculoskeletal disorder. The longer a person is exposed to the risk factors or the more frequent the exposure, the more likely an injury will occur. However, not every person exposed to risk factors will develop a musculoskeletal disorder, and there is no way to determine how much exposure will result in an injury.

Risk factors can be generally grouped as *occupational*, relating to the task or activity, or *individual*, taking into consideration a person's capabilities, physical attributes, and behaviors.

Occupational risk factors are those physical exposures that are inherent to the job or task. Occupational risk factors expose all workers performing the task to similar risks because the exposure is related to the task.

Engineering controls are the preferred method of addressing and resolving employee exposures to occupational risk factors. Examples of engineering controls include properly designed workstations, proper tools, and ergonomically designed facilities and equipment.

Administrative controls can also be used to significantly reduce daily exposure to occupational risk factors by altering the way in which work is performed. Examples of administrative controls include employee rotation, adjusting the pace of the work (i.e., slower pace), alternating tasks between employees, work processes that have taken ergonomics into consideration, and recovery rest breaks.

1.4.2.1 Repetition

A repetitive risk factor occurs when the same or similar movements are performed frequently. Repetition can still occur even when different tasks are performed if the repetitive motion is still similar. Inadequate recovery time may cause an injury.

The repetitive risk factor can be evaluated by

- Measuring the frequency or duration of tasks pertaining to certain movements,
- Measuring the ratio of work time to recovery time,
- Measuring the percentage of the workday spent on similar repetitive activities, and
- Measuring the quantity of work performed in a given time.

1.4.2.2 Force

A force risk factor is the amount of physical effort required by a person to perform a task or to maintain control of tools or an object involved in the activity. The type of grip required to hold the object can concentrate the force and the stress of individual muscles, tendons, or joints. Injury may result from excessive sustained force.

The force risk factor can be evaluated by

- Measuring the weight of the objects involved in the activity,
- Measuring the dimensions of the objects involved in the activity, and
- Measuring the amount of force required to manipulate the objects.

1.4.2.3 Awkward and Static Posture

A posture risk factor is created when the work activity frequently places the body out of the midrange or neutral position. Required positioning is often characterized as awkward or unnatural. The further away from neutral you stretch, the greater the stress on tendons, muscles, and joints. A posture risk can also occur if one position is held for a prolonged period of time. A static posture will result in reduced blood flow to the affected muscles and cause fatigue, which can lead to decreased muscle control, pain, discomfort, and injury.

The posture risk factor can be evaluated by

- Measuring the degree of bending or twisting while performing the activity;
- Measuring the reach distance;
- Measuring the length of time one position is held; and
- Measuring the total amount of time spent in one position during a work shift.

1.4.2.4 Contact Stress

A contact stress risk factor is caused by localized pressure on a body part in contact with a sharp edge or hard surface. The point of contact can irritate local tissues and interfere with blood circulation and nerve function.

The contact stress risk factor can be evaluated by

- Measuring the amount of time the body part is in contact with a sharp edge or hard surface and

- Measuring the degree of sharpness, hardness, or conformity to the body part.

1.4.2.5 Temperature Extremes

A temperature risk factor is caused by exposure to extreme cold or heat, which can be caused by environmental conditions or process equipment or from the temperature of objects being used. Direct contact or indirect exposure places stress on skin tissues. Extreme cold can cause blood vessels to constrict, resulting in reduced sensitivity and loss of hand coordination. Extreme heat can result in increased fatigue and lead to heat stress.

The temperature risk factor can be evaluated by

- Measuring the ambient temperature in the work environment and

- Measuring the temperatures associated with the task or process.

1.4.2.6 Vibration

A vibration risk factor can be exposure to whole body vibration or individual parts of the body. Whole body vibration can place stress on spinal tissues and typically results from operating equipment or driving long distances. Local vibration risk is typically associated with hand–arm vibration from power tools. This vibration exposure causes stress on the tissues of the fingers, hands, and arms.

Vibration risk factor can be evaluated by

- Measuring the amount of continuous exposure to vibration;

- Measuring the amplitude, frequency, and acceleration rates of the vibration; and

- Measuring the total amount of intermittent exposure over a period of time.

Knowing the risk factors, employees in an office setting can perform their own workstation evaluation. The workstation should be adjusted so that the most common work activities are performed in a neutral posture position. Items frequently used should be located close at hand to minimize reaching, bending, or twisting. The work environment also affects ergonomic posture. Lighting should be adjusted to provide optimal viewing without causing screen glare; task lights should be used as needed. If possible, varying work tasks should be scheduled to provide periodic changes in repetitive motions or fixed postures.

Individual risk factors include those individual actions that may mimic or duplicate the same physical exposures that are inherent to the job or task. Individual risk factors differ from occupational risk factors in that each individual may be affected differently by the same exposure because of their physical condition, size, shape, and body mechanics. People have different levels of tolerance and may be influenced by other lifestyle choices. Psychosocial issues from stress to boredom to anxiety can contribute to risk factors.

Stress can come from many non-occupational sources. Regardless of where it originated from, stress causes tension and results in an employee becoming more susceptible to an injury, which can lead to a musculoskeletal disorder. Distractions from heavy workloads, production deadlines, family, or emotional problems can all influence work habits and behaviors. Generally, people in good health, which encompasses eating a balanced diet and getting regular exercise and adequate sleep, can tolerate more stress and will recover faster from the daily demands placed on them.

After-work activities may also adversely affect the body's ability to rest and recover from work activities. High-impact activities can further damage muscles and other parts of the musculoskeletal system. Actions that pattern or use the same muscle groups can prevent adequate recovery. In some instances, a pre-existing medical condition can cause certain activities to have a much greater effect and result in a subsequent musculoskeletal disorder.

Wherever feasible, engineering controls are the preferred method for addressing risk factors associated with a musculoskeletal disorder. Examples of engineering controls include changing, modifying, or redesigning workstations, tools, facilities, equipment, materials and processes. The objective of engineering controls is to design the task or workstation to fit the employee's size, shape, physical tolerance, and capabilities.

The tool that is most appropriate for the job should be selected. A tool that is oversized may add more stress than is required to perform the task. A tool that is undersized may require more applied force to accomplish the task, again adding to overall stress. When selecting a tool, it is important to consider hand positioning and fit and if the worker will be wearing gloves. Handles should be round and fit the hand. Tools should be well-maintained, including sharpened cutting surfaces.

Administrative controls can be used to significantly reduce daily exposure to occupational risk factors by altering the way in which work is performed. Administrative controls are accomplished through work scheduling and procedures aimed at reducing the exposure. Training workers in ergonomically sound work practices, lifting techniques, and proper tool selection is critical to lessening the potential for developing a musculoskeletal disorder.

Ergonomics in industrial settings can be influenced by a number of factors. Choosing the best tool for the job and adjusting the work habits and techniques of the employee can reduce the risk factors associated with a musculoskeletal disorder. Long periods of bending or stretching can be avoided by placing equipment or materials at the appropriate working level. Additionally, factors contributing to fatigue such as poor lighting, noise, or temperature extremes can be reduced.

Workers should avoid sudden or jerky movements or awkward combinations of movements or positions such as bending and twisting at the same time. These movements can be especially damaging when combined with heavy pushing, pulling, or lifting.

Personal protective equipment provides barriers between a person and a hazard when other controls are limited or unavailable. Personal protective equipment is always the last consideration in reducing exposure to ergonomic risk factors.

Personal protective equipment may be effective in reducing risk factors associated with vibration, temperature extremes, or contact stress. For example, when chosen properly, gloves have proven to be an appropriate protective device. Gloves can protect hands from injury and damage from extreme heat and cold. Textured gloves can also enhance grip. Conversely, however, gloves can also reduce dexterity and sensitivity to touch. Gloves that are too stiff require more finger strength for a proper grip. Therefore, a glove should be selected that fits well and will minimize palm sweating. Padded gloves can provide useful protection when working with tools that vibrate.

Braces, splints, back belts, and other supporting apparatuses are not considered PPE. They are worn to reduce movement and as an aid to recovery and should only be used under the direction and guidance of a health care professional. It should be made clear that wearing a brace while performing the same activity will require additional effort to perform the act, which could cause further injury. Any employee diagnosed with a musculoskeletal disorder and prescribed to wear a support brace should have their work activity altered or reduced, as advised by their physician, to limit exposure and facilitate recovery.

A risk factor analysis may be performed at any time. Preferably, an analysis should be performed based on an awareness of potential risk factors prior to an employee's complaint of pain or discomfort. The advantage is clearly to prevent an injury and to optimize the working environment.

Being aware of ergonomic risk factors, any person may perform a self-assessment of their work activity. If an employee reports having pain or discomfort, his or her supervisor should assist the employee in considering the aforementioned risk factors as a potential contributor to the discomfort and complete an ergonomic risk factor analysis. When considering the various risk factors, describe how the activity is affected by that factor and estimate the frequency or duration of the activity relative to a normal work shift. Then list the control strategy that may influence the risk factor. For example, an activity may be described as lifting various boxes, 20 boxes per hour, and 4 hours per day. Another activity may be described as word processing, or data entry, 6 hours per day, 70% keyboard, and 30% mouse.

After consideration of the risk factors, immediate solutions may be readily available and easily resolved. This may be especially true for short-term tasks or work activities. Solutions may include changing the method, schedule, or process used to perform the task.

When pain or discomfort is recurring or associated with a normal job function or work activity, the solution may not be easily recognized. In fact, the cause of discomfort may be attributed to a number of interrelated factors. In some instances, a professional in the ergonomics field may be consulted for an expert opinion and could assist in completing and reviewing the ergonomic risk factor analysis and discuss possible control strategies to reduce or eliminate associated risk factors.

1.4.3 Proper Lifting

One of the most common types of injury is lower back injuries caused by improper lifting. Lifting should be done with leg muscles and not with the weaker back muscles. Training for workers who have to lift heavy objects should be provided and reinforced often. In this instance, *heavy* is a relative term with respect to the size of the worker. Generally, anything over 22.5 kg (50 lb) may fall into this category, but items that are bulky, awkward, or require a stretched or reaching posture can also cause an injury. The principal method of lifting to avoid this type of injury is to keep the back straight and to lift with the legs. A mechanical lifting device is a plausible alternate method to prevent injury. Finally, workers should ask for help whenever necessary.

2.0   CONTROL OF HAZARDOUS ENERGY

2.1   Lockout/Tagout

Procedures to isolate all sources of energy associated with a piece of equipment to be serviced, adjusted, or repaired are critical to the safety of maintenance workers. The fundamental part in these procedures is a process commonly known as *lockout/ tagout*. When properly applied and tested, lockout/tagout procedures are intended to prevent unexpected releases of energy.

Lockout is the safest means of isolating equipment for the maintenance employee. Lockout is accomplished by affixing a specially designed lockout device to isolate an energy source and securing the device with a lock in a predetermined position or state. An electrical breaker for a power source could be locked open. A valve isolating a pressure or fluid source could be locked closed and a vent or bleed valve could be locked open to prevent the accumulation of pressure. Most isolation devices today are engineered and manufactured with a means to install a lockout. In addition, several manufacturers have produced a wide variety of products capable of securely locking out even the most difficult systems.

Tagout is accomplished by placing a plainly visible tag on the energy isolation component. The tag acts as a warning and should clearly state the reason the device is the way it is. Tags can be useful in many situations, such as testing; however tags should never be a substitute for a lockout when personnel are at risk because of an unexpected return of energy. Tags must be made of a durable material that will hold up to environmental exposure without deterioration and while remaining legible.

Occupational Safety and Health Administration standards require employers to develop written plans for securing equipment known as *energy control procedures*. Depending on the size of the facility, the method used to group similar items, and the amount of detail included in these procedures, they could easily number into the hundreds. Significant investments of staff hours could go into developing well-detailed procedures. Once complete, these procedures become a valuable knowledge base for training and serve as the bulk of the energy control or lockout program. In addition to the procedures, the program must also include guidelines for training workers on these procedures and requirements for performing periodic inspections and program audits.

An industry-proven method for providing lockout protection is to install a key-operated, tamper-proof locking device on every valve, power disconnect, or energy control component identified in the energy control procedure. If more than one worker will be involved, each employee working on the system should apply an individual lock with its unique key or combination.

Rotating machine parts or parts with stored energy should be physically restrained or positioned in a zero mechanical state, removing any stored energy and preventing movement by gravity, wind, spring release, or fluid flow.

Many pieces of equipment also have auxiliary equipment that, if operated, could injure workers making repairs. Thus, to properly isolate a pump, both its electrical system and all appurtenant valves should be isolated. To ensure that all related equipment are properly locked out and secured in large systems, a responsible person who is familiar with the equipment and system should be designated to be an isolation supervisor and he or she should follow the energy control procedure.

When a machine or a system needs to be locked out for safety, all personnel who will be affected should be informed. Application of a lockout permit is an effective way to keep shift workers informed and provides a quick reference to track equipment out of service. The permit should include the following information: date, time, name of person applying and/or removing the locks and tags, and the equipment or system on which the work is to be performed. A brief summary of the work being performed may be beneficial.

Personnel should be taught to adhere to established lockout procedures for their own benefit and to respect all locks and tags for the safety of everyone involved. Locks and tags may be removed only by the person(s) they were meant to protect. Ignoring lockout/tagout procedures could result in personal injury or equipment damage.

2.2 Energy Isolation and Release

Isolation is about making sure that there are no alternative paths for the equipment to be energized. Energy can be stored as pressure or temperature and can be mechanical, electrical, or even gravitational. All sources must be considered when completing an energy control procedure. It is important to ensure that systems are depressurized and cooled. In addition, it is important to consider if the system is best drained or vented to ensure pressure does not build up or return. Components that could fall or move as the work is performed should be blocked.

Electrical grounding or discharging of stored electrical energy may be needed and must be performed by qualified personnel. Before any worker starts working on electrical equipment, equipment should be tested to ensure that it is isolated and properly grounded and that there is no stray or residual energy connected to the equipment. Simply throwing a single circuit breaker may not be enough; in some instances, equipment may have multiple power sources or share a common ground wire with other machinery that is still energized. When faulty electrical grounding is present, equipment can carry energy through its case or internals and deliver a deadly shock. For systems with self-contained energy such as large batteries or capacitors, it is important to ensure that these systems are either isolated or discharged before beginning to work on or around them. A simple voltmeter can be used for this purpose, but should only be performed by a qualified electrician. The reader is referred to Section 6.0 for more information on electrical safety.

2.3 Test and Verify

All associated sources of energy must be tested to ensure that the power to the machine is off, with the equipment in a de-energized state. The effectiveness of the lockout must be tested and verified for each machine or equipment item. Following a written hazardous energy control procedure is an effective way to make sure all energy is considered when performing the lockout.

Once the lockout is completed, ensure all employees are standing clear of the machine and attempt to start the machine at the local start control station. The machine should not start. If the machine has a remotely controlled starting feature, the control room should be contacted to request they attempt to start the equipment. The machine should not start. If either of these tests causes the equipment to start, all work should be stopped on the machine and the lockout reviewed for accuracy using the written procedure. Any errors in the lockout should be corrected and the tests repeated. All operating controls should be returned to the "off" position after each test.

2.4 Lockout Removal

When the work is completed and before circuits or equipment are re-energized, even temporarily, a visual inspection should be performed to verify that all tools, electrical jumpers, grounds, and other such devices have been removed. All affected employees should be informed of the intention to re-energize the circuit or equipment. All persons exposed to hazards associated with re-energizing the circuit or equipment should be warned to stay clear of the circuits and equipment and a visual determination should be made that will ensure the safety of all personnel.

3.0 WORKING AROUND MACHINERY

3.1 Machine Guarding

All rotating and moving equipment should be guarded. The best method for preventing machinery-related injuries is through use of equipment guards enforced through engineering and administrative controls. Left exposed, moving parts can create opportunities to catch fingers or hands, loose clothing, or other objects that may fall into their path. In addition to personal injury, equipment repairs can be expensive and seriously compromise process performance. The best way to prevent this type of injury is to install point-of-operation guards that prevent contact with ingoing nip points, pinch points, rotating parts, flying chips, and sparks. Examples of guarding methods include barrier guards, two-hand tripping devices, and electronic safety devices. Occupational Safety and Health Administration 29 CFR 1910.211 (Subpart O) (OSHA, 2011c) addresses standards for guarding machinery.

3.2 Safety Devices

Safety devices provide an immediate means for stopping a piece of equipment in an emergency situation. Common devices include electrical lockout–stop switches located adjacent to the equipment, proximity switches, light beam curtains, and mechanical interlocks. Some machines are equipped with an emergency pull cable. When the cable is pulled, machine operation is halted and an alarm generated. All safety devices should be periodically tested as part of the maintenance program.

3.3 Environmental Hazards

In addition to mechanical hazards of working around machinery, there are other hazards that need to be considered. Maintenance personnel must be trained and properly protected from these hazards as well.

3.3.1 Noise

Noise as a hazard is sound that is especially loud or impacting. A wastewater treatment plant has equipment that produces high noise levels both continuously and intermittently. As such, it is important to be aware of this hazard and to take preventive steps to reduce exposure to damaging noise levels by wearing effective hearing protection and to minimize the duration of the exposure to the noise. High levels of noise interfere with communication and can contribute to accidents and injuries by making it difficult for workers to hear warning signals. Repeated exposure may ultimately cause irreversible damage to ears, resulting in noise-induced hearing loss, which is recognized by the World Health Organization as a leading occupational illness.

Difficulty hearing a normal conversation is the first indication that noise may be a problem in the workplace. When noise levels increase above 80 dB, people have to speak loudly; when noise levels increase above 85 dB, people have to shout. Lastly, when noise levels increase above 95 dB, people have to crowd closely together to be heard.

The best way to deal with high levels of noise is through engineering controls when a facility is being designed. In situations where this is not possible, noise exposure must be monitored to determine the time-weighted average over an 8-hour period. If the value meets or exceeds 85 dB, federal regulations (CFR 29) require that a comprehensive hearing conservation program be implemented. Elements of the program include monitoring, audiometric testing, and provisions of hearing protection, training, and recordkeeping.

Employers must provide employees with a selection of at least one type of hearing plug and one type of hearing muff. The hearing plug and muff selected should be comfortable to wear and offer sufficient protection appropriate for the working environment. Assistance should be sought of a person knowledgeable in the available type and size of hearing protectors and trained to properly fit the devices. Most hearing protection devices have a manufacturer's noise reduction rating that represents the protector's ability to reduce noise under ideal laboratory conditions. To achieve this level of protection, the device must be properly fitted and the employee must be trained on how to insert or wear the protection.

3.3.2   Heat Insulation (Asbestos)

Asbestos is a mineral fiber that was added to a variety of products to strengthen them and to provide heat insulation and fire resistance. Most products made today do not contain asbestos. However, those few products that still contain asbestos could be inhaled and are required to be labeled. Prior to the 1970s, many types of building products and insulation materials contained asbestos. Common products that might have contained asbestos in the past, and conditions which may release fibers, include the following:

- Some roofing and siding shingles (made of asbestos cement);
- Insulation products installed between 1930 and 1950;
- Hot water and steam pipes in older installations may be coated with an asbestos material or covered with an asbestos blanket or tape;

- Prior to 1977, asbestos may be present in textured paint and in patching compounds used on wall and ceiling joints;

- Asbestos is found in some vinyl floor tiles and the backing on vinyl sheet flooring and adhesives; and

- Oil and coal furnaces and door gaskets may have asbestos insulation.

Asbestos material cannot be identified by looking at it unless it carries a label. Therefore, material in question should be sampled and analyzed by a qualified professional. There is no physical hazard from asbestos unless the material is damaged and the fibers are released. Once released, the fibers could be inhaled into the lungs.

Breathing asbestos fibers can create scar-like tissue in the lungs called *asbestosis*, which results in the loss of lung function and, possibly, disability and death. Asbestos also causes cancer of the lungs and other diseases such as mesothelioma of the pleura, which is a fatal malignant tumor of the membrane lining the cavity of the lungs or stomach.

3.3.3 *Heat Illness and Stress*

Heat stress falls into two categories: heat illness and heat stroke. Both are serious conditions and should not be taken lightly. Heat-related illness is typically associated with strenuous outdoor activities while working in hot air temperatures or in areas of high humidity. Other conditions that can result in a heat illness are cramps, heat rash, or heat exhaustion; if left unattended, these conditions can develop into heat stroke. Heat-related illnesses are medical emergencies that require proper care and treatment by trained medical personnel. Factors that may cause heat-related illnesses include

- High temperature and humidity,

- Dehydration from low fluid consumption,

- Direct sun exposure (with no shade) or extreme heat,

- Limited air movement (no breeze or wind),

- Physical exertion,

- Use of bulky protective clothing and equipment,

- Poor physical condition or ongoing health problems,

- Some medications,

- Pregnancy,

- Lack of previous exposure to hot workplaces, and

- Previous heat-related illness.

Heat stroke is the most serious heat-related health problem. Heat stroke occurs when the body temperature regulating system fails and body core temperature rises to critical levels. This is a medical emergency that may result in death. Signs of heat stroke are confusion, loss of consciousness, and seizures. Workers experiencing heat stroke have a very high body temperature and may stop sweating. If a worker shows signs of possible heat stroke, medical help should be sought immediately.

Until medical help arrives, the worker should be moved to a shady, cool area and as much clothing as possible should be removed. The worker should be wetted with cool water and the air circulated to speed cooling.

Heat illness is broken into several categories, including heat exhaustion, heat cramps, and heat rash. Heat exhaustion is the next most serious heat-related health problem. Signs and symptoms of heat exhaustion are headache, nausea, dizziness, weakness, irritability, confusion, thirst, heavy sweating, and a body temperature greater than 38 °C (100 °F). Workers suffering from heat exhaustion should be moved from the hot area and given liquids to drink. Any unnecessary clothing, including shoes and socks, should be removed. The worker should be cooled with cold compresses to the head, neck, and face or have the worker wash his or her head, face, and neck with cold water. Frequent sips of water should be encouraged. Workers with signs or symptoms of heat exhaustion should be taken to a clinic or emergency room for medical evaluation and treatment. Someone should stay with the worker until help arrives.

Heat cramps are muscle pains that are typically associated with physical labor in a hot work environment and are caused by the loss of body salts and fluid during sweating. Workers with heat cramps should replace fluid loss by drinking water and/or carbohydrate–electrolyte replacement liquids (e.g., sports drinks) every 15 to 20 minutes.

Heat rash is caused by sweating and looks like a red cluster of pimples or small blisters. Heat rash typically appears on the neck and upper chest, in the groin, under breasts, and in elbow creases. The best treatment for heat rash is to provide a cooler, less humid work environment. The rash area should be kept dry, and powder may be applied to increase comfort. Ointments and creams should not be used on a heat rash because anything that makes the skin warm or moist may make the rash worse.

To prevent heat stroke and related heat illness, the following procedures should be followed:

- Provide training on hazards leading to heat stress and ways to prevent them for workers and supervisors;

- Provide workers with plenty of cool water in convenient, visible locations close to the work area. The water should have a palatable (pleasant and odor-free) taste and water temperature should be 10 to 15.5 °C (50 to 60 °F), if possible. Workers should be reminded to frequently drink small amounts of water before they become thirsty to maintain good hydration. During moderate activity, or in moderately hot conditions, at least one pint of water per hour is needed. Workers should drink about 180 mL (6 oz) or a medium-sized glass full of water every 20 minutes. It is important to instruct workers that urine should be clear or lightly colored. Too much water can be just as harmful as not enough water. Workers should generally not drink more than a total of 11.4 L (12 qt) of fluid in 24 hours;

- Monitor weather reports daily and, if possible, schedule jobs with high heat exposure to cooler times of the day;

- Reduce the physical demands of the job, such as excessive lifting, climbing, or digging with heavy objects. Use mechanical devices or assign extra workers to alternate the activity;

- When possible, routine maintenance and repair projects should be scheduled during the cooler seasons of the year;

- Schedule frequent rest periods with water breaks in shaded or air-conditioned recovery areas; and

- Workers are at an increased risk of heat stress from PPE, especially from wearing semipermeable (penetrable) or impermeable clothing (such as Tyvek or rubber), when the outside temperature exceeds 21 °C (70 °F), or while working at high energy levels. These types of clothing materials trap heat close to a worker's body. Workers should be monitored by establishing a routine to periodically check them for signs and symptoms of overexposure.

4.0 MATERIAL HANDLING

Much of the wastewater works equipment requiring maintenance is mechanical but electrically driven, so a combination of safety practices is required. For example, pumps are electrically driven, but the pumps themselves are mechanical devices with associated valves, piping, and level controls. Because of size, the pump may need to be lifted with special electric equipment for repairs and/or replacement. Other heavy devices, such as valves, are entirely mechanical but may require electric lifting equipment for repairs.

Operating personnel coordinate closely to maintain, repair, or remove mechanical equipment with minimal shutdown time. Unfortunately, the need to restore service quickly may cause workers to disregard all appropriate safety measures; therefore, as much as is possible, it is important to plan, schedule, and perform maintenance with all the necessary tools, materials, and manpower available at the site of the operation. It is important to ensure that employees know their jobs and understand the potential hazards to themselves, other employees, and the wastewater system.

Care should be taken to follow lockout procedures for equipment that can be remotely or automatically operated. Equipment should be tagged and chocks or blocks should be used to prevent movement if all other measures fail.

4.1 Lifting Loads

Because of the size or location, equipment may need to be lifted to perform maintenance. Workers should be aware of the possibility of injury whether the equipment is lifted manually or with the aid of various lifting devices. When lifting an object manually, the object should be kept close to the body and leg strength should be used to lift rather than the back. Heavy objects should not be lifted without mechanical assistance.

Many wastewater plants are equipped with overhead traveling cranes to move materials and heavy equipment, such as pumps and valves. These cranes have rated capacities that should be posted and not exceeded. All crane-hoist hooks should be equipped with safety latches and tag lines should be attached to loads that may swing or must go through limited openings. Each load's balance should be checked by lifting it only slightly off the ground at first before attempting to move it. Workers should not stand or work under a suspended load or near a cable, chain, or rope under tension.

The difference between portable lifting equipment and permanently installed equipment is that portable equipment is less stable and communication is poorer; additionally, portable equipment can tip, touch power lines, two-block, overload, and overextend its reach. Therefore, it is important to use additional surveillance and care.

4.2 Crane Operations (Boom Trucks)

Only certified crane operators who have completed licensing requirements may operate a mobile crane. Individuals familiar with the facility should coordinate mobile crane use, taking into consideration the work surface, lift route, load weight, and lifting schedule to avoid overloading the crane, making it unstable, or tipping it over. The load moment can change substantially during a lift and could become irrecoverable, especially when a load is being lowered. Although some cranes are equipped with load moment indicators, it is important to not rely solely on these devices to prevent tipping. Because the load moment is a function of the distance between the load and the crane base, in addition to the angle of the boom and weight, operators should be especially alert when near the limits of the crane's rating to avoid overreaching and, consequently, tipping.

To avoid electrocution through contact with the lifting rope, load, boom, or crane, a minimum of 3.1 m (10 ft) of clearance should be maintained from any electrical source. Although some cranes can be equipped with devices that alert operators to nearby electric fields, it is important to not depend solely on these devices to alert the operator.

Besides electrocution and load-shifting problems, movements of the boom, jib, and load can cause *two-blocking*, a condition in which the lower load block or hook assembly comes in contact with the upper block or boom point sheave assembly. Elevating a load too high and telescoping where the load block touches the upper block can cause the rope to fail and the load to drop. The operator is responsible for watching the load to avoid two-blocking; he or she should not rely solely on anti-two-blocking devices.

To avoid confusion, only one person should be designated to signal crane operators. Standard hand signals should be used for safety and efficiency. The signaler and the operator should be able to see each other at all times and fully understand and comply with the signals given.

Only trained and certified operators should be permitted to operate lifting equipment. Operators should continuously watch for evidence of overload. They should only leave the lifting device after the load is lowered to the ground and all power is turned off; they should never leave the lifting device while the load is suspended.

Codes concerning the use of mobile and permanently installed cranes and hoists include the following:

- 29 CFR 1910.180 Subpart N, *Material Handling and Storage,* "Crawler, Locomotive, and Truck Cranes"; (OSHA, 2011e)

- 29 CFR 1910.550 Subpart N, *Cranes, Derricks, Hoists, Elevators, and Conveyors,* "Cranes and Derricks"; (OSHA,2011e)

- American National Standards Institute B30.5, *Mobile and Locomotive Cranes*;
- Society of Automobile Engineers J220, *Crane Boomstop*;
- American National Standards Institute B30.16, *Overhead Hoists*; and
- American National Standards Institute A10.5, *Safety Requirements for Material Hoists*.

5.0   PORTABLE POWER TOOLS

Before using any portable power tool, an employee must read the manufacturer's data as it pertains to proper selection, use, maintenance, repair, and required PPE. Most common power tools include electric, pneumatic, and powder-actuated. For additional information on portable power tools, the reader is referred to CFR 1910.241 (OSHA, 2011c) or CFR 1926.300 (OSHA, 2011g).

5.1   Tool Selection

Using the right tool for the job can make all the difference. Tools must be used as they were designed. All hand and power tools whether furnished by the employer or by the employee shall be maintained in a safe condition. All power tools must be grounded through the application of a three-prong plug or double insulated. Ergonomic risk factors should be considered when replacing or purchasing new hand tools (29 CFR 1926.300[a]) (OSHA, 2011g).

Common tool hazards include

- Machine guarding (lack of, missing, or removed);
- Improper electrical grounding;
- Lack of or ineffective use of proper PPE;
- Use of damaged or poorly maintained tools; and
- Using any tools without training or not as designed or intended.

Electrical tools are the most common power tools. The following are best practice tips for electrical tools:

- Never modify, bypass, or remove the grounding prong on power cord plugs and
- Never store or use electrical tools in damp or wet conditions.

Workers should be careful not to damage power cords. The cords should not be kinked or twisted because this could damage the wires running through the insulating jacket. A tool should not be lifted or suspended by its cord; finally, workers should be mindful of where cords are stretched to avoid tripping hazards.

Other power tools include pneumatic, fuel, and hydraulic fluid. *Pneumatic* means consisting of or resembling air. These compressed air power tools can be very dangerous. Even at low pressure, compressed air can cause injury; therefore, workers should wear the appropriate PPE. A primary danger of fuel-powered and hydraulic fluid tools is fire. Therefore, it is important to shut off these tools during refueling, servicing, and maintenance. Fuel should be transported, handled, and stored in compliance with CFR 1926 Subpart F, *Fire Protection and Prevention* (OSHA, 2011b). Section 7.0 provides more information on fire prevention.

5.2   Inspection and Servicing

Tools are safe when they are properly used and cared for. Although OSHA regulations do not specifically cover every tool that will ever be used, a few common sense guidelines are provided.

To maintain tools, they should be inspected often. Defective tools should be immediately removed from service. Power tools should always be inspected prior to use and frequently during use for defects. Safety guards should be kept in place and not altered or removed. Only authorized personnel should perform any service maintenance or repair on power tools. For more information, the reader is referred to CFR 1926 Subpart I, *Tools—Hand and Power.* (OSHA, 2011g)

5.3   Powder-Actuated Tools

A powder-actuated tool uses an explosive charge to drive a stud, pin, or fastener. Certified training is required, so only workers with extensive training are allowed to handle these tools. Like most firearms, powder-actuated tools are activated by pulling a trigger. They should be treated with the same respect as one would treat a gun. Safety glasses and hearing protection should be worn when using powder-actuated tools; the tools should never be pointed at anyone. The following are additional precautions that must be adhered to:

- Only authorized employees who have been trained to operate a particular tool in use should be allowed to operate a powder-actuated tool;
- All powder-actuated tools should be tested each day according to the manufacturer's recommended procedures to ensure proper operation;

- Any defected tools shall be removed from service immediately;
- Proper PPE should be worn;
- Tools should not be loaded until just before firing;
- Loaded tools should not be left attended; and
- Tools should not be used in an explosive or flammable atmosphere.

6.0   ELECTRICAL SAFETY

Electricity and electric power equipment should be treated cautiously. Ordinary 120-V electricity can be fatal; most wastewater facility electrical systems operate at 120 to 4000 V or more. All voltages should be considered dangerous and potentially life threatening.

Electricity kills by paralyzing the nervous system and stopping muscular action. It may hit the breathing center at the base of the brain, interrupting the transmission of nervous impulses to the muscles responsible for breathing; it may affect the heart, causing it to cease pumping blood; or it may cause severe and extensive tissue burns to the skin, penetrating all the way to the bone. The following sections provide an overview of good electrical safety practices and standards.

6.1   Non-Electrical Worker

Anyone not authorized, unfamiliar with, or untrained on electrical systems is considered a non-electrical worker and should not attempt to work on any electrical system. It is important to not make assumptions about qualifications of other workers or unfamiliar equipment.

6.2   Electrical Worker

An electrical worker is qualified, trained, and familiar with the electrical systems to be worked on. Such qualifications of training and experience must be documented.

6.2.1   General Safe Working Rules and Practices

The following are safe working rules and practices that should be followed when working on electrical systems:

- Before working on an electrical system, perform a job hazard analysis to determine any potential hazards and methods of abating those hazards;

- Assume a circuit is live unless you are certain it is dead and cannot be inadvertently energized;

- Avoid becoming grounded inadvertently to water piping or other metallic equipment when working on or in contact with electrical equipment or wiring, and do not touch or pass tools with a person who is grounded;

- Allow only qualified and authorized personnel to work on electrical equipment or perform electrical maintenance;

- Ensure overhead electrical power lines are neutralized or do not come in close proximity to tools or equipment; do not rely on electrical isolation devices for protection from such sources of electricity;

- Consult local authorities before digging or tunneling to prevent contact with buried electrical sources;

- Keep all electrical controls accessible, well marked, and in safe working order;

- Prevent wires or cords from becoming a tripping hazard;

- Do not use metal or conducting ladders, metal tape measures, or other metal tools around electrical equipment;

- Handle wires as if they were live;

- When working around electrical equipment, always keep the hazard in mind;

- Work from a firm base and cover energized buses or parts with a good electrical insulator such as a rubber blanket;

- Do not remove guards, use oversized fuses, or block or bypass protective devices unless it is absolutely essential to the repair or maintenance activity, and then only after alerting the operating personnel and maintenance supervisor; and

- When working on machinery remote from disconnect devices, especially at a long distance, ground the conductors to dissipate any stored energy and to prevent inadvertent energizing.

It is important to not work alone on energized equipment that operates at or above 480 V (such as a magnetic starter in a dead front motor control center). Contact with equipment and circuits at 480 V or higher may be lethal, so it is better to have two employees work as a team and only if equipment and circuits can be completely shut off and are located in a clean, dry, well-lighted area with good accessibility.

Two employees working together can double-check each other, and one of them can de-energize circuits, apply first aid, or summon assistance in the event of a mishap. Typically, there is sufficient work for both employees to work simultaneously.

It is important to notify others of intent to perform work on electrical systems or components. If interim repairs are necessary, supervisors should ensure that affected personnel know this and take remedial measures to reduce the opportunity for injury or damage.

6.2.2   Holding and Locking Out Electrical Circuits (Tagging and Locking)

It is important to create and adhere to a good system for holding and locking out electrical circuits when equipment is being repaired. Unexpected power in electrical equipment that can be started by automatic or manual remote control may injure persons who happen to be near enough to be struck.

When motors or other electrical equipment require repair, workers should open the circuit at the switch box and padlock the switch in the "off" position, tagging it with a description of the repair, the name of the repairer, and the department involved. Supervisors should emphasize the serious risks to maintenance personnel and ensure that a procedure is implemented with the necessary keys, locks, and arrangements. A system should be developed to suit the needs of the wastewater works maintenance organization and coordinated with the system for holding equipment out of service for mechanical maintenance. The system should be simple and clear responsibilities should be assigned to each person who is involved in the locking out or releasing operation. Accidentally opening the wrong valve may only give a pipe fitter a surprise shower or, if the contents are involuntarily ingested, make someone ill. Accidentally energizing an electrical circuit could cause death.

Electrical maintenance often involves performing equipment and diagnostic tests using electricity. Before conducting such tasks, the consequences of ordinary and fault condition reactions should be evaluated. Probes used to access terminals can cause short circuits or alternate electrical pathways. Introducing stray signals or commands that may affect the operation of programmable controllers and other logic-based electronic devices should be avoided. If these devices perform a safety function, the safety feature should be tested to ensure that it works.

Before working on a line or bus of at least 480 V, it should be grounded, de-energized, and locked out. Before grounding the line or bus, it should be tested with a pretested voltmeter to ensure that it is off.

Feedback is the return of a fraction of the electrical output signal to the input. It often occurs because of the impedance characteristics of a circuit and can cause component failure or, in control circuits, be misinterpreted as a control signal. Precautions should be taken to avoid feedback on a de-energized circuit. Feedback can occur from a control circuit interlocked with another control circuit that is fed from a different source; the high-voltage side of a potential or control transformer that is still connected to the bus; the low-voltage side of the transformer energized by an extraneous source acting as a step-up transformer; or standby on an emergency electrical power source. Symptoms of feedback conditions include premature failure of components, the presence of intermittent control and sensor signals, or surges within circuits. These conditions may be subtle and require extensive diagnostic routines to identify the origin of the problem.

Transformers are passive devices whose only indication of energy is a hysteresis hum, which may not be present at low or partial loads. It is important to ensure that both primary and secondary leads are disconnected before working on them. While ordinarily used for electrical flow in one direction, transformers are reversible. If only the primary lead is disconnected, an inadvertent cross-connection on the secondary side could induce high voltage on the primary side.

Electrical system grounding is the connection between an electrical circuit or equipment and the earth or some large conducting body that serves in place of the earth. Grounding is used to establish polarity or electrical potentials and to protect against electrical short circuits. The impedance separating an energized circuit from a ground may determine the path of electrical current flow and is a critical element in the potential for electrocution.

The mating contact in the grounding plug's receptacle is wired to a special grounding wire carded in the same conduit with the supply wires or else connected to a continuous metal conduit used as a ground path. This conductor is typically colored green and should be used only to ground equipment. It is important to remember to not break the ground blade off a three-prong plug so it will fit a two-wire receptacle. If a three-wire to two-wire plug adapter is being used, the ground should be continued by a separate wire or through the cover screw and ground wire or conduit supplying the receptacles. Poor or nonexistent connections to grounding for 15- or 20-Amp receptacles can be tested instantly by plugging in a tester with three lights and a quantity code for each light.

Grounding the neutral conductor of the electrical distribution system limits the voltage between any of the phases (86.6% of line voltage). Any piece of electrical equipment or wiring that accidentally grounds will cause ground fault current to flow and trip a circuit breaker, thereby separating the faulted circuit from the system.

However, neutral grounding systems have nothing to limit the voltage that might appear between a phase conductor and ground, which could reach several times the value of the system voltage. Thus, an employee working on 480-V equipment could receive a shock several times greater.

In many older plants, the neutral conductor of the power utilization voltage is left ungrounded so essential equipment may work temporarily, even during a single accidental ground. For safety, these ungrounded systems should be modified to grounded systems. At a minimum, ungrounded systems should be equipped with a ground detector and alarm to notify operating personnel immediately of an accidental ground so maintenance personnel can locate the ground and disconnect the grounded equipment or circuit from the system. Care should be taken to carry the ground wire through to a solid grounding location. Plastic is now used in the water and sewer piping industry and pipes are no longer a reliable ground source. Likewise, it is important to not assume that a building's structural steel will serve as an acceptable ground. The only "sure" ground is hard wire from the powered appliance back to an established ground source at the main distribution board.

Computer and digital sensors are extremely sensitive and can be damaged or destroyed by discharges of static electricity. Capacitors and solid-state voltage-increasing circuits can create high voltages in seemingly low-voltage electronic equipment. Computer and electronic equipment are susceptible to stray electrical currents. Therefore, special procedures and static discharge elimination equipment should be used to protect both workers and equipment.

The National Electrical Code requires green ground wires for computer and electronic equipment be the same size as current-carrying conductors. Care should be taken to bring back separate ground wires for each piece of equipment because looping ground wires or using the same ground wire in a series for several pieces of equipment can result in "ground loops," affect performance, and also create a safety hazard for maintenance personnel.

6.2.3   De-Energizing Lines and Buses

Insulation protects the current-carrying conductor from accidental grounding. For high-voltage conductors, especially those above 4 kV, a strong electromagnetic field is imposed in the insulation's dielectric material. When the power is disconnected, the magnetic field's collapse can re-energize the conductor to an unsafe level.

After disconnecting high-voltage lines and buses, they should be de-energized with a grounded conductor attached to an insulated handle ("dead man's stick").

The voltage and length of the conductor will determine the amount of energy stored in the dielectric (e.g., longer conductors and larger voltages mean more energy to dissipate). With high voltage, the stored energy will jump a substantial gap and the discharge will be accompanied by both flash and smoke. It is important to use safety goggles and electrically insulated tools of the proper voltage rating.

6.3 Working on Energized Equipment

Sometimes, maintenance personnel need to work on equipment that is electrically energized, such as when they are taking electrical measurements, opening and closing disconnects and circuit breakers, removing panels and/or opening electric equipment doors for inspection, observing polarity based on motor rotation, or performing diagnostics. Such activities should be avoided as much as possible; however, when they are necessary, additional precautions and protective measures should be taken. The following sections address some of these considerations.

When working on "hot" electrical systems, a team of at least two workers should be used. One team member is designated the safety observer, whose full attention is devoted to watching the work to make sure all safety rules are followed. The safety observer is trained in cardiopulmonary resuscitation (**CPR**), has grounding equipment available, and will review the procedure with workers before it is performed. This person's authority to stop the work is absolute. If a safety violation is observed, the safety observer will stop work until it is corrected. If an employee is injured, especially by contact with energized wires or equipment, the safety observer is the first line of rescue and first aid.

6.3.1   Use of Insulating Blankets and Non-Conducting Materials

Before working inside switchboards, power cabinets, and other locations where there are exposed energized buses or parts, it is important to ensure that all conductors are de-energized to the greatest extent practical. If some circuits remain energized, the following precautions should be taken to minimize the possibility of shock or short circuit:

- Cover all live buses with insulating blankets;
- Be careful to avoid accidental contact with live buses or parts within reach, and take extra care to prevent dropping tools on live buses or falling against live buses or parts;

- To prevent eye damage from possible high-intensity arcing, wear protective goggles for all work inside energized switchgear;

- Remove rings, watches, metal-framed glasses, and all other jewelry before performing such work. Key chains and key buckles can be a significant hazard in electrical work; they should be removed and stored in the toolbox for safety; and

- Avoid touching live parts, but, if absolutely necessary, touch them standing only on a dry insulating surface, clear of all other conductors or grounding surfaces. Wear rubber safety gloves in good tested condition that are approved for use on the voltage, and touch the circuit with only one hand.

Pliers, screwdrivers, wrenches, and other tools used in electrical work should have insulated handles; the un-insulated working surfaces of these tools should be as small as practicable to minimize the possibility of metal contacting live parts. Although electrical tape or other insulating materials may be used to cover metal surfaces, insulated tools should be used whenever possible. Using metal flashlights should be avoided.

6.3.2 Arc Flash Considerations

When working on electrically live or charged equipment, electrical energy may discharge, arcing or shooting sparks and potentially causing significant burns and injuries to occur. In addition,

- Arcs can produce temperatures 4 times hotter than the surface temperature of the sun. Human skin burns at 93.3 °C (200 °F);

- Fatal burns can occur up to 1.5 m (5 ft) from the arc;

- Severe burns can occur up to 3 m (10 ft) away from the arc; and

- Clothing can be ignited several meters away.

Before breaking the seal on an explosion-proof enclosure, it is important to make sure the work area is well ventilated. Workers should check for gas and shut down nearby equipment and facilities if practical; continually monitor the area for gas and use only nonsparking, nonferrous tools; and, when finished, make certain that the explosion-proof fittings are resealed.

6.3.3 Personal Protective Equipment

The Occupational Safety and Health Administration requires that workers be provided with PPE appropriate for the work to be performed and for the parts of the body that need protection. These include, but are not limited to, safety glasses, proper clothing, gloves, foot protection, hard hats, and hearing protection. The American National Standards Institute has established special designations for many items for personal protection when performing electrical work. Management should search out and use equipment approved for electrical work designed to protect workers from electrical shocks and other injuries. The reader is referred to Chapter 10 for more information on PPE.

Arc-rated PPE is typically expressed in small calories of heat energy per square centimeter (cal/cm²). Tests for determining arc rating are defined in American Society for Testing and Materials F1506, *Standard Performance Specification for Flame Resistant Textile Materials for Wearing Apparel for Use by Electrical Workers Exposed to Momentary Electric Arc and Related Thermal Hazards* (ASTM, http://www.astm.org/standards/F106.htm).

Selection of appropriate PPE, given a certain task to be performed, is typically handled in one of two possible ways. The first method is to consult a hazard category classification table like that found in the National Fire Protection Association's (NFPA) *Handbook for Electrical Safety in the Workplace* (Table 130.7[C][9][a]) (NFPA, 2009). It lists a number of typical electrical tasks performed at various voltage levels and recommends the category of PPE that should be worn. The minimum rating of PPE necessary for any category is the maximum available energy for that category.

The second method of selecting PPE is to perform an arc flash hazard calculation to determine the available incident arc energy. The Institute of Electrical and Electronics Engineers Standard 1584, *Guide for Performing Arc-Flash Hazard Calculations* (IEEESA, 2002) provides a guide to perform these calculations if the bolted fault current, duration of the fault, and other general equipment information is known. Once the incident energy is calculated, the appropriate ensemble of PPE that offers protection greater than the energy available can be selected.

6.3.4 Approach Boundaries

The risk from exposed live parts depends on an individual's distance from the parts. These boundaries are set by the National Fire Protection Association (NFPA) (2009). According to the *Handbook for Electrical Safety in the Workplace* (NFPA, 2009), electrical shock boundaries to live parts for 300 to 600 V are as follows:

- The *limited approach* boundary is 1 m (3 ft, 6 in.), which is the closest an unqualified person can approach unless accompanied by a qualified person;

- The *restricted approach* boundary is 0.3 m (1 ft), which is the closest to exposed live parts that a qualified person can go without proper PPE and insulated tools; and

- The *prohibited approach* boundary is 0.25 m (1 in.), which is the distance you must stay from exposed live parts to prevent flashover or arcing in the air.

The *flash protection* boundary for live parts for 300 to 600 V is 1.2 m (4 ft) and PPE is needed to prevent burns in the event of an arc flash.

Tables 5.1 through 5.5 provide OSHA-required approach distances under given circumstances. Table 5.2, 5.3, and 5.4, in particular, provide safe approach and working distances in the vicinity of energized electric apparatuses so that work can be done safely without risk of electrical flashover. The working distances must withstand the maximum transient overvoltage that can reach the worksite under the working conditions and practices in use. Technical information for U.S. electrical systems indicates that current design provides for the following maximum transient overvoltage values (typically produced by switching surges): 362 kV and less, 3.0 per unit; 552 kV, 2.4 per unit; and 800 kV, 2.0 per unit. For further information on electrical standards, the reader is referred to OSHA's 29 CFR 1910, NFPA's *Handbook for Electrical Safety in the Workplace* (NFPA, 2009), and the National Electrical Code or local building codes with jurisdictional authority for each location and industry.

TABLE 5.1   Approach distances for qualified employees—alternating current (CFR 1910.333[c][ii][C]).

Voltage range (phase to phase)	minimum approach distance
300 V and less	Avoid contact
Over 300 V, not over 750 V	1 ft 0 in. (0.3 m)
Over 750 V, not over 2 kV	1 ft 6 in. (0.4 m)
Over 2 kV, not over 15 kV	2 ft 0 in. (0.6 m)
Over 15 kV, not over 37 kV	3 ft 0 in. (0.9 m)
Over 37 kV, not over 87.5 kV	3 ft 6 in. (10 m)
Over 87.5 kV, not over 121 kV	4 ft 0 in. (1.2 m)
Over 121 kV, not over 140 kV	4 ft 6 in. (1.4 m)

TABLE 5.2 Alternating current live-line work minimum approach distance (CFR 1910.269).

Nominal voltage in kilovolts [b] phase to phase	Distance [a]			
	Phase-to-ground exposure		Phase-to-phase exposure	
	(ft-in.)	(m)	(ft-in.)	(m)
0.05 to 1.0	c	c	c	c
1.1 to 15.0	2–1	0.64	2–2	0.66
15.1 to 36.0	2–4	0.72	2–7	0.77
36.1 to 46.0	2–7	0.77	2–10	0.85
46.1 to 72.5	3–0	0.90	3–6	1.05
72.6 to 121	3–2	0.95	4–3	1.29
138 to 145	3–7	1.09	4–11	1.50
161 to 169	4–0	1.22	5–8	1.71
230 to 242	5–3	1.59	7–6	2.27
345 to 362	8–6	2.59	12–6	3.80
500 to 550	11–3	3.42	18–1	5.50
765 to 800	14–11	4.53	26–0	7.91

[a] These distances take into consideration the highest switching surge an employee will be exposed to on any system with air as the insulating medium and the maximum voltages shown.
[b] The clear live-line tool distance shall equal or exceed the values for the indicated voltage ranges.
[c] Avoid contact.

7.0 FIRE PREVENTION

Understanding the mechanics of making a fire is paramount to understanding how to prevent fires. There are four ingredients necessary to support a fire: a fuel source, an oxygen source, a heat source, and the chemical chain reaction. This chemical chain reaction that sustains the fire occurs when the fuel, oxygen, and heat are present in appropriate proportions; all three must be present to support combustion. Vapors are released during the burning process and are carried into the flame. Heat from the flames drives the chemical reaction. If any one of the ingredients is removed, the fire can be extinguished.

TABLE 5.3   Alternating current live-line work minimum approach distance with overvoltage factor phase-to-ground exposure (29 CFR 1910.269).

Maximum anticipated per-unit transient overvoltage	Distance in feet-inches [a,b]						
	Maximum phase-to-phase voltage in kilovolts						
	121	145	169	242	362	552	800
1.5	...	...	...	...	...	6–0	9–8
1.6	...	...	...	...	...	6–6	10–8
1.7	...	...	...	...	...	7–0	11–8
1.8	...	...	...	...	...	7–7	12–8
1.9	...	...	...	...	...	8–1	13–9
2.0	2–5	2–9	3–0	3–10	5–3	8–9	14–11
2.1	2–6	2–10	3–2	4–0	5–5	9–4	...
2.2	2–7	2–11	3–3	4–1	5–9	9–11	...
2.3	2–8	3–0	3–4	4–3	6–1	10–6	...
2.4	2–9	3–1	3–5	4–5	6–4	6–4	...
2.5	2–9	3–2	3–6	4–6	6–8	11–3	...
2.6	2–10	3–3	3–8	4–8	7–1	...	...
2.7	2–11	3–4	3–9	4–10	7–5	...	...
2.8	3–0	3–5	3–10	4–11	7–9	...	...
2.9	3–1	3–6	3–11	5–1	8–2	...	...
3.0	3–2	3–7	4–0	5–3	8–6	...	...

[a] The distance specified in this table may be applied only where the maximum anticipated per-unit transient overvoltage has been determined by engineering analysis and has been supplied by the employer. Table 5.2 applies otherwise.

[b] The distances specified in this table are the air, bare-hand, and live-line tool distances.

A fire prevention plan sets minimum requirements to protect affected personnel and to mitigate the extent of damage from a fire-related incident. The fire safety plan further details individual responsibilities regarding the implementation, training, testing, evaluation, and enforcement of the fire prevention plan.

The workplace should be evaluated to determine situations where there is a risk of fire. Control measures must be put in place to remove those risks. If this is not

TABLE 5.4   Alternating current live-line work minimum approach distance with overvoltage factor phase-to-phase exposure (29 CFR 1910.269).

Maximum anticipated	Distance in feet-inches [a,b]						
per-unit transient overvoltage	Maximum phase-to-phase voltage in kilovolts						
	121	145	169	242	362	552	800
1.5	...	...	...	...	...	7–4	12–1
1.6	...	...	...	...	...	8–9	14–6
1.7	...	...	...	...	...	10–2	17–2
1.8	...	...	...	...	...	11–7	19–11
1.9	...	...	...	...	...	13–2	22–11
2.0	3–7	4–1	4–8	6–1	8–7	14–10	26–0
2.1	3–7	4–2	4–9	6–3	8–10	15–7	
2.2	3–8	4–3	4–10	6–4	9–2	16–4	...
2.3	3–9	4–4	4–11	6–6	9–6	17–2	...
2.4	3–10	4–5	5–0	6–7	9–11	18–1	...
2.5	3–11	4–6	5–2	6–9	10–4	...	...
2.6	4–0	4–7	5–3	6–11	10–9	...	...
2.7	4–1	4–8	5–4	7–0	11–2	...	...
2.8	4–1	4–9	5–5	7–2	11–7	...	...
2.9	4–2	4–10	5–6	7–4	12–1	...	...
3.0	4–3	4–11	5–8	7–6	12–6	...	...

[a] The distance specified in this table may be applied only where the maximum anticipated per-unit transient overvoltage has been determined by engineering analysis and has been supplied by the employer. Table 5.2 applies otherwise.

[b] The distances specified in this table are the air, bare-hand, and live-line tool distances.

possible, controls must be put in place to reduce the effects of a fire incident. Finally, plans and procedures must be developed and implemented to deal with a fire event.

Areas of the workplace where flammable atmospheres may occur should be identified and classified; ignition sources (from unprotected equipment, for example) should be avoided in those areas. Likely areas include the collections system and anaerobic digesters. Areas with potential flammability include

- Collections system,

- Anaerobic digesters,

- Sludge dryers, and

- Any oxygen-enriched system.

When working in these areas, it is important to keep the following points in mind:

- Store oily rags in a metal container;

- Smoking should not be allowed within 15 m (50 ft) of the digester or the collections system;

- Use nonsparking tools when working on equipment; and

- Flammable gases should be stored away from potential ignition sources (e.g., methane and acetylene).

Typically, sludge dryers are contained in enclosed vessels with minimal exposure potential for employees. However, fires associated with sludge dryers can occur within the dryer, in product storage containers, or from dust that accumulates in areas

TABLE 5.5   Direct current live-line work minimum approach distance with overvoltage factor (29 CFR 1910.269).

Maximum anticipated per-unit transient overvoltage	Distance in feet-inches [a,b]				
	Maximum line-to-ground voltage in kilovolts				
	250	400	500	600	750
1.5 or lower	3–8	5–3	6–9	8–7	11–10
1.6	3–10	5–7	7–4	9–5	13–1
1.7	4–1	6–0	7–11	10–3	14–4
1.8	4–3	6–5	8–7	11–2	15–9

[a] The distances specified in this table may be applied only where the maximum anticipated per-unit transient overvoltage has been determined by engineering analysis and has been supplied by the employer. However, if the transient overvoltage factor is not known, a factor of 1.8 shall be assumed.
[b] The distances specified in this table are the air, bare-hand, and live-line tool distances.

of the facility where temperature and oxygen conditions could lead to ignition. It is imperative that the dryer be operated to create a product with design pellet moisture content to prevent formation of product that is excessively dusty. Good housekeeping and maintenance are essential to removing the buildup of combustible dust or residue.

7.1 Hot Work

Fire hazards must be identified and controlled at all times. *Hot work* is defined as any activity that creates a potential ignition source for flammable or explosive substances. This definition obviously includes activities such as welding or using a cutting torch or open flame; however, it may also include use of power tools while working in areas susceptible to a potentially explosive atmosphere. Using a grinder, drill, electric or manual saw, and even a hammer may create a sufficient spark to ignite a flammable substance. Space heaters, strip heaters, and temporary lighting equipment all produce heat and must be considered a hazard with the potential to start a fire under certain conditions.

A hot work craftsperson is responsible for the safe operation of his or her equipment and the safe conduct of hot work techniques and processes, ensuring that they are either working in an approved hot work area or seeking authorization of a hot work permit from their supervisor to perform hot work outside of the approved area. Use of a hot work permit is intended as a tool to assist in the control of potential fire hazards.

Any area where flammable vapors may collect or settle in a low area or where ventilation is limited should always be tested for an explosive atmosphere and monitored before and throughout any hot work evolution. All hot work will be prohibited from starting or, if in progress, stopped if there is any suspected or detectable sign of an explosive atmosphere. When measuring for a combustible atmosphere, a gas detector or air meter should be used that will indicate a percentage of the lower explosive level.

The maintenance department should establish several work areas approved to perform hot work. Approved hot work areas should be routinely inspected by the supervisor assigned responsibility for that area to ensure the areas are maintained in a condition to minimize a fire hazard. Generally, a hot work permit is not required in an approved hot work area; however, the area supervisor has the right to request a permit be issued whenever he or she believes the hot work creates a potential fire hazard that warrants the added scrutiny of the permit process. Approved hot work areas should be

- Free of combustibles and any flammable materials except those directly involved in the work being performed;
- Free of flammable liquids, vapors, or gasses not directly involved in the hot work process;
- Effectively protected against any possible incursion of flammable oils, liquids, vapors, or gasses that may be released from pipelines, sewers, drains, or any other source or that may drift into the area from an adjacent area;
- Equipped with a readily accessible fire extinguisher appropriate for the work being performed;
- Cleaned of any residual flammable material or substances upon completion of the hot work; and
- Posted as an approved hot work area or station.

All tools used in the hot work process should be properly secured and stored with gas cylinder isolation valves closed, pressure regulators set to minimum, and hoses vented of residual pressure.

The employee performing hot work in an approved hot work area must ensure that the area complies with all required conditions. A fire watch is typically not required in an approved hot work area, but may be requested by the craftsperson or directed by the area supervisor for certain hot work evolutions that may produce a greater fire hazard.

7.2 Flammable Materials

All flammable liquids should be properly labeled and stored in NFPA-approved storage lockers. Flammable material storage lockers should be clearly identified and used exclusively for the storage of flammable liquids. Materials should not be stored in a flammable material storage locker that is not part of the original manufacturer's packaging.

Flammable liquids in their original factory-sealed containers may be stored on the shelf or in non-fire-rated lockers until initially opened. Once opened, the material must be properly stored in a double-wall storage locker. Flammable materials storage lockers should be clearly marked. Accumulation of flammable liquids and combustible materials should be minimized and only the smallest quantity necessary to effectively perform work should be stored.

Bulk storage of flammable chemicals can have potentially disastrous consequences if the tanks are not properly maintained or if safe work practices are ignored. It is important to ensure that all safety features of the tanks, such as overpressure reliefs and flame arrestors, are working and properly serviced. Tanks should be clearly labeled and warning signs should be posted to identify hazards and necessary precautions. Finally, it is important to ensure that any repair work on the tank or in close proximity to the tank, especially work involving a flame or ignition source, is performed under the strictest safety procedures.

7.3 Fire Extinguishers

Fire extinguishers are rated based on the type or classification of material they are intended to extinguish. Class A fires are organic combustibles, such as wood, paper, or plastics. Class B fires are flammable liquids, such as fuels, grease, lubricants, or paints. Class C fires are fires in energized electrical equipment. Class D fires involve combustible metals such as magnesium and sodium. The most common type of extinguisher in use today is rated "ABC" and contains a chemical that is effective for multiple classes of fires, but perhaps less effective than an extinguisher rated for a single purpose and properly used. Maintenance personnel should be trained in the proper use and limitations of fire extinguishers. In addition, any person expected to combat a fire should receive awareness training of the dangers of heat, smoke, and toxic vapors and on defensive measures including an avenue for escape.

Class C fire extinguishers should be mounted near motor control centers, transformer banks, and switchgear installations for potential electrical fires. Water or other conductive liquids and materials should not be used on electrical fires.

Portable fire extinguishers need to be inspected and serviced periodically to ensure they are ready for use when needed. Supervisors should check with local fire codes for servicing requirements.

8.0 CONFINED SPACE ENTRY

Performing maintenance in a wastewater treatment plant may involve activities in which the mechanic will be required to work in a space where access is restricted or difficult, where breathing air may be harmful because of toxic contaminants, or where there is a greater risk for an explosion because of residual vapors. Additionally, there may be other hazards from mechanical motion, flooding of the space from varied sources, and physical entrapment that could lead to crushing or death by asphyxiation. If any of these conditions exist, the work environment is likely a confined space.

8.1 Space Classification

The Occupational Safety and Health Administration has defined a *confined space* using three conditional criteria. First, the space must be of adequate size and have a configuration where a worker can enter the space. That seems simple enough; the space must be big enough to get into and there must be a way in. Second, the space has a limited means of access or egress. Although this seems relatively straightforward, there are conditions or circumstances that may warrant further consideration. For example, a 0.75-m (30-in.) manhole located near the bottom of a tank may appear to provide an adequate access point; however, could five workers exit through that opening in a timely manner under emergency conditions? Test questions for this criterion may include: can the worker get in or out of the space unassisted, is self-rescue a realistic option, or are there sufficient access points so that all workers can exit the space in a timely manner?

The third criterion for a confined space is that the space was not designed for continuous human occupancy. This criterion needs some interpretation. For instance, some people might think that only a space such as a living room would qualify as being designed for continuous occupancy. However, if the design of the space took into consideration the work to be performed and provided adequate space, lighting, and clean air for breathing, then it was intended for continuous occupancy. For more information, the reader is referred to OSHA's *Letter of Interpretation—Permit Required Confined Space Standard As It Applies to Certain Operations* (OSHA, 1993).

It is prudent at this point to give further thought to space classification. There are many things to consider with space classification, including consequences for resulting decisions. One factor on the side of the wastewater industry is history; rarely will one be entering a space, such as the wastewater treatment plant, for the first time. The hazards are generally well known and consistent and the work is typically well planned out, perhaps even scheduled weeks or months in advance. If conditions are not ideal, work can often be deferred or delayed in the interest of safety.

There may be a number of spaces that are classified as confined spaces that, upon close scrutiny, may meet habitability considerations for continuous occupancy and could, therefore, be not treated as a confined space. Take, for example, an open metering vault that is 3 m (10 ft) deep. It clearly is large enough to enter and has limited egress because of a fixed ladder, but does it meet the continuous occupancy test? Being an open vault, there is natural lighting and ventilation, and the vault is periodically entered for meter calibration. Clearly, it could be argued that the space was designed for human occupancy and, therefore, does not meet all three criteria to be classified as a confined space.

A well-developed pre-entry checklist can be a valuable safety tool that can guide a confined space entry team to identify all hazards that could reasonably be expected when performing an entry. Section 8.3 provides greater detail on developing a pre-entry checklist. A thorough checklist takes time to complete and should be given proper consideration. Regarding the metering vault mentioned previously, if the policy was to classify any suspect space as a confined space thinking that would be the safer option, maintenance personnel may become complacent during routine or seemingly non-hazardous entries. Because it was classified as a confined space, a pre-entry check would be required and the tendency would be for the worker to shortcut the process knowing there are no serious safety concerns. This could begin a slide down a slippery slope to an unsafe condition.

The point of this discussion is to outline two typical options facing maintenance leaders and then to suggest a third option. As presented, maintenance staff could closely evaluate a potential confined space and find reasonable arguments to satisfy a claim it is not a confined space, thereby avoiding the scrutiny of the confined space program. This could cause potential hazards to be overlooked. Conversely, a confined space program could be overly cautious and overrate spaces, which would require maintenance staff to perform pre-entry checks and paperwork that may be unnecessary, tying up needed personnel resources and valuable time. A third option is to do the honest and defensible evaluation of the space in question and, if conditions do meet the three criteria for a confined space, then take all the prescribed steps to comply with the confined space program. However, if through an honest and defensible evaluation of the space it can be argued that the space was designed for human occupancy and the scope of work does not present any hazards to workers that would warrant the safeguards of a watchful attendant, then the space should not be called a confined space. Rather, time should be taken to identify any real or potential hazards and prudent measures should be taken to safeguard against them. Monitoring air quality for any space below grade is always a good idea and highly recommended.

A confined space may be classified as either a non-permit-required confined space or a permit-required confined space. Under certain conditions, a permit-required confined space may allow for alternate entry procedures. It is never appropriate to assume the classification of a confined space based solely on past practice or to under-classify a space for reasons influenced by available staffing, rescue personnel, or time. When classifying a confined space, it is important to take into consideration design and physical configuration of the space and known hazards that must be considered that are supported by actual testing or the past history of working within the space. If for any reason (e.g., the purpose of the entry is not routine) the conditions are not as expected or the work to be performed will cause or create a health or safety hazard, then the space must be evaluated and classified appropriately as the actual conditions dictate.

A non-permit-required confined space is a confined space that does not contain or have the potential to contain any recognized hazard capable of causing death or serious physical harm. This also includes any hazard or potential hazard associated with breathing air within the space.

Permit-required confined space entries are expected to be relatively infrequent and involve little to no risk. Most entries will be scheduled and well planned for the purpose of inspections or routine maintenance. Typically, all work in a permit-required confined space involving significant maintenance, construction, or repair work or lasting for extended periods of time will be performed by qualified contractors. However, in rare instances (i.e., emergency repairs), trained personnel may be required to perform work in a permit-required confined space.

A permit-required confined space entry will include, at a minimum, the following three individuals: the attendant, the entrant, and the entry supervisor. An emergency rescue plan, appropriate for hazards associated with the entry, must be considered. Entrant self-rescue or rapid retrieval are typical plans. In rare instances, on-site rescue services may be necessary.

Alternate entry procedures may be used for entering a permit-required confined space provided that the only hazard posed by the permit space is an actual or potential hazardous atmosphere and continuous forced air ventilation alone is sufficient to maintain that permit space safe for entry.

8.2 Personnel Responsibilities

8.2.1 Entry Supervisor

The confined space entry supervisor must be trained in the specific duties of the position and have the requisite knowledge to conduct a confined space activity. The entry supervisor must be aware of the general hazards that may be encountered during a confined space entry and the specific hazard(s) unique to each confined space. The person filling the position does not have to be a supervisor by title or position within the organization, but will be designated as the entry supervisor by his or her supervisor.

The primary duty of the entry supervisor is to ensure all precautions are taken, all possible hazards are considered, and all safety equipment is in place to reduce, to the greatest extent, any health or safety risk to personnel performing work in a confined space. A technical knowledge of the work is not required, but a general understanding of the scope of the work that may affect conditions in the space is necessary. The entry supervisor should have a thorough knowledge of confined space entry procedures and the specific duties assigned to the entry supervisor.

Before authorizing a confined space entry, the entry supervisor is expected to have full knowledge of hazards associated with the confined space entry and to understand the specific purpose of the entry and the work to be performed. The entry supervisor should question or evaluate if any of the work may be prestaged or completed prior to entering the space.

In preparation for the confined space entry, the entry supervisor must fully assess all hazards associated with the entry. A confined space pre-entry checklist is a useful tool and should be completed prior to the entry. Based on the space hazard evaluation, the scope of the work to be performed, past experience, and best safe work practices, the entry supervisor should determine if this is a permit-required confined space entry. If available, he or she should refer to historical entry permit records from previous entries into this space or identical spaces under similar conditions and incorporate that knowledge in the determination. Additionally, the entry supervisor should establish if alternate entry procedures are applicable to this entry.

Based on the hazard assessment, the entry supervisor should determine the number of attendants required to safely monitor the entry. The entry supervisor should also verify that the attendant or attendants are trained and familiar with his or her required duties. Under rare circumstances, one attendant may monitor more than one entry point if the spaces are close and the hazards are minimal.

The entry supervisor should verify all entrants are aware of any potential hazards and that all safety measures are in place to reduce, limit, or mitigate their exposure. The rescue plan should be reviewed with each entrant so they clearly understand the expectations and the process.

The entry supervisor should verify that the rescue person, team, or rescue service is on alert and available for immediate response in the event of an emergency. The entry supervisor should also verify that all required rescue equipment is available on-site and ready for use. Listing required safety equipment on the confined space pre-entry checklist is recommended. Rescue plans are discussed further in Section 8.3.3.

The method of communication to be used between the attendant and all entrants should be approved by the entry Supervisor and tested. For small spaces, verbal communication may be acceptable. If the space allows entrants to move beyond the view of the attendant or if the work may cause the entrant's or entrants' hearing to be impaired or compromised, a more definite and unquestionable communication method must be used. In some instances, a tag line may be required.

With the possible exception of the most routine nonpermit confined space entries, it is recommended that the entry supervisor coordinate a confined space pre-entry brief. The entry supervisor does not need to conduct the briefing if someone more qualified is available to discuss hazards associated with the entry and the work to be performed. At a minimum, the attendant and all planned entrants should attend the pre-entry brief. If the rescue person is on-site, he or she should also attend the brief.

After confirming that acceptable entry conditions exist, the entry supervisor will sign the confined space entry permit authorizing entry. During a confined space entry, the entry supervisor should prohibit any unplanned action or change of conditions that would adversely alter or affect the confined space in any way. He or she should remain available to the attendant to address any issues, questions, or concerns that may develop. The entry supervisor is not required to remain at the entry site; however, some situations may warrant the added scrutiny and attentiveness of an on-site supervisor to ensure the safety of the entrants.

If at any time the health or safety of the entrant or entrants is in question, the entry supervisor should direct that all entrants immediately be removed from the confined space and he or she should be on standby outside the space until the concern is resolved. The entry supervisor has the duty and authority to terminate a confined space entry for any cause, but especially if the safety of any person involved with the entry is in jeopardy. The entry supervisor will direct all entrants to exit the space, secure the entry, and cancel the permit pending an investigation.

8.2.2   Attendant

A permit-required confined space attendant must be trained in the specific duties of the position and have the requisite knowledge to conduct a confined space activity. The attendant must be aware of the general hazards that may be encountered during a confined space entry and the specific hazard(s) unique to the confined space they will be attending. The person filling the position does not require any additional training to fill the position other than that of the attendant.

The primary duty of the attendant is to ensure the safety and wellbeing of entrants from all possible health or safety hazards. A technical knowledge of the work is not required, but a general understanding of the scope of the work that may affect conditions in the space is necessary.

The entry supervisor should determine the number of attendants required for a confined space entry after completing the pre-entry checklist. Several factors should be considered, including the number of entrants, the complexity of the job, the configuration of the space, the number of possible entry points, any communication difficulty or interference with entrants, and a full assessment of hazards associated with the entry.

Positioning of the attendant with respect to the entry point should be established such that communication between the entrant and the attendant is never in question or compromised. The attendant should remain close to the entry point to ensure access control; however, as with open spaces, he or she may relocate to better observe the entrants. For a closed space with a single entry point, the attendant should remain at or near the entry point.

8.2.3   Entrant

The permit-required confined space entrant must be trained in the specific duties of the position and have the requisite knowledge to conduct a confined space activity. The entrant must be aware of general hazards that may be encountered during a confined space entry and specific hazards unique to the confined space they will be entering. The person filling the position does not require any additional training to fill the position other than that of the entrant.

The primary duty of the entrant is to perform his or her work in a safe manner as quickly as possible and to minimize the exposure to all possible health or safety hazards. A technical knowledge of the work is required and the entrant must have a full understanding of how the work may affect the conditions in the space.

8.2.4   Training

All personnel associated with a confined space entry must be trained to the specific duties and responsibilities of their position. Personnel who are not involved with confined space entry as part of their job duties still need to be trained to recognize the type and method of posting and warning signs used to identify confined spaces, and must be aware of access restrictions and permit requirements. It is important to check local codes for specific training requirements.

8.3   Pre-Entry Checklist

The pre-entry checklist identifies many potential hazards associated with a confined space entry and requires that positive actions be taken to eliminate or reduce the hazard. Actions may include system lineup or configurations, blank flanging, lock-out/tagout, and ensuring adequate ventilation. There are different ways to prepare a checklist. A checklist can be detailed and specific to cover every potential or conceivable hazard or more general and suggestive of areas or types of hazards to consider. Training on how to use the checklist and knowing how maintenance personnel work with checklists are factors to success in properly and fully identifying hazards associated with working within the confined space.

8.3.1   Air Monitoring

While many confined space hazards can be easily recognized or identified, a hidden danger may be present in the air that entrants are breathing. The oxygen content may be too low to sustain life. The air may be contaminated by toxic fumes or there may be a mixture of combustible gases, creating the potential for an explosion. Although undetectable to human perception, the atmosphere in a confined space could be deadly. For this reason, air monitoring is essential before entering and while working in a confined space.

When preparing to enter a confined space, especially one that has poor circulation of air or one that has multiple levels, an air-monitoring profile of different levels throughout the space should be performed. As part of the pre-entry check, air should be tested in several areas. Gases of varying density will rise or settle or may accumulate in pockets of still air. For this reason, it is important to sample the air toward the top, middle, and bottom of the space, paying particular attention to areas where the work will be performed.

In most instances, a portable air-monitoring device with a pump to draw in the sample will be required. It is important to allow the meter sufficient time to draw in and analyze the sample before moving to the next sample point. As a general rule, gas monitors with pumps drawing a sample through an attached tube will require 6 seconds per meter (2 seconds per foot) of tube. Given a 5-m (15-ft) sample tube, the tube should be monitored for at least 30 seconds to get an accurate reading before moving on to the next monitored location. Gas meter manufacturer's recommendations should be referred to for sample limitations and best metering practices. Air-monitoring technology has improved over the years and manufacturers offer a wide range of features. Useful options may include such things as self-calibration or data logging. Physical size, sensor service life, durability, and ease of use are all factors influencing the usefulness of a gas monitor; as such, prudent users should take many things into consideration when deciding which detectors to purchase.

8.3.2   Job Brief

Conducting a job safety brief immediately prior to confined space entry is a valuable teaching opportunity to ensure all participants are fully aware of their role and responsibility during the entry evolution. The briefing should include a discussion of specific hazards related to the space and the preventive measures in place. It should also detail emergency procedures to be followed if rescue should become necessary. The briefing is typically conducted by an entry supervisor, although individuals most familiar with the job may be involved as appropriate. All personnel involved in the entry, including rescue personnel, should attend the briefing.

8.3.3   Rescue Plan

Statistically, more than half of all fatalities associated with confined space entries involve persons attempting rescue operations. Attempting a rescue must be a well-planned evolution using only trained personnel. Most of the confined spaces entered by maintenance personnel are controlled evolutions and involve little risk to the entrant.

A confined space rescuer or rescue team should comply with the following minimum requirements:

- Trained and equipped with PPE;
- Trained in CPR and basic first aid;
- Fully compliant with the respiratory protection program;
- Wear a full body harness with a retrieval line attached to a mechanical device (i.e., tripod, davit arm, or other fixed point outside the space throughout the rescue effort);
- A mechanical hoisting device should be available to retrieve personnel from vertical-type spaces more than 1.5 m (5 ft) deep; and
- All rescue personnel should be trained annually in simulated rescue operations including removing dummies, manikins, or persons from actual or

representative permit spaces; maintenance departments should work with local fire departments and contracted rescue services to ensure the readiness and capabilities of those services.

9.0 REFERENCES

American Society for Testing and Materials, F1506, *Standard Performance Specification for Flame Resistant Textile Materials for Wearing Apparel for Use by Electrical Workers Exposed to Momentary Electric Arc and Related Thermal Hazards.* http://www.astm.org/standards/F106.htm (accessed Jan 2011).

Institute of Electrical and Electronics Engineers Standards Association (2002) *1584–2002, IEEE Guide for Performing Arc-Flash Hazard Calculations.* http://standards.ieee.org/findstds/standard/1584–2002.html (accessed Jan 2012).

National Fire Protection Association (2009) *Handbook for Electrical Safety in the Workplace*; NFPA 70E; National Fire Protection Association: Quincy, Massachusetts.

Occupational Safety and Health Administration (1993) *Letter of Interpretation—Permit Required Confined Space Standard As It Applies to Certain Operations*; Occupational Safety and Health Administration: Washington, D.C.

Occupational Safety and Health Administration (2011a) *Electrical*; OSHA Title 29 CFR Part 1910 Subpart S; Occupational Safety and Health Administration: Washington, D.C.

Occupational Safety and Health Administration (2011b) *Fire Protection and Prevention*; OSHA Title 29 CFR Part 1926 Subpart F; Occupational Safety and Health Administration: Washington, D.C.

Occupational Safety and Health Administration (2011c) *Hand and Portable Powered Tools*; OSHA Title 29 CFR Part 1910 Subpart P; Occupational Safety and Health Administration: Washington, D.C.

Occupational Safety and Health Administration (2011d) *Machinery and Machine Guarding*; OSHA Title 29 CFR Part 1910 Subpart O; Occupational Safety and Health Administration: Washington, D.C.

Occupational Safety and Health Administration (2011e) *Material Handling and Storage*; OSHA Title 29 CFR Part 1910 Subpart N; Occupational Safety and Health Administration: Washington, D.C.

Occupational Safety and Health Administration (2011f) *Scaffolding*; OSHA Title 29 CFR Part 1926 Subpart L; Occupational Safety and Health Administration: Washington, D.C.

Occupational Safety and Health Administration (2011g) *Tools—Hand and Power*; OSHA Title 29 CFR Part 1926 Subpart I; Occupational Safety and Health Administration: Washington, D.C.

Occupational Safety and Health Administration (2011h) *Walking-Working Surfaces*; OSHA Title 29 CFR Part 1910 Subpart D; Occupational Safety and Health Administration: Washington, D.C.

10.0 SUGGESTED READINGS

American Society of Safety Engineers (2008) *Control of Hazardous Energy Lockout/ Tag Out and Alternate Methods*; ANSI/ASSE Z244.1–2003 (R2008); American Society of Safety Engineers: Des Plaines, Illinois.

American Society of Safety Engineers (2009) *Criteria for Accepted Practices in Safety, Health, and Environmental Training*; ANSI/ASSE Z490.1– 009; American Society of Safety Engineers: Des Plaines, Illinois.

American Society of Safety Engineers (2009) *Definitions and Nomenclature Used for Fall Protection and Fall Arrest*; ANSI/ASSE Z359.0–2009; American Society of Safety Engineers: Des Plaines, Illinois.

National Fire Protection Association (2007) *Standard for Portable Fire Extinguishers*; NFPA 10; National Fire Protection Association: Quincy, Massachusetts.

Nelson, D. I.; Nelson, R. Y.; Concha-Barrientos, M.; Fingerhut, M. (2005) The Global Burden of Occupational Noise-Induced Hearing Loss; *Am. J. Ind. Med.*; World Health Organization: Geneva, Switzerland.

Occupational Safety and Health Administration (2011) *Electric Power Generation, Transmission, and Distribution*; OSHA Title 29 CFR Part 1910.269 Subpart R; Occupational Safety and Health Administration: Washington, D.C.

Chapter 6

Safety and Health in Sewer Collections and Remote Locations

(continued)

1.0 HAZARDS SPECIFIC TO SEWER COLLECTION SYSTEMS

Every employee, regardless of rank, has a personal responsibility to ensure on-the-job safety that equals the organization's obligation to provide a safe work environment. Working safely around the many hazards at wastewater collection systems and remote treatment facilities requires continuous effort. Although collection systems and wastewater treatment facilities may vary widely, this chapter presents work rules, procedures, guidelines, and other useful information that operators, consultants, engineers, and other personnel need to know to work safely in and around the workplace.

People who work around collection systems may be exposed to many hazards within or adjacent to the facility infrastructure that include the following:

- Infectious diseases
  - Pathogen inhalation or
  - Contact with skin, eyes, burns, cuts, scrapes, and mouth;
- Physical injury
  - Falls,
  - Slips,
  - Moving machinery,
  - Lack of physical safeguards,
  - Improper lifting, pushing, and pulling,
  - Repetitive action, or
  - Contact with chemicals and gases;
- Confined spaces
  - Limited access and egress,
  - Poor ventilation, or
  - Not intended for worker occupancy;
- Oxygen-deficient spaces
  - Limited ventilation,
  - Sewer gas production,
  - Chemical reactions, or
  - High heat and humidity;
- Toxic, corrosive, or harmful chemicals, gases, and vapors
  - Chemicals,
  - Chemical reactions,
  - Sewer gas,

- o   Industrial wastes, or
- o   Lack of ventilation;
- Explosive gas mixtures
  - o   Sewer gas,
  - o   Oxygen- and hydrogen-enriched areas,
  - o   Lack of ventilation, or
  - o   Ignition source;
- Fires
  - o   Improper material and chemical storage with ignition source or
  - o   Combustible materials potentially present in sewer (or combined sewers), which may ignite or explode;
- Electrical shock
  - o   Faulty equipment,
  - o   Improper grounding;
  - o   Unqualified servicing,
  - o   Poor insulation, or
  - o   Short circuits;
- Noise
  - o   Equipment,
  - o   Amplification in confined space, or
  - o   Explosions; and
- Dust, fumes, and mists
  - o   Chemical reactions,
  - o   Bulk off-loading, or
  - o   Transfer to mix tanks.

1.1 Hydrocarbons

Hydrocarbons found in collection systems include lubricating oils, greases, aerosol sprays, pesticides, herbicides, insecticides, chemical reagents used in a laboratory, gasoline, diesel fuel, butane, propane, methanol, and methane. Hydrocarbons may be aqueous, liquid, or gaseous compounds with fumes and vapors. Many hydrocarbons are flammable, combustible, or otherwise harmful and should be considered dangerous. Hydrocarbons should not be inhaled, allowed to touch the skin or other body parts, or stored near acids, caustics, or chlorine compounds.

1.2   Radiological Hazards

Although the hazards are not fully documented, collection system operators are potentially exposed to radioactive wastes because radioisotopes are used in hospitals, research laboratories, and other industries; additionally, some instrumentation used by operators, such as sludge density meters, may use a radioactive isotope. Radon gas may also find its way into confined spaces, particularly in below-grade structures constructed in a granite stratum. Radon should be tested for periodically if the general collection system area is known to experience this phenomenon.

The U.S. Nuclear Regulatory Commission (NRC) stringently controls handling and disposal of nuclear materials; however, accidental discharges occur and the operator may be exposed to enough radioactive wastes to cause acute or chronic injury. Therefore, the following precautions should be taken to reduce the risk of injuries and problems associated with radioactive wastes:

- Routinely check radioactive levels in collection systems and wastewater facilities. Report excessive levels to the health department and NRC;

- If radioactive wastes that could discharge accidentally or without authorization are known to exist, routinely monitor operators for exposure levels using pocket dosimeters or film badges;

- Wear special protective clothing and allow only qualified persons to work in a potentially contaminated area;

- Have the manufacturer train and certify all persons who use instruments containing radioactive isotopes to operate, calibrate, and service the equipment; and

- If radiological sources are present, establish a prearranged method for handling spills.

2.0 SAFETY PLANS AND STANDARD PROCEDURES

2.1 Development

A safety and health program aims to protect employees from undue exposure to chemical, physical, and other health hazards in the work environment. Program details should be distributed to all employees.

Implementing the program will also require setting goals and developing an action plan. Setting and attaining realistic goals requires identifying the magnitude of past or present risk and injuries, identifying preventive solutions, and developing a prioritized list of actions to implement those solutions. Safety data that are currently collected may not be adequate to monitor the effect of the safety program; as such, accident reporting forms and procedures may need to be revised.

Hazards have three possible causes: environment, equipment, and employee. Preventive safety inspections made with these causes in mind and a job safety analysis (JSA) will provide the basis for selecting controls and achieving desired risk reduction.

Safety inspection checklists should be developed for specific areas. The JSA identifies all hazards by inspecting each basic step of the job. A supervisor should look for specific types of potential accidents and ask the following questions about each basic step:

- Can the employee strike against or otherwise make injurious contact with the object?
- Can the employee be caught in, on, or between objects?
- Can the employee strain muscles by pushing, pulling, or lifting?
- Is exposure to toxic gases, vapors, dust, heat, or radiation possible?

Job observations should be repeated for each job element until all hazards have been identified.

Emergency planning identifies possible types of emergencies and hazards to the collection system and treatment plant and develops procedures to deal with them. Regulatory authorities should be contacted for information on which regulations apply. In addition to the federal Title III Superfund Amendments and Reauthorization Act, also known as the Emergency Planning and Community Right to Know Act, several states and municipalities have passed "right-to-know" legislation.

A priority list should be established that contains essential equipment and unit processes that should operate during a power outage to provide maximum protection of public health and safety and private and public property. Next, a corresponding prioritized list of personnel actions and support plans should be developed from cooperating outside agencies.

Supervisors should determine the vulnerability of wastewater system components to all foreseeable events, including conditions that could pose a threat to the work force, cause damage to equipment, or be toxic to biological processes. Additionally, supervisors should analyze which protective measures will eliminate or minimize adverse effects.

While typically not a safety tool, a sewer use ordinance may be one of the most effective tools available to collection system personnel. The industrial pretreatment program and local limits portions of the sewer use code of ordinances can be particularly effective in protecting workers by preventing hazardous material from entering the sewer system. However, such ordinances should contain certain basic elements to be legally enforceable. In addition, specific items are unique to each agency. In general, an ordinance should include the following:

- Definition,
- Prohibitions and limitations of wastewater discharges,
- Control of prohibited wastes,
- Industrial wastewater monitoring and reporting,
- Industrial discharge permit system,
- Enforcement procedures,
- Penalties and costs,
- Saving clause (if a portion of the ordinance is ruled to be invalid, the remainder of the ordinance remains valid),
- Resolution of conflicts,
- Effective date, and
- Enacting clause.

Most ordinances regulate both domestic and industrial wastewater disposal and, in some communities, the industrial waste (pretreatment) inspector may be responsible for both aspects of the ordinance.

Typically, the wastewater ordinance will be preceded by a section that grants specific authority for the sanitation agency to regulate wastewater disposal under state law and specifies any regulations under which the agency is required to operate. Additional statements may be made limiting wastes accepted by the sanitation agency to those that will not

- Damage the system;
- Create nuisances;
- Menace public health;
- Impose unreasonable cost;
- Interfere with wastewater treatment processes, including sludge disposal and biosolids reuse;
- Violate any quality requirements set by regulatory governmental agencies; or
- Be detrimental to the environment.

An agency may establish local pretreatment standards that are more stringent than U.S. Environmental Protection Agency standards if it can demonstrate that such limitations are necessary to meet or exceed state and local limitations on publicly owned treatment works effluent or to accomplish wastewater reclamation objectives. The wastewater ordinance should include the details of the control mechanism to be used to regulate dischargers to the agency and should specify the conditions and limitations of discharge. The control mechanism may be a permit, contract, administrative order, or some other type of arrangement with dischargers. The ordinance should grant specific inspection authority and right of access to pretreatment facilities and processes generating industrial wastewaters. Such authority includes the ability to take samples and examine records on the operation and maintenance of the contributing facility and other waste handling or chemical records, such as purchases and waste manifests.

Agency personnel should be notified immediately whenever pretreatment standards are violated. Supervisory personnel should then evaluate the effect of the violations and determine if the existing procedures need to be altered to provide continued worker safety.

The following questions should be considered when developing safety work rules and procedures for any sewer collection system:

- Are they formulated with the cooperation and participation of supervisors, management, and workers?

- Are they easily understood, realistic, and in accordance with applicable federal, state, and local laws?
- Are they logical and stress the individual's responsibility?
- Are they enforceable?

The system size, number of employees, and accident record should be considered when establishing reasonable rules and procedures.

Federal and state agencies have issued many rules, regulations, and standards that apply to wastewater treatment facility safety programs. For example, the Occupational Safety and Health Administration (OSHA) regulates safe practices associated with construction and maintenance. Ignoring these rules and regulations can result in serious civil and/or criminal penalties, so employees should be aware of existing requirements and keep up to date on them.

Several U.S. agencies and organizations provide safety information on safe exposure limits, testing, and performance of safety equipment. Their publications are useful to any safety program. A few of these associations include the American Society for Testing and Materials, the American Conference of Governmental Industrial Hygienists (ACGIH), the National Safety Council, and the National Fire Protection Association.

2.2 Training

Safety training should focus on the organization's needs and may take several forms, including regular prescheduled and formal meetings, smaller informal tailgate meetings, and infield demonstrations. Safety training should be scheduled to meet seasonal needs and regular refresher training should be provided in addition to training for new employees. Other resources for safety training include employees and organizations such as the American Red Cross or Water Environment Federation, subgroups such as the California Water Environment Association, and others. Following training, employees should practice their responses to hazards requiring quick action under pressure in a simulated test or drill.

2.3 Evaluation and Updating

Accidents and injuries often may appear to occur unpredictably, and the accident scene may need to be returned to service quickly. To expedite matters, a formal accident reporting and investigation program pre-assigns responsibilities, details procedures, provides checklists, and establishes lines of authority and communication. The information collected and analyzed can identify causes related to improper procedures, inadequate equipment, poor training, or miscommunication. The formal plan should

- Identify individuals responsible for initial and detailed investigations;
- Provide written authority;
- Provide the training, materials, and equipment needed;
- Include standard forms;
- Provide regularly compiled statistics; and
- Produce written investigation results.

Initial investigation involves collecting and documenting facts surrounding the accident for subsequent detailed analysis. The follow up investigation may be a simple review or a complete reconstruction of the accident. The goals are to identify the cause, provide guidance on possible remedial actions, and comply with regulatory requirements. Results may not identify a single cause, requiring management to provide a judicial solution. Employees should be informed of the causes and remedial actions to be taken. Employers should monitor the success of the remedial plan.

Risk evaluation identifies the cause of undesirable consequences and the likelihood of occurrence so that proper controls can be selected. The challenge is to set a level of acceptable risk that is low enough for improvement, but not so low that it is unattainable. The definition of *acceptable risk* will vary according to an individual's experience, knowledge, and perception of benefit.

To measure risk, one must first recognize that a hazard to human health or the environment exists in the machine, process, or operation and determine the potential severity of harm the hazard may cause. The third element of measuring risk is determining how the risk is created in the operation. What combination of events can lead to the hazard causing harm? Most accidents happen because of several things going wrong in sequence or at once. Once the combinations of events are found, the probability of those combinations occurring can be assessed and mitigated.

2.4 Ergonomics

Workplace injury prevention (in addition to hazard mitigation) includes consideration of repetitive motions, forceful or prolonged exertions, heavy lifting or carrying, and awkward postures. Other factors such as vibration or temperature may add risk to these work conditions. Working conditions with multiple risk factors have a higher probability of causing musculoskeletal problems.

The Occupational Safety and Health Act of 1970, Section 5(a) and (b), states that employers shall provide a place of employment " ... free from recognized hazards that are causing or likely to cause death or serious physical harm ...," and that employees "... shall comply with occupational safety and health standards and all rules, regulations, and orders issued pursuant to this Act which are applicable to his own actions and conduct." This general duty clause has been interpreted to apply to jobsite conditions related to ergonomic stressors.

When OSHA uses the general duty clause to cite an employer, OSHA must demonstrate that

- The employer failed to keep the workplace free of a hazard to which employees were exposed,

- The hazard was causing or likely to cause death or serious physical harm,

- The hazard was recognized, and

- A feasible means of abatement for that hazard exists.

Development of safety plans for sewer collection systems and remote locations should include an evaluation of ergonomic considerations.

2.5 Vehicle Safety

Besides typical hazards associated with motor vehicles, it is important to consider some of the other dangers associated with wastewater district vehicles when developing a vehicle safety program. Vehicle operators should wear ear protection and observe the threshold limits of vacuum trucks and jet trucks, which can produce noise levels in excess of 100 db while operating. Moving mechanical parts, such as pumps, are just as hazardous on vehicles as they are on standing equipment. Operators of chemical transport vehicles should be trained to handle chemical spills. It is important to be aware of electrical hazards on vehicles that carry generators.

3.0 PUMPING STATIONS

In this section, we lift stations and pumping stations will be referred to collectively as *pumping stations*. A pumping station (in the context of a sewer collection system) is a facility that receives wastewater via a gravity or pressure main and pumps the wastewater to another receiving facility via a pressure pipe or force main. A lift station is a facility that receives wastewater via a gravity main and pumps the wastewater a relatively short distance to a receiving facility at a higher elevation. Lift stations typically discharge into a gravity collection system or a headworks facility immediately adjacent to the lift station, whereas the force main discharge for a pumping station may be located a significant distance away. A pumping station force main could be discharged into a gravity collection system, headworks facility, or another pumping station and the elevation of the discharge could be above or below the pumping station infrastructure. Pumping stations can be constructed above or below ground and inside or outside of buildings. Any station located below ground or in a building should be considered a confined space. As such, operators should take all necessary precautions every time the station is entered, whether for routine checks or to perform maintenance. Dangerous concentrations of sewer gases may be present or released while performing maintenance. Additionally, slabs and floors may become wet, which can contribute to slips and falls.

Pumps may become clogged, bearings may need replacement, or other maintenance may be needed. Because of the size or location, equipment may need to be lifted to perform maintenance. Operators should beware of injury whether the equipment is lifted manually or with the aid of various lifting devices. When manually lifting an object, the object should be kept close to the body and leg strength should be used to lift rather than the back. Heavy objects should not be lifted without mechanical assistance.

When pumps are pulled, a chain and hoist rated for handling the load plus a safety factor should be used. A block of wood or other suitable support should be placed under the pumps or motors in case the hoist, chain, or lifting eyes fail. Hands, feet, or other body parts should never be placed under suspended equipment.

Rotating equipment can cause injuries to workers with rings, jewelry, long hair and beards, or loose, baggy clothing. Sleeves may also tangle in moving parts. Supervisors should make employees aware of these hazards.

Before performing any work, electrical controls should be locked out and tagged so the pump or other equipment cannot be turned on accidentally. The following sections discuss some of the safety considerations associated with using cranes, hoists, and forklift trucks as lifting devices.

3.1   Wet and Dry Wells

Wet wells are sumps that provide operational storage (flow equalization) for waste-water from upstream gravity collection systems (and sometimes force mains) prior to being pumped to the next downstream sewer collection facility. A pumping station wet well may include pumps, valves, controls, and discharge piping within the wet well space depending on design configurations.

Dry pits (or dry wells) contain pumps and other necessary equipment and controls for removing wastewater from a wet well. They are often constructed below ground with a common wall to the wet well. Dry wells that have adequate ventilation and do not have limited egress or entry are not automatically classified as a confined space. However, one should always treat wet wells and dry pits with respect. The reader is referred to Section 6.3, "Wet Wells" and Section 6.4 "Dry Pits," for additional precautions and guidelines.

3.2   Force Mains and Appurtenances

Force mains may include several types of mechanical and electrical infrastructure in addition to pressure pipes, such as

- Isolation valves,
- Air-release valves,
- Check valves,
- Flow meters,
- Pigging stations,
- Anticorrosion devices or systems,
- Chemical injection systems, and
- Odor control devices or systems.

Section 7.1 provides more information on working on force mains.

3.3   Chemicals (Odor and Corrosion Control)

A material and safety data sheet (MSDS) should be located every place chemicals are used or stored (including on service vehicles). Several common chemicals used or found in sewer collection systems are presented in this section; however, this is not intended to be an exhaustive list of chemicals potentially present in collection systems.

3.3.1   Chlorine

Besides disinfecting treated effluent, chlorine is used for odor control in sewers, wet wells, and headworks and for grease removal and as wastewater "freshener" in primary sedimentation units. It is important that workers understand the dangers and necessary precautions for handling chlorine.

The ACGIH has established the threshold limit vapor concentration at 0.5 ppm. A chlorine concentration of 0.3 ppm can be detected by smell, although odor threshold is highly variable, especially among individuals who are routinely exposed. Chlorine is available in gaseous, liquid, and aqueous states or in granular (powdered) form. Chlorine gas is yellow-green at normal temperatures and pressures and may be detected as a sharp, pungent odor. It is heavier than air and, therefore, will "flow" along the ground and spread. Under pressure, chlorine becomes a transportable liquid form. In any form, it is corrosive when mixed with water, dangerous to workers if inhaled or if it comes in contact with skin or eyes, and highly toxic in small concentrations.

Chlorine vapor attacks the respiratory system; however inhalation damage, unless severe, is generally reversible with time. Persons with a respiratory ailment such as asthma, bronchitis, or emphysema or suffering from a cold or sinus problem are particularly susceptible to chlorine inhalation. Immediate reactions can include nausea, vomiting, dizziness, shortness of breath, and chest pain. Pulmonary edema and chemical pneumonia may occur hours after exposure even if no immediate reaction occurred. Skin contact can cause irritation, burns, and blisters. Ingested chlorine can severely burn the mouth, esophagus, and stomach, causing nausea and vomiting.

There is no known antidote to chlorine. Clothing and shoes that become contaminated with any form of chlorine should be removed immediately and laundered thoroughly. Guidance should be sought from an MSDS for ingestion of liquids containing chlorine, which may not include recommendations to induce vomiting. Depending on the chemical composition, an MSDS may recommend the victim drink water or milk.

Cylinders should be unloaded carefully to avoid physical injury and cylinder damage. The cap, cylinder, and valves should be inspected for corrosion. Smaller chlorine cylinders should be stored upright in covered areas and secured with chains to prevent tipping. Storage cylinders should not be crowded or exposed to high temperatures. Storage areas should be well ventilated and kept away from chlorinators and other equipment that may be damaged if leaks occur. Chlorine leak detection equipment should be installed and maintained and solvents, oils, greases, or other chemicals should not be stored in the same area as chlorine.

Granular, or powdered, chlorine (calcium hypochlorite, 65% available chlorine) is highly caustic. The dry powder or granules may be applied directly or mixed with water to form a chlorine solution in a tank. This solution will typically contain hydrochloric or hydrochlorous acids, which are corrosive. When transporting or mixing granular forms, a dry, clean container should always be used to avoid an explosive reaction with traces of organic or petroleum products. A chemical feed pump should be used to deliver the chlorine solution to the application point from a mix tank. The chlorine granules should only be handled in well-ventilated areas free from excessive moisture and away from any water line. Chlorine is highly reactive to tin and titanium. Butyl-coated nylon gloves should be used when transferring chlorine from a storage container to a mixing tank and fumes from the open container should not be inhaled. Proper respirators and clothing should be worn when handling any hypochlorite.

Hypochlorite is also available as a liquid, typically as sodium hypochlorite. Although it is typically less than 10% available chlorine, it should be stored and handled with extreme caution. Protective clothing and gear should be worn during handling.

Chlorine leaks may develop at connections to chlorinators, pressure gauges, vacuum gauges, fittings, valves, ejectors, and chlorine solution lines. If moisture or water is present at the site of a chlorine leak, the resulting acidic and corrosive conditions may damage equipment. Leaks can be the result of incorrect tool use. Adjustable wrenches, pliers, cheater bars, or other standard tools should not be used on cylinder valves because the tools will apply too much torque to the valves, possibly shearing them.

Leaks can be detected by using aqueous ammonia vapors, which form a white ammonia chloride vapor in the presence of chlorine. However, it is important to not breathe ammonia chloride because it is poisonous. One should not add ammonia solution directly to a suspected leak because it will cause corrosion directly at the source. Instead, a cloth should be moistened with ammonia solution and placed over a suspected leak. An appropriate personal protective equipment (PPE) breathing apparatus should be worn if using ammonia to detect chlorine leaks. Some leaks can be detected by smell, but a small leak can go undetected by smell or ammonia vapor method until the metal is corroded, causing a dangerous significant leak. Discolored pressure joints or moisture droplets on the underside of a joint may indicate a small leak. If a leak is in progress, cadmium plating (used over copper tubing and bronze or brass fittings) will disappear. The base metal will become reddish and green copper chloride may appear. Painting chlorine lines with a bright yellow, durable paint can help identify small leaks. The first evidence of a small leak will be a highly visible moist spot of brown rust. Small leaks can also be identified by chlorine leak detectors. Most detectors are capable of registering chlorine concentrations as low as 0.5 ppm in the air. Remote alarms and automatic dialers can be activated if a leak is detected; all leaks should be fixed immediately.

Only heavy-gauge pipes, tubing, fittings, and valves should be used for chlorine supply to chlorinators and ejectors and chlorine solution lines from the ejector to the point of application.

The chlorinator room should be separate from other parts of the facility, with positive ventilation provided at the ceiling and floor level. Ventilation should be continuous, and at least start ventilating before entering the room. Ventilation controls should be interlocked with a light switch located outside the room. Other electrical controls should be placed outside the room to prevent corrosion. Self-contained breathing apparatuses (SCBAs) suitable for protection against chlorine gas should be stored nearby, but also outside the room. The door to the room should open out and have a window for observing chlorine equipment. Entry and exit areas should be kept free from obstacles and have clear pathways; emergency hardware should be stored nearby.

The Chlorine Institute (1988) specifies proper repair kits for chlorine storage containers: type "A" kits for 68-kg (150-lb) cylinders, type "B" kits for 907-kg (1-ton) cylinders, and type "C" kits for rail cars. Personnel likely to make repairs should be trained annually. Chlorine repairs should not be authorized if personnel are untrained or unqualified. Personnel should wear full-face respirators and impervious gloves and clothing when changing cylinders, repairing leaks, or making routine inspections because a dangerous leak can occur at any time.

Although chlorine itself is not flammable, it will support combustion. Personnel should only apply water to cylinders in the event of a nearby fire to keep the cylinders cool and avoid melting their fusible plugs, which would allow gaseous and/ or liquid chlorine to escape. Otherwise, water should be kept away from chlorine cylinders and powdered chlorine at all times to prevent corrosion of cylinder walls. Water or moisture in contact with powdered chlorine may chemically react, causing fires.

Personnel should know and have posted the telephone numbers of local fire departments and industrial emergency response teams who have experience handling chlorine emergencies. Personnel should be provided with eye-wash stations and shower areas for neutralizing contaminants; adequate safety signing; and frequent drills on the properties of chlorine, the use of SCBAs, and emergency procedures for evacuating, stopping a leak, and neutralizing a spill area.

3.3.2   Ozone

Although it has other uses, ozone is typically used for disinfection and odor control. It is a powerful oxidizing agent produced on-site from air or oxygen-carrier gas passing between narrowly spaced electrodes under high voltage. Ozone contact vessels must be covered to control offgas discharges. Offgases must be treated to destroy remaining ozone, typically by thermal or thermal-catalytic means. It is important to avoid breathing and contact with ozone and offgases because ozone is an irritant and may cause serious respiratory problems. Electrical hazards exist because high voltage is used to produce ozone. Feed gas compressors should be enclosed in a soundproof room or otherwise sound-attenuated to acceptable levels.

As recommended by the National Institute for Occupational Safety and Health (1990), exposure levels should not exceed a threshold limit of 0.2 mg/m^3 (0.1 ppm by volume) for 8 hours per workday and/or 0.6 mg/m^3 (0.3 ppm by volume) for more than 10 minutes. Typically, ozone can be detected by individuals at concentrations ranging from 0.02 to 0.1 mg/m^3 (0.01 to 0.05 ppm by volume). However, frequent exposure to ozone may dull an individual's ability to detect it. Ozone monitors can detect ozone leaks; maintenance personnel should repair leaks promptly and shut down the ozone system until repairs are complete.

3.3.3   Caustic

Collection systems that serve commercial and/or industrial users may encounter pH adjustment chemicals or plant spills associated with industrial operations. Caustic chemicals include any chemical with a pH higher than 9. Examples of commonly used caustic chemicals are calcium hydroxide (hydrated lime), sodium hydroxide (caustic soda), ammonia (in some food processing facilities), and calcium oxide (quicklime, unslaked lime, and burnt lime). These types of chemicals are used to aid coagulation, adjust pH, clean filters, and neutralize acid spills.

When the dry form of these chemicals or concentrated liquid forms are mixed with water, the chemical reaction creates heat and rapidly liberates hydrogen gas, which creates a potentially explosive atmosphere. If mixed in enclosed areas, rapid expansion of gas may rupture the vessel in which the reaction takes place.

Workers should not inhale vapors and fumes and should wear eye protection to avoid contact with splashes, fumes, and vapors. Caustic spills should be flushed with large amounts of water and neutralized with dilute acids.

3.4 Electrical Safety

Much of the wastewater works equipment requiring maintenance is mechanical, but electrically driven; as such, a combination of safety practices is required. For example, pumps are electrically driven, but the pumps themselves are mechanical devices with associated valves, piping, and level controls. Because of the size or installation requirements, the pump may need to be lifted with special electric equipment for repairs and/or replacement. Other heavy devices, such as valves, are entirely mechanical but may require electric lifting equipment for repairs.

Collection system personnel are pressed to maintain, repair, or remove mechanical equipment with minimal shutdown time. Unfortunately, the need to restore service quickly may lead workers to disregard appropriate safety measures. It is important to ensure employees know their jobs and understand the potential hazards to the public, themselves, other employees, and the wastewater system. A licensed electrician should be used for work within electrical panels and on electrical components. A licensed electrician on staff may be beneficial to an organization. As much as is possible, it is important to plan, schedule, and perform maintenance with all the necessary tools, materials, and manpower staged or in use at the site of the operation.

Care should be taken to follow lockout procedures for equipment that can be remotely or automatically operated. Equipment should be tagged and chocks or blocks should be used to prevent movement if other measures fail. Properly isolating, or locking out and tagging, equipment is one way to reduce the chance that equipment will accidentally operate during maintenance or repair work. Appropriate controls are physically locked and marked with a written tag that describes why the equipment is locked out of service.

One of the safest means of isolating equipment is for the maintenance employee to install a key-operated, tamperproof locking device on the valve, power disconnect, or control. If more than one worker will be involved, each employee working on the system should apply an individual lock with its unique key or combination.

It is important to physically restrain rotating machine parts or parts with stored energy or position them in a zero mechanical state, removing any stored energy and preventing movement by gravity, wind, spring release, or water flow.

Many pieces of equipment also have auxiliary equipment that, if operated, could injure workers making repairs. Thus, to properly isolate a pump, both its electrical system and all appurtenant valves should be isolated. To ensure that all related equipment is properly tagged out and secured in large systems, a responsible person who is familiar with the equipment and system should be designated as an isolation supervisor.

Hold cards should be logged centrally so supervisors will be aware of tagged-out units and can easily check for clearance. When a system needs to be locked out for safety, it is important to inform the personnel who will be affected and record the following information: date, time, name of person applying and/or removing hold cards, and the equipment or system on which work is to be performed.

Personnel should be taught to adhere to established lockout procedures for their own benefit and to respect hold or tagout cards regardless of the isolation method. Locks and tags may be removed only by the person(s) they were meant to protect. Ignoring lockout/tagout procedures could result in personal injury or equipment damage.

All electricity and electric power equipment should be treated cautiously. According to extensive studies, currents as low as 10 to 15 mA can cause loss of muscle control and, upon complete contact, 12 V may cause injury (Bridges et al., 1985). Ordinary 120-V electricity can be fatal, and most collection system electrical facilities operate at voltages from 120 to 480 V or more. Therefore, all voltages should be considered dangerous.

Electricity kills by paralyzing the nervous system and stopping muscular action. It may hit the breathing center at the base of the brain, interrupting the transmission of nervous impulses to the muscles responsible for breathing; it may affect the heart, causing it to cease pumping blood; or it may cause severe and extensive burns.

If someone does come in contact with electricity, the victim should be freed from the live conductor promptly using a dry stick or other nonconductor or by turning off the electricity. Bare hands should never be used to remove a live wire from a victim or a victim from an electrical source. Next, it is important to begin cardiopulmonary resuscitation (CPR) or artificial respiration immediately and to continue until breathing is restored or until a doctor or emergency medical technician arrives.

A circuit should be assumed to be live unless one is certain it is dead and cannot be inadvertently energized. Additional rules for electrical maintenance safety include the following:

- Avoid becoming grounded inadvertently to water piping or other metallic equipment when working on or in contact with electrical equipment or wiring, and do not touch or pass tools with a person who is grounded;

- Allow only qualified and authorized personnel to work on electrical equipment or to perform electrical maintenance;

- Be sure overhead electrical power lines are neutralized or do not come in close proximity to tools or equipment; do not rely on electrical isolation devices for protection from such sources of electricity;

- Consult local authorities before digging or tunneling to prevent contact with buried electrical sources;

- Keep all electrical controls accessible, well marked, and in safe working order;

- Prevent wires from becoming a tripping hazard;

- Do not use metal or conducting ladders, metal tape measures, or other metal tools around electrical equipment;

- Handle wires as if they were live;

- When working around electrical equipment, always keep the hazard in mind;

- Work from a firm base and cover energized buses or parts with a good electrical insulator such as a rubber blanket;

- Do not remove guards, use oversized fuses, or block or bypass protective devices unless it is absolutely essential to the repair or maintenance activity, and then only after alerting the operating personnel and maintenance supervisor; and

- When working on machinery remote from disconnect devices, especially at a long distance, ground the conductors to dissipate any stored energy and to prevent inadvertent energizing.

Employees should not work alone on energized equipment that operates at or above 480 V (such as a magnetic starter in a dead front motor control center). Contact with equipment and circuits at 480 V or higher may be fatal, so it is better to have two employees work as a team and only if equipment and circuits can be completely shut off and are located in a clean, dry, well-lighted area with good accessibility. Two employees working together can double check each other and one of them can de-energize circuits, apply first aid, or summon assistance in the event of a mishap.

It is important to notify others of the intent to perform work on electrical systems or components. If interim repairs are necessary, ensure that affected personnel know this and take remedial measures to reduce the opportunity for injury or damage.

3.4.1   Tagging and Lockout

It is important to create and adhere to a good system for holding and locking out electrical circuits when equipment is being repaired. Unexpected power in electrical equipment that can be started by automatic or manual remote control may injure persons who happen to be near enough to be struck.

When motors or other electrical equipment require repair, an employee should open the circuit at the switch box and padlock the switch in the "off" position, tagging it with a description of the repair, the name of the repairer, and the department involved. Supervisors should emphasize the serious risks to maintenance personnel and ensure that the procedure is implemented with the necessary keys, locks, and arrangements.

Individual locks should be issued for which each worker keeps one key and the supervisor keeps the other. The supervisor should have a master list of key numbers for each lock in the department. Only the supervisor will use the extra key until the lock and keys are destroyed and replaced with new equipment. The locks should be painted different colors to indicate types of craft or to differentiate shifts; each lock should be stamped with the employee's name or clock number or a metal tag attached.

Maintenance personnel should be taught the following lockout procedure:

- Alert the operator;
- Before starting work on any power transmission equipment or power-driven machine, be sure it cannot be set in motion without the maintenance worker's permission;
- Make sure each worker places individual padlocks on each control switch, lever, or valve so every worker must remove one padlock per block before the equipment can be operated again;

- If no padlock is available, place an "at work" sign at the control and block the mechanism, fastening both the sign and blocking securely so they cannot be removed easily;

- At the end of each shift, make sure workers remove their individual padlocks, signs, and blocking themselves, but only if removing them will not expose another person to danger; and

- If the padlock key is lost, immediately report it to the supervisor and get a new padlock.

This system should be developed to suit the needs of the wastewater works maintenance organization and coordinated with the system for holding equipment out of service for mechanical maintenance. The system should be made simple and clear responsibilities should be assigned to each person who is involved in the locking out or releasing operation. Accidentally opening the wrong valve may only give a pipe fitter a surprise shower or, if the contents are involuntarily ingested, make someone ill; however, accidentally energizing an electrical circuit could cause death.

3.4.2   Testing

Electrical maintenance often involves performing equipment and diagnostic tests using electricity. These tasks may require exercising switches, relays, and equipment protective devices, bypassing other controls or lockout devices. Before conducting such tasks, the consequences of ordinary- and fault-condition reactions should be evaluated. Similarly, when measuring electrically live circuits, it is important to be sure to use the appropriate capacity testing device and cables. Probes used to access terminals can cause short circuits or alternate electrical pathways.

Introducing stray signals or commands that may affect the operation of programmable controllers and other logic-based electronic devices should be avoided. If these devices perform a safety function, the safety feature should be tested to be sure it works. Before working on a line or bus of at least 480 V, it should be ground and de-energized before being locked out. However, before grounding the line or bus, it should be tested with a pretested voltmeter to be sure it is off.

3.4.3   Feedback

Feedback is the return of a fraction of the electrical output signal to the input. It often occurs because of the impedance characteristics of a circuit and can cause component failure or, in control circuits, be misinterpreted as a control signal.

Precautions should be taken to avoid feedback on a de-energized circuit. Feedback can occur from a control circuit interlocked with another control circuit that is fed from a different source; the high-voltage side of a potential or control transformer that is still connected to the bus; the low-voltage side of the transformer energized by an extraneous source acting as a step-up transformer; or standby on an emergency electrical power source. Symptoms of feedback conditions include premature failure of components, the presence of intermittent control or sensor signals, or surges within circuits. These conditions may be subtle and require extensive diagnostic routines to identify the problem's origin.

3.4.4 System Grounding

Electrical system grounding is the connection between an electrical circuit or equipment and the earth or some large conducting body that serves in place of the earth. Grounding is used to establish polarity or electrical potentials and to protect against electrical short circuits. The impedance separating an energized circuit from a ground may determine the path of electrical current flow and is a critical element in the potential for electrocution.

3.4.5 Grounding Portable Tools

Each portable electrical tool that is not inherently double insulated should be equipped with a separate electrical conductor in or on the cord that will effectively ground the metallic case of the tool. Single-phase, 120-V tools should have a three-conductor cord, with the case-grounding conductor wired to a three-prong polarized plug. The plug should be designed to be inserted into the receptacle in only one way.

The mating contact in the grounding plug's receptacle is wired to a special grounding wire carded in the same conduit with the supply wires or else connected to a continuous metal conduit used as a ground path. This conductor is typically colored green and should be used only to ground equipment. The ground blade should not be broken off of a grounding plug so it will fit a two-wire receptacle. If a three-wire to two-wire plug adapter is being used, it is important to be sure the ground is continued by a separate wire or through the cover screw and ground wire or conduit supplying the receptacles. Poor or nonexistent connections to grounding for 15- or 20-A receptacles can be tested instantly by plugging in a tester with three lights and a quantity code for each light.

When used around water or wastewater, the portable tool should be plugged into a ground fault interrupter to protect the user. The grounding circuit should be checked periodically to be sure it is intact between the plug–receptacle interface and the tool case. A broken ground wire in the tool's cord could lead to an accident. At least once a quarter, all tools should be checked with a megohmmeter (megger) to verify the grounding circuit is complete.

Double-insulated, portable electrical tools do not require a grounding conductor. It is important to periodically check to be sure the double insulation has not been damaged, which could cause dangerous electrical leakage, and to examine the cord for wear, cuts, or abrasions. Extreme care should be taken when working in wet locations and portable electrical tools should not be used near an explosive hazard. Tools should be tested with a portable ground fault interrupter before being checked out of a tool room, regardless of whether the tool is double insulated or has three prongs.

3.4.6 Computer and Electronic Equipment

Special training and static discharge elimination equipment should be used to protect both workers and equipment. Computer and digital sensors are extremely sensitive and can be damaged or destroyed by as small an electrical charge as the static charge generated by moving one's hand to touch the electrical board. Conversely, capacitors and solid-state voltage-increasing circuits can create high voltages in seemingly low-voltage electronic equipment. Computer and electronic equipment are susceptible to stray electrical currents. The small independence in a grounding circuit, invisible to ordinary electrical power, can become significant voltage when subjected to the extremely high frequency waveforms found in modern electronics.

The National Electrical Code requires the green ground wires for computer and electronic equipment to be the same size as current-carrying conductors. Care should be taken to bring back separate ground wires for each piece of equipment because of looping ground wires or using the same ground wire in a series for several pieces of equipment can result in "ground loops," affect performance, and create a safety hazard for maintenance personnel.

3.4.7 De-Energizing Lines and Buses

Insulation protects the current-carrying conductor from accidental grounding. For high-voltage conductors, especially those above 4 kV, a strong electromagnetic field is imposed in the insulation's dielectric material. When the power is disconnected, the magnetic field's collapse can re-energize the conductor to an unsafe level.

After disconnecting high-voltage lines and buses, they should be de-energized with a grounded conductor attached to an insulated handle ("deadman's stick"). The voltage and the length of the conductor will determine the amount of energy stored in the dielectric; longer conductors and larger voltages mean more energy to dissipate. With high voltage, the stored energy will jump a substantial gap and the discharge will be accompanied by both flash and smoke. Safety goggles and electrically insulated tools of the proper voltage rating should be used.

While the deadman's stick will discharge the original stored energy, the dielectric material's stored energy will take longer to dissipate. This energy can also recharge high-voltage conductors, albeit over a longer time. After "sticking," the conductor or bus should be temporarily grounded to something substantial that is bolted or clamped so it cannot be knocked loose accidentally.

3.4.8   Working on a Live Circuit

Sometimes, maintenance personnel need to work on equipment that is electrically energized, such as when they are taking electrical measurements, functionally exercising electrical components, observing polarity based on motor rotation, or performing diagnostics. Such activities should be avoided as much as possible; however, when they are necessary, additional precautions and protective measures should be used. The following sections address some of these considerations.

3.4.9   Buddy System

When working on "hot" electrical systems, a team of at least two workers should be used. One team member is designated the safety observer, whose full attention is devoted to watching the work to make sure all safety rules are followed. The safety observer is trained in CPR, has grounding equipment available, and will review the procedure with workers before it is performed. This person's authority to stop the work is absolute. If a safety violation is observed, the safety observer will stop work until it is corrected. If an employee is injured, especially by contact with energized wires or equipment, the safety observer is the first line of rescue and first aid.

3.4.10   Insulating Blankets

Before working inside switchboards, power cabinets, and other locations where there are exposed energized buses or parts, it is important to be sure all conductors are de-energized to the greatest degree practical. If some circuits remain energized, the following precautions should be taken to minimize the possibility of shock or short circuit:

- Cover all live buses with insulating blankets;
- Be careful to avoid accidental contact with live buses or parts within reach, and take extra care to prevent dropping tools on live buses or falling against live buses or parts;

- To prevent eye damage from possible high-intensity arcing, wear protective goggles for all work inside energized switchgear;

- Remove rings, watches, metal-framed glasses, and all other jewelry before performing such work; and

- Avoid touching live parts, but if absolutely necessary, touch them standing only on a dry insulating surface, clear of all other conductors or grounding surfaces; and

- Wear rubber safety gloves in good tested condition and approved for use on the voltage, and touch the circuit with only one hand.

Small metallic objects, such as tools, flashlights, and jewelry, can make an electrical contact with or cause a short across live electrical parts. Jewelry should not be worn when working with or near electrical circuitry. Key chains and key buckles can be a significant hazard in electrical work; therefore, they should be removed and stored in a toolbox for safety.

Pliers, screwdrivers, wrenches, and other tools used in electrical work should have insulated handles, and the uninsulated working surfaces of these tools should be as small as practicable to minimize the possibility of metal contacting live parts. Electrical tape or other insulating materials may be used to cover metal surfaces, but insulated tools should be used whenever possible. Using metal flashlights should be avoided.

3.4.11 Explosive Gas Considerations

When working on electrically live or charged equipment, electrical energy may discharge, arcing or shooting sparks. This can present an explosion hazard in areas containing potentially flammable or combustible mixtures. Before breaking the seal on an explosion-proof enclosure, it is important to make sure the work area is well ventilated. Workers should check for gasses and shut down nearby equipment and facilities if practical. The area should be continually monitored for gas and only non-sparking, nonferrous tools should be used. When finished, it is important to make certain that the explosion-proof fittings are resealed.

3.4.12 Fire Extinguisher

Class C fire extinguishers for electrical fires should be mounted at or near all motor control centers, transformer banks, and switchgear installations. Water or other conductive liquids and materials should not be used on electrical fires.

3.5 Site Security

The following general security measures should be provided at facilities:

- Erect and maintain intruder-resistant fences;

- Post appropriate warning signs on fences, doors, and buildings;

- Contact information in case of emergency or suspicious activity;

- Ask nearby residents or neighborhood watch groups to report loitering or other questionable behavior;

- Consider using security companies or the local police department for additional surveillance or other security services; and

- Implement adequate fire and emergency procedures, including installing and maintaining fire alarms and fire-suppression equipment near every potential fire hazard, developing evacuation procedures and plans, and conducting fire and emergency drills regularly.

Warning devices are local or remote alarms, such as flashing lights, sirens, or horns, which activate when specific events occur. Available devices and instrumentation should be used to monitor detection of unauthorized entry; excessive levels of combustible gas concentrations; temperature; leaks; oxygen deficiency; and critical levels, flows, or pressures.

To curtail unauthorized entry into an area, the following measures should be taken:

- Install locks on doors and/or gates. Distribute non-duplicating keys for keyed locks and maintain a key assignment log or consider using combination locks or electronic locks with programmable entry codes, which can be changed as needed. Install panic hardware to override locks in emergencies;

- Eliminate unnecessary windows and install burglar bars on the remaining ones;

- Install sensors and detectors that tie into local alarms and annunciators. Link automatic dialing or other communication equipment with detection equipment to report an unauthorized entry to security personnel; and

- Station security guards to monitor a site, and consider using cameras and monitors.

Good security can reduce illegal dumping, tampering, and vandalism and prevent injury to unauthorized persons. A wastewater facility's security requirements will depend on the protection that workers and the public need, past problems or monetary losses from lack of security, anticipated problems, the confidence level needed, and the resources available. Larger facilities may need more elaborate security than smaller facilities.

3.6 Site Safety

Entrances and exits should be clearly marked and warning signs and other devices should be placed in prominent areas to identify head clearance and step-up and step-down hazards. Lighting systems should be maintained and lights that burn out should be replaced. Caution should be exercised when opening doors, especially ones that open outward. Workers should hold on to handrails when walking up or down stairs. Nonslip surfaces should be used on floors, catwalks, walkways, ladders, and scaffolds, and they should be periodically checked and maintained. Damaged sidewalks, stairs, and ladders should be replaced.

Gratings and manhole covers should be replaced as soon as possible after removing them. Open pits and trenches should be covered and backfilled as soon as practical. Care should be taken when mowing and trimming vegetation, and grass and vegetation should be removed that may hide hazards. Leaves, rubbish, or debris should be prevented from accumulating. Snow and ice should be removed frequently from walkways, parking lots, sidewalks, and stairways. Appropriate traffic-control devices and signs should be used in travel areas, such as stop signs at intersections, speed limit signs and speed bumps, and barricades and cones at construction sites. Clearances should be posted for overhead wires and piping; all piping should be prominently marked or color-coded to identify the contents of the pipe and direction of flow.

Valves should be clearly marked and labeled so they are easy to locate and shut down in an emergency. Fire hoses should be placed at strategic and easily accessible locations. Fire-actuated sprinkler systems should be installed where possible, and fire extinguishers should be located near all electrical control panels and other fire hazards.

4.0 GRIT CHAMBERS, SCREENS, AND COMMINUTORS

Manually or mechanically cleaned bar screens, comminutors, and other screening devices are typically constructed at the headworks of a treatment plant. However, they may be in sewer collection systems upstream of pumping stations or flow equalization basins. Their primary purpose is to remove relatively large objects and materials that may interfere with plant equipment and processes. Toxic industrial waste and sewer gases may accumulate, causing explosive, flammable, or oxygen-deficient atmospheres. These hazards are of particular concern when the screens are housed in buildings or constructed below ground.

Mechanically cleaned screens have moving mechanisms and devices such as motors, reduction gears, endless chains or cables, and rakes with teeth. Comminutors incorporate a rotating blade that cuts and shreds the solid material, eliminating the need to remove it from the wastewater flow. Large objects can jam mechanical screens. Therefore, it is important to disable all moving equipment before working around them. Additionally, workers should lock out and tag electrical equipment and physically block off the drive mechanism.

5.0 TRENCHING AND EXCAVATIONS

5.1 Coordination with Other Agencies and Utilities

There may be a tendency to overlook the significant hazard and risk increase caused by in-house construction because in-house staff is performing the work. Employees should perform their jobs safely and supervisors should ensure all necessary safety equipment is available and used. Employees should be trained to recognize job hazards and how to avoid injury. The worksite should be inspected periodically for safe conditions and working procedures.

Preplanning is an integral part of construction safety. Meetings should be held with all parties involved to discuss the hazards associated with upcoming projects and what measures can be taken to reduce or eliminate the risks. The methods, equipment, and employees to be used should be determined. The jobsite itself should be evaluated for potential hazards such as unstable or contaminated soil or exposure to vehicular traffic.

Proper follow through of safety planning is critical. A system to monitor and inspect worksites should be set up. Deficiencies found during inspections should be documented and corrective actions initiated that will not only fix the deficiency, but prevent its recurrence. The same care and concern should be used for in-house construction activities as for contractor construction. The hazards are no less because the workers are familiar; actually, if utility systems personnel are not regularly involved in such construction, they may be greater.

When the work is complete, the worksite should be thoroughly inspected. All material and debris should be removed to avoid leaving any tripping or falling hazards for the general public. Indeed, the site should be cleaner than before work began. Sites should be reviewed at a later date to check for ground or pavement settling. The reader is referred to Section 8.1 ("Notifications") for additional precautions and guidelines.

5.2 Public Safety and Crowd Control

Any construction activities in public spaces present a public hazard. The responsibility to protect the public rests with the organization performing the work, including the contractor or the public organization. It is important to warn both motor and pedestrian traffic of the construction activity, prevent them from entering the work area, and keep adjacent areas clear of construction materials and debris. Warning signs should be used indicating that work is in progress, in addition to barricades, emergency cones, and reflective barricade tape.

5.3 Shoring

Because sewers are designed and constructed to operate by gravity flow, they are often located at depths greater than 1.5 m (5 ft). When sewers and appurtenances deeper than 1.5 m (5 ft) must be excavated for repairs, cave-in protection is required by OSHA 29 CFR 1910 (Office of the Federal Register, 1989). The excavation should be adequately sloped and/or braced and shored and excavated materials placed at least 1 m (3 ft) away from the edge of the trench. Additionally, proper traffic control, rescue plans, and equipment operations are needed to fully protect equipment, workers, and the public.

5.4 Parking and Backing Vehicles

Minor fender benders or serious injuries can happen when parking and backing vehicles. To reduce the dangers associated with these operations, a skilled, alert driver and a "spotter" should be used. A spotter is an individual outside the vehicle, with a clear view of the area, who assists the driver. Spotters are typically used for backing; entering narrow locations, such as a garage; or assisting in precise parking situations, such as at jobsites. The driver should always have an unobstructed view of the spotter. If the spotter moves out of the driver's range of vision, the driver should stop the vehicle immediately and wait for the spotter to come back into view. This may prevent hitting an inattentive spotter. When parking on the side of the road, the driver should be sure that oncoming vehicles have a safe clearance and set out appropriate warning signs.

6.0 CONFINED SPACES

Performing maintenance in a sewer collection system may involve entry into a space where access is restricted or difficult or where the atmosphere may be harmful, toxic, and/or explosive. There may be other potential hazards such as flooding of the work space, physical entrapment, biting insects or animals, chemical contact, or electrical hazards. If any of these conditions exist, there is a good chance one may be entering a confined space. The reader is referred to Section 8.1 of Chapter 5 for confined space classification criteria.

6.1 Manholes

Sewers, manholes, and traps are confined spaces, which have many hazards. In addition to wastewater, sewers may also carry many sewer gases and, in some instances, toxic industrial wastes. Methane, carbon monoxide, and carbon dioxide may be present in harmful concentrations and, depending on pH and temperature, septic wastewater bacteria can reduce sulfate, which will generate toxic and potentially explosive hydrogen sulfide gas. The areas over sewers and near manholes can collapse because of corrosion and/or leaks. It is important to be aware of these hazards and to follow the proper precautions and procedures when working in sewers.

Adequate equipment for work crews in confined spaces includes the following:

- Two fresh air blowers (one for backup) and large-diameter flexible hoses for manhole ventilation;

- Atmosphere testing equipment for testing and monitoring to guard against oxygen deficiency and explosive and toxic gases;

- Harnesses and individual life lines for each person going underground and for standby personnel;

- A SCBA for each person going underground and for standby personnel;

- Protective clothing, including rubber boots, gloves, rain gear, hard hats, and face shields or goggles;

- Explosion-proof lights;

- Communications equipment;

- A first aid kit;

- Barricades, traffic cones, and warning signs;

- Miscellaneous tools, including shovels, pike poles, chain jacks, pry bars, and manhole hooks;

- Portable ladders and tripod-type lifting equipment with parachute-type harnesses; and

- Dual lifting devices (one for backup).

All workers should be properly trained to use all equipment and have a confined space entry permit signed by an upper level supervisor authorizing entry if a confined space will be entered. Before entering a sewer or manhole, the following precautions should be taken:

- Adequately ventilate the area and test for oxygen sufficiency, toxic gas, and combustible gas from top to bottom. Check temperature and humidity for safe levels;

- Obtain confined space entry permit, if necessary;

- Implement traffic controls;

- Use proper tools to remove manhole covers and lift using leg strength. Lay covers flat on the ground at least 1 m (3 ft) from the opening;

- Wear approved PPE and enter only if confined space entry requirements are met; and

- Be aware that cockroaches, spiders, snakes, toads, frogs, lizards, rats, ants, and stinging insects may be found inside and outside of the sewers and manholes.

Upon entering a sewer or manhole, the following procedures should be followed:

- When possible, use portable ladders to avoid loose, corroded, and broken steps and keep firm footing and a handhold at all times. Otherwise, use a safety harness and a lifting and lowering winch for entry and egress;

- Be alert, stay in communication, get the job done, and get out;

- Descend one at a time using an adequately supported safety harness in good condition;

- Use only explosion-proof portable lights and nonsparking tools and continue gas monitoring while workers are below ground; clean up all tools and equipment and put them back in their proper places;

- Remove traffic control devices only after all work is completed and the manhole cover replaced; and

- Change out of contaminated clothes and wash hands, face, and any other exposed body parts.

It is important to continue to ventilate the confined space while the entrant is inside.

6.2 Valve and Meter Vaults

Sewer system protection includes bolting down vault covers, surrounding lift stations with intruder-resistant fencing and locked gates, locking dry wells, using tamper-proof locks on control panels and electrical feed boxes, and installing alarms or security systems to report unauthorized entries.

6.3 Wet Wells

All wet wells are confined spaces and should be treated accordingly. Ventilation requirements vary according to the well's area and depth. Relatively large amounts of organic material may settle and decompose, producing dangerous gases, and additional dissolved sewer gases may be released from flow agitation as wastewater enters the well. Installing permanent gas detectors with alarms should be considered.

Enclosed wet wells should be continuously ventilated to prevent excessive accumulation of gases in the upper level. This type of ventilation is typically a pipe positioned to deter small rodents from gaining entry and screened to keep out larger insects. The screen should be checked periodically. All conduit and pipe entrances should have gas-tight seals. Adequate guardrails and safety chains should be provided around all pits, wells, and floor openings. Collection system and maintenance personnel should be aware that wastewater may rise rapidly during rainfall events or pump failure. The reader is referred to Section 3.0 ("Pumping Stations") and Section 6.1 ("Manholes") for additional precautions and guidelines.

6.4 Dry Pits

Dry pits (or dry wells) are typically considered confined spaces. The pumps present mechanical hazards, but leaking walls, pumps, seals, valves, packing glands, gauges, and other equipment can cause slippery conditions and sewer gas accumulation. Improperly sealed conduits for the level control system between the wet well and the dry well can allow sewer gas to accumulate in the dry well. Forced air ventilation should be initiated before entering a dry well.

To prevent injury, all leaks should be repaired and floors kept clean. All equipment should also be kept clean and painted so it is easy to identify small leaks before they become dangerous problems. The entire room should be illuminated well and kept free from clutter. Whether permanent or portable, nonslip, secured ladders should be used.

There should be a sump with two pumps (one for backup) and level controls to prevent flooding of the area if a leak develops. The pumps should be checked routinely to ensure proper operation. Valves should be operated periodically so they will work if an emergency situation develops. It is important to be sure that all electrical equipment is explosion-proof and to mount a Class C fire extinguisher in the room. The reader is referred to Section 3.0 ("Pumping Stations") and Section 6.1 ("Manholes") for additional precautions and guidelines.

6.5 Personnel Responsibilities

Personnel involved in confined space entry, whether acting as the entrant or as support for the entrant, must be trained and understand responsibilities included with this type of work. Emergency contact procedures, equipment operation, hazard identification, site safety, and first aid are the responsibility of all persons involved. Team practice, under controlled simulated situations, will help build worker confidence and reinforce appropriate actions and reactions to potential hazards.

7.0 PIPELINE REPAIR AND MAINTENANCE

Proper workplace equipment and practices are necessary to prevent illness and injury and to protect the environment when working on sewer pipelines. Sewer spills can contaminate the soil, groundwater, surface waters, and public travel ways. Proper planning, training, and evaluation of operating procedures are necessary to prevent illness and injury.

7.1   Force Mains

Prior to working on sewer force mains, all pumping stations tributary to the force main should be turned off. An agency's sewer atlas should be reviewed to determine all possible agency and private pumping stations that may be connected to the force main. Bypass pumping or standby tanker trucks may be necessary during a prolonged maintenance event; as such, it is important to schedule (on call) or stage bypass pumping equipment before beginning work.

Even when pumping stations connected to a force main have been shut down, the contents of a force main may still be under pressure because of the slope of the discharge pipe, a pipe blockage, or discharge into a surcharged receiving vessel and tank. Special care should be taken when exposing or cutting into a buried force main. The volume of stored wastewater between the point of work and isolation valves (upstream and downstream) should be considered when planning for spill mitigation.

7.2   Gravity Sewers

Gravity sewers are designed to operate partially full, but may be surcharged (pressurized) because of downstream blockages or pipe failure. Tree roots, trash, fats, oils, and grease, slipped joints, pipe sags, and/or excavation damage could contribute to a blocked gravity sewer pipe. Sewer blockages identified by video inspection or found during maintenance and cleaning operations should be scheduled for further investigation and possibly repair and replacement. Line cleaning may be necessary prior to additional inspection and assessment.

Repair or replacement of gravity sewers may be performed via open-trench excavation, slip lining, or pipe bursting. Typically, outside contractors will be hired to perform slip-lining or pipe-bursting repair work. However, agency personnel will typically be required to observe and inspect work performed by outside contractors. Bypass pumping and notification of service area users upstream of the work may be necessary prior to (or during) work. The reader is referred to Section 6.1 ("Manholes") for additional precautions and guidelines.

7.3   Trunk Mains and Interceptors

Trunk mains and interceptor sewers refers to larger sewer collection piping, typically gravity sewers, which collect wastewater from multiple and/or remote gravity sewers and force mains. Trunk mains do not have sewer laterals for direct collection of wastewater. An interceptor sewer is a dedicated sewer main often designed to convey flow around an older (or smaller) sewer system to a receiving location downstream of the older or smaller sewer system to prevent surcharge within the (bypassed) gravity sewer mains. Bypass pumping or storage is most likely required when working on a trunk main or interceptor sewer. An agency's sewer atlas should be reviewed to determine all possible pumping stations and tributary gravity collection systems, which may be connected to the trunk main or interceptor.

7.4 Combined Sewer Systems

Combined sewer systems use sewer collection system piping to convey stormwater runoff as well as domestic wastewater. Area drains, roof runoff, and other direct connections to the sewer system may be present in combined sewers. Combined sewers may be more prone to blockage because of increased amounts of dirt, trash, and other debris, which enter the system via storm drainages. Also, runoff from private land, streets, and parking lots poses additional risk for spilled chemicals or hydrocarbons (such as gasoline) to enter the collection system. Combined sewers are highly affected by rainfall events, and extreme changes in flowrates can be observed in a short period of time. Special considerations for spill prevention and safety must be addressed when working on or around combined sewer systems.

8.0 TEMPORARY TRAFFIC CONTROL

Proper traffic control at a jobsite helps keep workers safe. All vehicles and workers involved in a job in a traffic area should comply with state and local requirements for traffic control. The American Traffic Safety Services Association in Fredericksburg, Virginia, has some useful pamphlets on flagging and setting up traffic control signs. For information about specific state traffic control requirements, an organization should contact local police, a state highway department, or the U.S. Federal Highway Administration.

8.1 Notifications

An agency should develop and adopt programs for notifying other crews, departments, agencies, and the public before beginning work on sewer collection systems. Other work crews within the department may be called upon to lend support in the event of an equipment or infrastructure failure. Other departments (water, street, storm drain, etc.) may also be working at or near the site, and may have traffic control systems in place that would interfere with the work proposed.

Many sewer agencies' service areas overlap the jurisdiction of other city, county, and state agencies responsible for street maintenance and overall street safety. It may be necessary to obtain an encroachment permit and prepare a traffic control plan for the approval of other agencies prior to beginning scheduled work. This often requires a certain amount of lead time for review of proposed traffic control plans, even when standard plans provided by the jurisdictional agency are available for reference and use. Emergency maintenance provisions can reduce lead time on notification (depending on the jurisdictional agency). However, not all maintenance is considered an emergency; as such, emergency notification procedures should not be the typical rule of practice.

Public notification of work within roadways that could pose a hazard to commuters, residents, businesses, or pedestrians should be provided in advance when possible. Notification signs, flyers (for residents and/or businesses), digital communication outlets (Web sites, Facebook, Twitter, etc.), and/or public workshops may be appropriate when members of the public may be affected by sewer maintenance activities.

8.2   Standard Plans

Whenever practical, standard traffic control plans for work within or near roadways should be developed or used. Standard plans can reduce lead-time preparation for repair and maintenance activities in the following two ways:

- Standard plans reduce traffic control plan preparation time and
- Standard plans are (by design) generally approved, which typically reduces any required review time before approval.

Standard plans can also be used for training personnel during mockups or actual maintenance activities; the experience gained during training is directly applicable to future events.

8.2.1   Day

Traffic controls during a daytime event must provide warning and directions for drivers, warning and access limitations for pedestrians, and protection for employees. Barricades, guardrails, and traffic cones and signs should be erected to protect workers, equipment, and traffic. Vehicles should be placed between traffic and the manhole. Work should be hidden from view of drivers, if possible, because driver curiosity will tend to dramatically slow traffic and may even lead to accidents.

8.2.2 Night

Areas should be brightly illuminated at night. Additional sight distances, lighted warning signs, and provisions may be necessary to provide worker and traffic and pedestrian safety at night.

A daytime maintenance or repair project can easily stretch into a nighttime event if a few unforeseen events occur. Crews should have additional traffic control devices and equipment available on-site or readily accessible in case work stretches into evening hours.

8.2.3 Inclement Weather

Traffic control requirements during inclement weather may require additional sight and stopping distance, setbacks from open trenches or workers, and other special considerations. Placement of traffic control devices (signs and delineators) may be affected by surface runoff during rain events, and additional weights (sandbags) or anchors may be necessary for signage during heavy winds. Weather forecasts should be considered when preparing and implementing traffic control plans.

8.3 Equipment and Personnel

An updated log of traffic control equipment should be maintained that includes equipment age, condition, and date inspected. Traffic control laws are constantly updated and older devices may not be compliant with newer jurisdictional agency requirements. Anytime new plans or requirements for traffic controls are adopted, equipment inventories must be checked and brought up to date. Personnel training for specific traffic control functions is necessary to protect property, equipment, the public, and employees. Updated records should be kept for employee training and experience with placement of traffic control devices, flagging, inspecting or auditing worksites for traffic control, or preparation of traffic control plans.

9.0 REFERENCES

Bridges, J. E.; Ford, G. L.; Sherman, I. A. (1985) Electrical Shock Safety Criteria. *Proceedings of the 1st International Symposium on Electrical Shock Safety Criteria*; Pergamon Press: New York.

Chlorine Institute, Inc. (1988) *Chlorine Manual*; Chlorine Institute, Inc.: Arlington, Virginia.

National Institute for Occupational Safety and Health (1990) *Pocket Guide to Chemical Hazards*; Publication No. 90–117; National Institute for Occupational Safety and Health: Cincinnati, Ohio.

Office of the Federal Register (1989) *Occupational Safety and Health Standards*; 29 CFR, Part 1910; National Archives and Records Administration, U.S. Government Printing Office: Washington, D.C.

Chapter 7

Commercial and Powered Industrial Vehicles

(continued)

1.0 COMMERCIAL DRIVERS

1.1 The Federal Motor Carrier Safety Administration

The Federal Motor Carrier Safety Administration (FMCSA) was established within the U.S. Department of Transportation (USDOT) on January 1, 2000, pursuant to the Motor Carrier Safety Improvement Act of 1999. The primary mission of FMCSA is to prevent commercial motor vehicle-related fatalities and injuries. The Federal Motor Carrier Safety Administration, which is headquartered in Washington, D.C., consists of service centers (eastern, midwestern, southern, and western) and field offices in all 50 states and the District of Columbia that are all dedicated to improving the safety of commercial motor vehicles (CMVs) and saving lives. The activities of FMCSA contribute to ensuring safety in motor carrier operations through strong enforcement of safety regulations, targeting high-risk carriers and CMV drivers, strengthening commercial motor vehicle equipment and operating standards, and increasing safety awareness.

1.2 Commercial Safety Act of 1986

The Commercial Motor Vehicle Safety Act of 1986 was signed into law on October 27, 1986. This act applies to anyone who operates a CMV including employees of federal, state, and local governments. The act requires each state to meet the same minimum standards for commercial driver licensing. The goal of the act is to improve highway safety by ensuring that drivers of large trucks and buses are qualified to operate those vehicles and to remove unsafe and unqualified drivers from the highways. The act addresses circumstances that existed prior to 1986 by

- Making it illegal for commercial driver's license (CDL) holders to possess more than one license;

- Requiring states to adopt knowledge and skills testing to ensure that individuals required to have a CDL are qualified to operate heavy trucks and buses; and

- Establishing minimum licensing standards and information requirements for the CDLs that states issue.

1.3 Driver Standards Requirements

The Federal Motor Carrier Safety Administration has developed and issued standards for testing and licensing CDL holders. These standards require states to issue

CDLs to certain CMV drivers only after the driver passes knowledge and skills tests administered by the state and related to the type of vehicle the driver expects to operate.

1.4 Commercial Driver License

Drivers are required to obtain and hold a CDL if they operate in interstate, intrastate, or foreign commerce and if they drive a vehicle that meets any of the classifications of a CMV mentioned in the following sections.

1.4.1 Class A

Class A vehicles are any combination of vehicles with a gross combination weight rating (GCWR) of 11 794 kg (26 001 lb) or more provided the gross vehicle weight rating (GVWR) of the vehicle(s) being towed is in excess of 4536 kg (10 000 lb).

1.4.2 Class B

A Class B vehicle is any single vehicle with a gross vehicle weight rating of 11 794 kg (26 001 lb) or more or any such vehicle towing a vehicle not in excess of 4536 kg (10 000 lb) GVWR.

1.4.3 Class C

A Class C vehicle is any single vehicle, or combination of vehicles, that does not meet the definition of Class A or Class B vehicles described in the preceding sections.

1.4.4 Endorsements and Restrictions

Drivers who operate special types of CMVs also need to pass additional tests to obtain any of the following endorsements on their CDL:

- T—double and triple trailers (knowledge test only),
- P—passenger (knowledge and skills tests),
- N—tank vehicle (knowledge test only),
- H—hazardous materials (knowledge test and Transportation Security Administration (TSA) threat assessment),
- X—combination of tank vehicle and hazardous materials, and
- S—school bus (knowledge and skills tests).

A driver must take the skills test in a motor vehicle that represents the type of motor vehicle that a driver applicant operates or expects to operate as defined by the vehicle classifications described previously. While these classifications are general for the class of vehicle, additional requirements exist for the passenger and school bus endorsements. To obtain a passenger endorsement, the driver must test in a passenger vehicle. To obtain a school bus endorsement, the driver must test in a passenger vehicle equipped with school bus features (lights, signs, etc.).

1.4.5 Certificates and Record Checks

When an individual applies for a CDL or attempts to renew or update his or her CDL, the state must perform a check of its own database, the Commercial Driver's License Information System, and the National Driver Register to ensure the driver is not disqualified and does not possess a license from more than one jurisdiction. If the driver possesses a license from another jurisdiction, the state must require the driver applicant to surrender his or her driver's license issued by that state before issuing a new license. The state must request the complete driving record of the applicant from all jurisdictions where the driver was previously licensed in the past 10 years. For persons applying for a hazardous materials endorsement, compliance is required with the standards for such endorsement specified in TSA requirements; proof of citizenship or immigration status should also be provided. If a state determines in its check of an applicant's license status and record prior to issuing a CDL, or at any time after the CDL is issued, that the applicant has falsified information or any of the required certifications, the state shall at a minimum suspend, cancel, or revoke the person's CDL or his or her pending application or disqualify the person from operating a commercial motor vehicle for a period of at least 60 consecutive days.

1.5 Vehicle Weight

Vehicle weight is expressed in terms of gross vehicle weight, GVWR, and GCWR, which are described as follows:

- Gross vehicle weight—the maximum allowable fully laden weight of the vehicle and its payload. The most common classification scheme used by manufacturers and by states, often for both trucks and tractors;

- Gross vehicle weight rating—a value specified by the manufacturer for a single-unit truck, track tractor, or trailer or the gross combined weight rating the sum of such values for the units, which make up a truck combination. In the absence of a GVWR, an estimate of the gross weight of a fully loaded unit may be substituted for such a rating;

- Gross combination weight rating—the GVWR of a truck combination may be called the *GCWR*. It is the value specified by the manufacturer as the loaded weight of a combination (articulated) vehicle. In the absence of a value specified by the manufacturer, GCWR will be determined by adding the GVWR of the power unit and the total weight of the towed unit and any load thereon.

1.6   Maintaining a Log

Any person who is subject to the safety regulations and drives a CMV must complete a logbook page for any day that includes CMV driving and for the prior 7 days. The person must also account for every day on their log, even days off, unless they are covered by a logbook exception on any of the days. The log must cover all 24 hours of every day. Authorized government inspectors may check the logs at any time. Inspectors check the logs to see if the person has violated the hours-of-service regulations. Violations of the hours-of-service regulations can result in being fined and/or placed out of service.

1.7   Hazardous Materials Transportation

The definition of *hazardous materials* includes those materials that pose an unreasonable threat to the public and the environment. Hazardous materials include the following: (1) hazardous substances, (2) hazardous wastes, (3) marine pollutants, (4) elevated temperature material, (5) materials identified in 49 *Code of Federal Regulations* (CFR) 172.101, and (6) materials meeting the definitions contained in 49 CFR Part 173.

As of January 1, 2005, FMCSA requires motor carriers to obtain a Hazardous Materials Safety Permit (HMSP) prior to transporting certain highly hazardous materials. An HMSP is required to transport any of the following materials:

- A highway route-controlled quantity of a Class 7 (radioactive) material;
- More than 25 kg (55 lb) of a Division 1.1, 1.2, or 1.3 (explosive) material or an amount of a Division 1.5 (explosive) material requiring placarding under 49 CFR 172;
- More than 1 L per package of a "material poisonous by inhalation" that meets the criteria for "hazard zone A";
- A "material poisonous by inhalation" that meets the criteria for "hazard zone B" in a bulk packaging (capacity greater than 450 L [119 gal]);

- A "material poisonous by inhalation" that meets the criteria for "hazard zone C" or "hazard zone D" in a packaging having a capacity equal to or greater than 13 249 L (3500 gal); or

- A shipment of compressed or refrigerated liquefied methane, liquefied natural gas, or other liquefied gas with a methane content of at least 85% in bulk packaging having a capacity equal to or greater than 13 249 L (3500 gal).

1.8 Employer Requirements

All employers shall request and all person's applying for employment as a CMV operator shall provide employment history information for the 10 years preceding the date the application is submitted. The request shall be made at the time of application for employment.

1.8.1 Significant Violations

Significant violations include the following:

- Being under the influence of alcohol (concentration of 0.04 or greater) while operating a CMV;

- Refusing to take an alcohol test as required by a state or jurisdiction under its implied consent laws or regulations;

- Being under the influence of a controlled substance;

- Leaving the scene of an accident;

- Driving a CMV when, as a result of prior violations committed operating a CMV, the driver's CDL is revoked, suspended, or canceled or the driver is disqualified from operating a CMV;

- Causing a fatality through the negligent operation of a CMV, including but not limited to the crimes of motor vehicle manslaughter, homicide by motor vehicle, and negligent homicide; and

- Using the vehicle in the commission of a felony involving manufacturing, distributing, or dispensing a controlled substance.

1.8.2 Serious Violations

Serious violations include the following:

- Speeding excessively, which involves any speed of 6.7 m/s (15 mph) or more above the posted speed limit;

- Driving a CMV without obtaining a CDL;

- Driving a CMV without a CDL in the driver's possession;

- Driving a CMV without the proper class of CDL and/or endorsements for the specific vehicle group being operated or for the passengers or type of cargo being transported;

- Driving recklessly as defined by state, local law, or regulation;

- Making improper or erratic traffic lane changes; and

- Following the vehicle ahead too closely.

1.8.3 Disqualifications

The following are types of disqualifications that apply to CDL holders because of the violations caused by them.

1.8.3.1 Disqualifications for Felony

Using a CMV or non-CMV in the commission of a felony involving manufacturing, distributing, or dispensing a controlled substance will result in a disqualification for life, without the possibility of reinstatement.

1.8.3.2 Disqualification for Significant Offenses

The first violation for a significant offense in a CMV or a non-CMV results in a 1-year disqualification or a 3-year disqualification if a driver is transporting hazardous materials that are required to be placarded. The second violation for a significant offense, in a CMV or a non-CMV, results in a lifetime disqualification. The driver may be eligible for reinstatement under certain conditions after 10 years.

1.8.3.3 Disqualification for Serious Traffic Violations

The first violation for a serious violation does not result in a disqualification. A second serious violation within 3 years results in a 60-day disqualification and a third serious violation within 3 years results in a 120-day disqualification. Serious disqualifications must be served consecutively. All serious violations in a CMV are included. Serious violations in a non-CMV must not be included unless it results in the revocation, cancellation, or suspension of the CDL holder's license or non-CMV driving privileges.

1.8.3.4 *Disqualification for Violating Out-of-Service Orders While Operating a Commercial Motor Vehicle*

Category 1 describes a driver who was transporting placarded hazardous materials or operating a vehicle designed to transport 16 or more passengers. Category 2 describes drivers not in Category 1.

In Category 1, the first violation results in a disqualification of no less than 180 days or more than 2 years. The second and subsequent violations within 10 years results in a disqualification of no less than 3 years or more than 5 years.

In Category 2, the first violation results in a disqualification of no less than 180 days or more than 1 year. The second violation within 10 years results in a disqualification of no less than 2 years or more than 5 years. The third and subsequent violations result in disqualifications of no less than 3 years or more than 5 years.

1.9 Safety and Security

1.9.1 *Company Safety Records*

The FMCSA maintains several Web sites that provide easy access to valuable safety-related information. Users only need a company's name, USDOT number, or motor carrier number to perform a search. Some of these Web sites are as follows:

- Motor Carrier Safety Measurement System Online—Figure 7.1 shows FMCSA's motor carrier safety measurement system Web site where motor carrier safety data can be searched and information on how FMCSA uses this data to enhance safety can be ascertained (http://www.fmcsa.dot.gov/redirect.asp?page=http://ai.fmcsa.dot.gov/sms/default.aspx). SafeStat combines current and historical safety performance information to measure the relative safety fitness of commercial motor carriers. This information includes federal and state data on crashes, roadside inspections, on-site compliance review results, and enforcement history.

- Safety and Fitness Electronic Records System—The Company Snapshot is a free service that provides a concise record of a company's identification, size, cargo, inspection and out-of-service summary, crash data, and safety rating (if any). The Company Safety Profile is a fee-based service that offers more safety-related information about an individual company's operation, including selected items from inspection and crash reports and results of any reviews

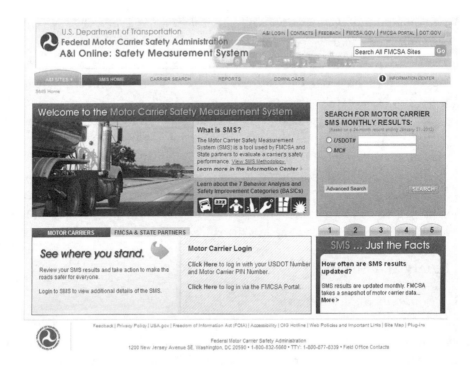

Figure 7.1   Safety measurement system online (courtesy of U.S. Department of Transportation).

or enforcement actions involving the requested company (http://www.fmcsa.dot.gov/redirect.asp?page=http://safer.fmcsa.dot.gov/).

- *Analysis and Information Online*—To arrange transportation for a group, the Passenger Carrier Safety Web site helps select the right vehicle and find the safest passenger carrier companies (http://www.fmcsa.dot.gov/redirect.asp?page=http://ai.fmcsa.dot.gov/).

1.9.2   Hazardous Materials

The mission of FMCSA is to reduce the number of serious hazardous materials transportation incidents 20% by 2010 compared to fiscal year 2000. In addition, FMCSA seeks to reduce hazardous materials security risks that could potentially harm the public and environment. Developing programs to accomplish these goals is the responsibility of the FMCSA Hazardous Materials Program.

1.10 How to Comply with Federal Regulations

1.10.1 Safety Permits

All registered intrastate, interstate, and foreign motor carriers transporting certain types and amounts of hazardous materials are required to have an HMSP. All motor carriers having the FMCSA safety permit also need to register with the Pipeline and Hazardous Materials Safety Administration (PHMSA) to receive a certificate of registration.

1.10.2 Security

In response to the terrorist atrocities committed against the World Trade Center and the Pentagon on September 11, 2001, and subsequent threats to the transportation system, FMCSA has initiated programs to protect the public from terrorists using CMVs as weapons or targets. A top priority for commercial vehicle security is protecting the transportation of hazardous materials.

1.10.3 Shipper Check Report

The FMCSA placed additional emphasis on the safety of shippers of hazardous materials for transportation by highway during March and April 2002. This special emphasis project was designated "Hazardous Materials Shipper Check 2002." The goal of this project was to reduce the risk of hazardous materials incidents (spills) by targeting hazardous materials shippers. Shipper Check 2002 consisted of packaging inspections conducted at dockside, less-than truckload facilities, intermodal facilities, and roadside. It relied on the data export feature of the Hazardous Materials Package Inspection Program (HMPIP) software to generate reports. A total of 128 federal and 64 state personnel representing 41 FMCSA division offices and 18 different state agencies completed HMPIP inspection forms. The participants made Shipper Check 2002 a successful operation resulting in 5618 inspections with 1089 violations found with 91 planned enforcement cases. The results indicate that one of every five packages checked was in violation of the Federal Hazardous Materials Regulations. A 16% violation rate indicates a significant compliance problem on the part of hazardous materials shippers.

1.10.4 Risk Assessment and Analysis

The purpose of the Hazardous Materials Transportation Program is to identify and manage risks presented by transportation of hazardous materials in commerce. The USDOT Hazardous Materials Risk Management Program encompasses different modes of transportation, a wide assortment of hazardous materials, manufacturers, shippers, and carriers of all sizes. Information on unintentional releases of hazardous materials and the consequences are collected and analyzed. Identifying low-probability, high-consequence events (which may not be apparent from incident data) and providing appropriate levels of protection are among the more demanding aspects of a risk management program.

1.10.5 Reporting Hazardous Materials Complaints

Currently, all complaints involving hazardous materials transported by commercial motor vehicle can be reported online at the FMCSA Web site (http://www.fmcsa.dot.gov/) or by calling their toll-free hotline at 1-888-DOT-SAFT (1-888-368-7238), which is available from 9:00 a.m. to 7:00 p.m. (Eastern time), Monday through Friday. A complaint can also be filed by contacting a FMCSA state field office.

1.10.6 Incident (Spill) Reporting and Prevention

When release or a suspected release of a hazardous material has taken place in transportation, then the incidents (spills) should be reported directly to the 24-hour National Response Center (NRC). The regulations in 49 CFR 171.15 and 171.16 govern such situations. Two phases of incident reporting are required in the regulations. Section 171.15 covers immediate telephonic notification following an incident and Section 171.16 outlines written reporting procedures. As soon as practical, but no later than 12 hours after the occurrence of any incident, each person in physical possession of the hazardous material must provide notice to NRC by telephone at 800-424-8802 (toll free) or 202-267-2675 (toll call) or online at NRC's Web site (http://www.nrc.uscg.mil). In place of notice to NRC, notice involving an infectious substance (etiologic agent) may be given to the director of the Centers for Disease Control and Prevention (CDC), U.S. Public Health Service, in Atlanta, Georgia, by calling 800–232-0124 (toll free).

1.10.7 Pipeline and Hazardous Materials Safety Administration Office of Hazardous Materials Safety

As one of 10 agencies within USDOT, PHMSA works to protect the American public and the environment by ensuring safe and secure movement of hazardous materials to industry and consumers by all transportation modes, including the nation's pipelines. The Pipeline and Hazardous Materials Safety Administration was created under the Norman Y. Mineta Research and Special Programs Improvement Act of

2004, which was signed into law by President Bush on November 20, 2004. Through PHMSA, the department develops and enforces regulations for the safe, reliable, and environmentally sound operation of the nation's 3.7 million kilometer (2.3 million mile) pipeline transportation system and the nearly 1 million daily shipments of hazardous materials by land, sea, and air.

1.10.8 Top 20 Hazardous Materials Violations

The top 20 hazardous materials violations in fiscal year 2010 as listed by FMCSA are as follows:

- Placard damaged, deteriorated, or obscured;
- Package not secure in vehicle;
- No copy of certificate of registration or registration number on subject vehicle;
- Vehicle not placarded as required;
- Failing to provide carrier-required placards;
- Shipping paper accessibility;
- No shipping papers (carrier);
- Emergency response information missing;
- Offering a hazardous material without preparing a shipping paper;
- Emergency response information not available;
- No placards or markings when required;
- Cargo tank test or inspection markings (hazardous material);
- State or local laws ordinance regulations;
- Placard or device could be confused or conflicted with USDOT placard;
- Failing to enter proper shipping name on shipping paper;
- Placard not reading horizontally;
- Package or containment not labeled as required;
- Failing to enter hazardous material description on ship paper in the manner required;
- Failing to enter emergency response phone number on shipping paper; and
- Maintenance and accessibility of emergency response information.

1.10.9 Hazardous Materials Security

Access to hazardous materials during transportation to a facility should be another security concern. Using one or more of the following security measures to prevent unauthorized access should be considered:

- Establish partnerships with local law enforcement officials, emergency responders, and other public safety agencies with jurisdiction over the facility to exchange information about threats, trends, and unsuccessful security programs;

- Restrict the availability of information related to your facility and the materials you handle;

- Add security guards and increase off-hour patrols by private security personnel. Request that law enforcement personnel increase off-hour patrols;

- Check the adequacy of locks and other protective equipment. Conduct frequent inspections;

- Install additional lights, alarm systems, or surveillance cameras;

- Restrict access to a single entry or gate;

- Require employees to display identification cards or badges;

- Conduct security spot checks of personnel and vehicles;

- Upgrade security procedures for handling pickups and deliveries at facilities. Accept packages and deliveries only at the facility front gate;

- Secure hazardous materials in locked buildings or fenced areas. Have a sign-out system for keys;

- Secure valves, passageways, and other fixtures on transportation equipment when not in use;

- Periodically inventory the quantity of hazardous materials on-site to recognize if a theft has occurred; and

- Keep records of security incidents. Review records to identify trends and potential vulnerabilities.

1.10.10 Field Operational Test

Following the September 11, 2001, terrorist attacks on the United States, USDOT was asked to identify areas within the transportation system that were vulnerable to terrorist attack. The Federal Motor Carrier Safety Administration conducted a field operational test (FOT) to quantify the security costs and benefits of an operational concept that applied technology and improved enforcement procedures to hazardous materials (hazmat) transportation. The FOT demonstrated an approach that enhances the safety and security of hazmat shipments from origin to destination by examining possible vulnerabilities in the hazmat transportation system. An independent evaluation was conducted in parallel with FOT. The evaluation team determined whether or not FOT met the objective of ensuring the safety and security of hazmat shipments from origin to destination. The project also included development of a technology compendium designed to be a comprehensive listing of the different safety and security technologies that are available. The technology compendium is an ongoing effort that will continue to expand and be updated.

1.10.11 Training Requirements

The following are training requirements for persons dealing with hazardous materials:

- General awareness/familiarization—general awareness and familiarization training is intended to raise the hazmat employee's awareness of hazardous material remediation and the purpose and meaning of hazard communication requirements. All hazmat employees must have this training.

- Function-specific training—function-specific training is intended to teach the necessary knowledge, skills, and abilities for an individual's job function.

- Safety training—this training provides information concerning the hazards posed by materials in the workplace, personal protection measures. The training may also include basic emergency response procedures.

2.0 POWERED INDUSTRIAL VEHICLES

Wastewater treatment facilities, like most other industrial facilities, manufacturing plants, and so on, have the need to handle large, heavy materials. Most wastewater treatment plants rely on powered industrial vehicles (PIVs), especially forklifts and hand trucks, to load, unload, and move and stack materials, thereby reducing the strain on employees through manual force. However, operation and use of PIVs present their own safety hazards. Powered industrial vehicles can cause damage to materials and/or other property while drivers and/or other people can be injured or killed by rollovers, by being hit, or by being pinned against a solid object. Therefore, it is essential for operators to be properly trained on the safe and proper operation of such equipment.

2.1 Types of Powered Industrial Vehicles

Powered industrial vehicles typically include forklifts, tractors, platform lift trucks, motorized hand trucks, and other specialized equipment powered by electrical motors or internal combustion engines. Some PIVs can also be operated by compressed air or compressed gas (i.e., propane), but are not covered under the same OSHA standard as the former. The Occupational Safety and Health Administration classifies the most commonly used PIVs into the following seven classes:

- Class I: Electric Motor Rider Trucks;

- Class II: Electric Motor Narrow Isle Trucks;

- Class III: Electric Motor Hand Trucks or Hand/Rider Trucks (i.e., pallet jack);

- Class IV: Internal Combustion Engine Trucks on Solid or Cushion Tires (i.e., common forklift; see Figure 7.2);

- Class V: Internal Combustion Engine Trucks on Pneumatic Tires;

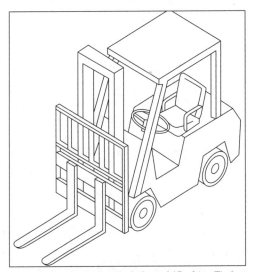

Lift Code 3: Fork, Counterbalanced (Cushion Tire).

FIGURE 7.2   Class IV: Internal combustion engine truck (solid tires) (OSHA, 2008).

- Class VI: Electric and Internal Combustion Engine Tractors; and
- Class VII: Rough Terrain Forklift Trucks.

2.2 Center of Gravity

Most PIVs are used for lifting and/or moving materials or equipment throughout the facility. It is especially important to remember that many PIVs operate on a center of gravity that allows the PIV to stay stable, especially when carrying loads. To prevent the PIV from tipping, weight must be distributed evenly, especially when carrying irregular-sized loads. Loads should also be kept as close to the front wheels of the PIV as possible and in the center of the forks.

2.3 Load Center

According to OSHA (2008), the load center is the distance from the face of the forks to the center of gravity of the load. Many forklifts are rated using a 61-cm (24-in.) load center, which means that the center of gravity of the load must be 61 cm (24 in.) or less from the face of the forks (OSHA, 1998). Before handling a load, determine what the load center is for your forklift, and position load accordingly.

2.4 Occupational Safety and Health Administration Powered Industrial Vehicle Standard

The OSHA PIV Standard, 29 CFR 1910.178, covers a range of PIVs. Specifically, the standard covers fire protection, design, inspection, maintenance, use, operation, and training for PIVs powered by electric motors or internal combustion engines. Although this OSHA standard does not apply to compressed air or nonflammable compressed-gas-operated industrial trucks, following the requirements is recommended.

2.5 Pallet Jack Safety

Pallet jacks are a common piece of equipment used to move materials on pallets. Although they are not as dangerous as PIVs, they do have hazards to be aware of. Pallet jacks can cause injuries such as crushed toes or feet. Therefore, it is important to always wear PPE such as steel-toe boots, leather gloves, and safety glasses when using pallet jacks. Similar to driving a PIV, it is important for operators to be aware of their surroundings and surfaces when preparing to move a load on a pallet jack. Operators should make sure they have a clear view of their path or have a coworker help guide them. People should never be allowed to ride on the pallet jack.

It is important to be aware of areas where feet and/or hands can be caught between the jack and/or load and other stationary objects. Operators should also be aware of where they park or leave the pallet jack unattended so that it does not pose a tripping hazard for others.

2.6 Hazards and Hazard Controls

Powered industrial vehicles present health and safety hazards to both drivers and pedestrians. It is important to be aware of these hazards and how to control them prior to operating a PIV. The most common danger to drivers is the forklift tipping over, especially when the driver is not wearing a seatbelt. Drivers also need to be aware of pedestrians or other workers in the area that he or she is working. Besides being hit by the forklift itself, an unstable load can also fall on a person. To reduce the likelihood of a tip-over or of dropping a load, drivers should be aware and familiar with workplace conditions and pedestrian traffic and be able to properly load and carry materials. Of course, drivers should always be aware of pedestrian traffic and remember that they always have the right of way.

In addition to physical dangers, there are atmospheric hazards to be aware of when operating certain types of PIVs in potentially hazardous or poorly ventilated areas. The OSHA PIV standard (based on Table N-1 located in 1910.178[c]; see Tables 7.1 through 7.4) presents information on the various types, classes, and divisions of PIVs in addition to recommendations for which PIVs can be used in certain locations. Most wastewater treatment plants are considered unclassified locations. An unclassified location has no hazardous atmosphere, that is, an atmosphere where no flammable or explosive gas is present. Diesel, electric, gasoline, and liquid propane gas-operated PIVs can all be used freely in areas with no flammable or explosive atmospheres. If the area contains flammable gases that are contained and not expected to be released except in instances of malfunction or accident, then diesel, electric, gasoline, and liquid propane gas-operated PIVs may all be used. However, Table N-1 should be consulted for operating in specific hazardous atmospheres. Finally, diesel and gasoline-operated PIVs always need proper ventilation to prevent buildup of carbon monoxide.

2.7 Training Requirements

The OSHA PIV standard requires initial training that includes procedures for the safe operation of a PIV, types of PIVs, safety hazards associated with operating and working near PIVs, and the requirements of the OSHA PIV standard.

TABLE 7.1 Types of PIVs.

Diesel	Electrical	Gasoline	Liquified petroleum/propane gas
D = diesel (minimal to no safeguards against fire hazards)	E = electrical (minimal to no safeguards against fire hazards)	G = gasoline (minimal to no safeguards against fire hazards)	LP = liquified petroleum/propane (minimal to no safeguards against fire hazards)
DS = diesel with additional safeguards against inherent fire hazards	ES = electrical with additional safeguards to electrical system	GS = gasoline with additional exhaust, fuel, and electrical system safeguards	LPS = LP with additional exhaust, fuel, and electrical system safeguards
DY = safeguards of DS, but with enclosed electrical and other safeguards	EE = safeguards of E and ES PIVs, but have enclosed electrical motors and equipment		
	EX = safeguards of E, ES, and EE models, but specifically constructed and assembled to be used in atmospheres containing flammable vapors or dusts		

Training must be provided by knowledgeable and experienced instructors and delivered through a combination of instruction including lecture, discussion, interactive computer learning, video, written material, and practical training. An evaluation must also be performed to evaluate the operator's competency.

Additionally, a driver's competency must be recertified at least every 3 years and refresher training must be conducted whenever a driver shows deficiency in their PIV driving skills or is assigned to a new type of PIV.

Finally, it is essential to keep training records for each driver who has been trained and evaluated in accordance with the OSHA PIV standard. Each training record must include the operator's name, the date of training, date of evaluation, and the name of

TABLE 7.2   Powered industrial vehicle classes.

Classes	Description of Classes
Class I locations	Flammable gases or vapors are or are potentially present in quantities (in the air) sufficient to produce explosive or ignitable mixtures
Class II locations	Combustible dust present
Class III locations	Easily ignitable fibers or flyings present, but not likely to be in suspension in quantities sufficient to produce ignitable mixtures
Unclassifield	Locations not possessing atmospheres as described in rows above

person(s) performing the training or evaluation. The OSHA PIV standard for training is located in 1910.178(l)(3).

2.7.1   Prequalification of Candidates

Because PIVs can pose a hazard to drivers and passersby, potential operators should be determined to be competent prior to operating a PIV. This can be achieved through completion of training and a successful evaluation. In addition, a potential PIV driver must have or meet the following basic requirements:

- A valid driver's license;
- Good driving record;
- Good vision (adequately corrected by glasses or contacts);
- Good hearing (adequately enhanced by hearing aid);
- Physical condition that allows for full and safe operation of the vehicle;
- No impairments that affect the balance and/or consciousness of the operator; and
- No medications or other drugs that affect vision, perception, or other physical capabilities.

2.7.2   Requirements

Once a potential PIV operator has fulfilled minimum competency requirements, he or she may participate in initial training. As listed in OSHA Standard

TABLE 7.3 Powered industrial vehicle divisions (nature of hazardous conditions).

1	Condition exists continuously, intermittently, or periodically under normal operating conditions
	Explosive mixture may be present under normal operating conditions, where failure of equipment may cause the condition to exist simultaneously with arcing or sparking of electrical equipment, or where dusts of an electrically conducting nature may be present
	Explosive mixture may be present under normal operating conditions, where failure of equipment may cause the condition to exist simultaneously with arcing or sparking of electrical equipment, or where dusts of an electrically conducting nature may be present
2	Condition may occur accidentally because of a storage drum puncture
	Explosive mixture not normally present, but where deposits of dust may cause heat rise in electrical equipment or where such deposits may be ignited by arcs or sparks from electrical equipment
	Explosive mixture not normally present, but where deposits of dust may cause heat rise in electrical equipment or where such deposits may be ignited by arcs or sparks from electrical equipment
No division	None of the conditions above exists

1910.178(l)(3)(i)(A) through (M), training should include the following PIV-related topics:

- Operating instructions, warnings, and precautions for the types of truck the operator will be authorized to operate;
- Differences between the PIV he or she will be operating and an automobile;
- Operation of the engine or motor;
- Steering and maneuvering;
- Visibility (including restrictions because of loading);

TABLE 7.4 Types of atmospheres and recommended PIVs.

Group	Examples of locations or atmospheres	Class I suggested PIV type (flammable gas or vapors)	Class II suggested PIV type (combustible dust)	Class III suggested PIV type (ignitable fibers or flyings)	Unclassified
None	Piers and wharves inside and outside general storage, general industrial or commercial properties; Baled waste, cocoa fiber, cotton excelsior, hemp, istle, jute, kapok, oakum, sisal, Spanish moss, synthetic fibers, tow	—	—	Division (Div) 1: DY, EE, EX Div 2: DS, DY, E, ES, EE, EX, GS, LPS	Any D, E, G, or LP PIV
A	Acetylene	No PIV can be used	No PIV can be used	—	—
B	Hydrogen	No PIV can be used	No PIV can be used	—	—
C	Ethyl ether	No PIV can be used	No PIV can be used	—	—
D	Gasoline, naphtha, alcohols, acetone, lacquer solvent, benzene.	Div 1: EX Div 2: DS, DY, ES, EE, EX, GS, LPS	Div 1: EX Div 2: DS, DY, ES, EE, EX, GS, LPS	—	—
E	Metal dust	—	No PIV can be used	—	—
F	Carbon black coal dust, coke dust	—	Div 1: EX Div 2: EX, DY, EE	—	—
G	Grain dust, flour dust, starch dust, organic dust	—	Div 1: EX Div 2: DS, DY, ES, EE, EX, GS, LPS	—	—

- Fork and attachment adaptation, operation, and use limitations;

- Vehicle capacity and stability;

- Any vehicle inspection and maintenance that the operator will be required to perform;

- Refueling and/or charging and recharging of batteries;

- Operating limitations; and

- Any other operating instructions, warnings, or precautions listed in the operator's manual for the types of vehicle that the employee is being trained to operate.

Operators are also required to be trained on workplace-specific information such as the type of surface conditions; type of loads to be carried and their stability; load manipulation; stacking and unstacking process; type of pedestrian and/or other traffic to be encountered in the workplace, narrow aisles or other restrictions where the PIV will be operated; any hazardous location or insufficiently ventilated area that the PIV will be operated in; and ramps and/or sloped surfaces where the PIV may be operated.

2.7.3 Performance Testing

After successful completion of a classroom training course, drivers must be given an opportunity to complete practical, hands-on training with the type of PIV they will be operating. The hands-on training may include how to perform a pre-operational inspection of the PIV; how to operate and move the PIV; how to pick up, travel, set, and stack a load; and refueling and/or charging or recharging of batteries. The driver should then be evaluated on proper implementation of training and competency of operation of the PIV.

2.7.4 Obstacle Course Setup

To evaluate the PIV driver's skill and competency operating a PIV, an obstacle course should be constructed. Although the obstacle course's length and difficulty is up to the trainer, the course should provide some realistic scenarios the driver will encounter. Some suggested scenarios and obstacles may include the following:

- Boarding and starting the PIV,

- Driving forward and backward,

- Parking,

- Picking up a load and moving forward,
- Placing and/or stacking a load,
- Driving through narrow or variously sized "aisles,"
- Picking up a load and driving in reverse, and
- Parking and turning off the PIV.

The driver's performance on the course should be recorded by the trainer and kept with his or her training records.

2.7.5 Safe Operating Procedures

Although driving a PIV is unlike driving a typical automobile, many of the driving rules are still the same. For instance, PIV drivers should always drive on the right side of the road or aisle and should not speed or tailgate other vehicles. Additionally, PIV drivers should remember that pedestrians always have the right of way. Finally, PIV drivers should always wear their seatbelt.

2.7.6 Changing and Charging Storage Batteries

The Occupational Safety and Health Administration's Standard 1910.178(g) describes requirements for changing and charging storage batteries for PIVs. Because handling batteries can pose a health and safety hazard, a designated area for the purpose of battery charging and installation is required. This designated area must have a station for flushing and neutralizing spilled electrolyte. Additionally, because batteries can be heavy, an overhead hoist or other similar method for moving batteries is required. The area must also have fire protection and a protective system of posts or curbs around the charging apparatus to prevent damage from PIVs. Fumes can also be released during charging; as such, adequate ventilation is necessary.

Because handling and maintaining batteries involves corrosive chemicals and battery acid, additional standards apply to these activities. Staff involved in battery charging and/or changing activities should wear steel-toe boots, chemical-resistant gloves, an acid apron, and eyewear and face protection (29 CFR 1910.13[a][1]). This PPE will reduce injury if acid is splashed or spilled on the operator. Face protection such as safety goggles and face shields should be worn in accordance with the American National Standards Institute (ANSI) Z87.1-1989 specifications. Finally, in accordance with OSHA 29 CFR 1910.151, " ... suitable facilities for quick drenching or flushing of the eyes and body (i.e., eye/face wash and shower) shall be provided within the work area for immediate emergency use" because the eyes or body of any person may be exposed to injurious corrosive materials during battery handling. According to the American National Standards Act (2004), *Emergency Eye Wash and Shower Equipment,* the eye/face wash and shower must be within 10 seconds in distance of the hazard and on the same level as the hazard. This unit needs to be clearly identified with proper signs and adequate lighting.

The following are additional practices that should be followed when working with batteries:

- A carbon filter or siphon should be used when handling electrolyte;

- Acid should always be poured into water. Never pour water into acid;

- Check to be sure ventilation caps are functioning. The battery (or compartment) cover(s) must be open to dissipate heat;

- Be sure to properly position and chock tires of the PIV before attempting to change or charge batteries;

- Never smoke in battery charging areas;

- Open flames, sparks, and/or electric arcs should be prevented in battery charging areas; and

- Keep metal tools and other metallic objects away from the top of uncovered batteries.

2.7.7 *Operations*

In addition to being proven a competent PIV driver (through successful completion of training and evaluation), the driver should inspect the PIV prior to use each day. According to OSHA PIV Standard 1910.178(p), anytime the PIV is observed to be in "need of repair, defective, or in any way unsafe, the truck shall be taken out of service until it has been restored to safe operating condition." In addition, OSHA also states that fuel tanks are not to be filled while the engine is running. Spills should be prevented; however, if a spill occurs, it should be properly cleaned or allowed to evaporate before restarting the PIV. Any fuel leaks should be repaired before the PIV is operated. Finally, an open flame (e.g., a lighter) should not be used to check electrolyte levels in storage batteries or gasoline levels in fuel tanks.

2.7.8   Traveling

When driving a PIV, it is important to remember the rules of the road. In addition to the safe operating procedures discussed in OSHA 1910.178(n), Section 2.7.5 states that

- All traffic regulations shall be observed, including authorized plant speed limits;
- A safe distance shall be maintained approximately three truck lengths from the truck ahead and the truck shall be kept under control at all times;
- The right of way shall be yielded to ambulances, fire trucks, or other vehicles in emergency situations;
- Other trucks traveling in the same direction at intersections, blind spots, or other dangerous locations shall not be passed;
- The driver shall be required to slow down and sound the horn at cross-aisles and other locations where vision is obstructed. If the load being carried obstructs forward view, the driver shall be required to travel with the load trailing;
- Railroad tracks shall be crossed diagonally wherever possible. Parking closer than 2.4 m (8 ft) from the center of railroad tracks is prohibited;
- The driver shall be required to look in the direction of, and keep a clear view of, the path of travel;
- Grades shall be ascended or descended slowly; and
- When ascending or descending grades in excess of 10%, loaded trucks shall be driven with the load upgrade.

2.7.9   Handling of Liquid Propane Gas

Proper procedures should be used when handling or changing liquid propane gas cylinders in the PIV. Refer to the manufacturer's instructions for changing the tank on that specific PIV. However, best practices include the following:

- Park, turn off the PIV, and set the brake;
- Turn off the gas tank (typically by turning the cylinder's valve) and disconnect cylinder;
- Remove the cylinder using proper lifting techniques;
- Lift and place a new cylinder in place on the PIV;

- Reconnect the clamp and turn the cylinder valve; and

- Check for leaks before restarting the PIV.

Storage of forklift cylinders should be in accordance with the National Fire Protection Association's liquefied petroleum gas code (NFPA, 2011). Cylinders must be secure and protected from tampering and damage. They should not be stored in areas with high temperatures or near ignition sources. Finally, when not in use, the service valves on the cylinders should be closed.

2.8 Checklist/Pre-Inspection Form Samples

Occupational Safety and Health Administration 1910.178(q) requires that all forklifts be examined at least daily or after each shift. Tables 7.5 and 7.6 present examples of pre-inspection forms that can be used for a typical gasoline, diesel, electric, or liquid propane PIV. The forms are based on example forms provided by OSHA at http://www.osha.gov/dte/library/pit/daily_pit_checklist.html.

3.0 ARTICULATING AERIAL PLATFORMS

An articulating aerial platform is a type of aerial lift; it is often referred to as a *cherry picker* or *bucket truck*. These types of equipment present serious safety hazards to operators because of falls, electrocutions, collapses, and tip overs. Occupational Safety and Health Administration Standard 1910.67 is the regulation that covers aerial and boom lifts (which conform to national standards for *Vehicle Mounted Elevating and Rotating Work Platforms*, ANSI A92.2–1969).

3.1 Types of Boom Lifts

Aerial and/or boom lifts are types of vehicle-mounted aerial devices used to elevate personnel to jobsites aboveground such as extensible boom platforms, aerial ladders, articulating boom platforms, vertical towers, and/or a combination of any such devices. They may be constructed of metal, wood, fiberglass reinforced plastic (FRP), or other material. They are either powered or manually operated, and may or may not be capable of rotating about a substantially vertical axis. In addition, they may have multiple-section extensible ladders.

3.2 Operation of Equipment

Boom buckets designed for holding a person should have both platform (upper) and lower controls. According to 1910.67(c) (2), "Upper controls shall be in or beside the

TABLE 7.5   Example daily preinspection form for combustion engine PIV.

Driver/operator name:_____ Date:_____ Time:_____

Gas/diesel/liquid propane (LP)PIV inspection form	Okay? Yes/no/NA	Maintenance required?
Engine off inspection		
Leaks—fuel, hydraulic oil, engine oil or radiator coolant		
Tires—condition and pressure		
Forks, top clip retaining pin and heel—check condition		
Load backrest—securely attached		
Hydraulic hoses, mast chains, cables, and stops—check visually		
Overhead guard—attached		
Finger guards—attached		
Propane tank (LP truck)—rust corrosion, damage		
Safety warnings—attached (refer to parts manual for location)		
Battery—check water/electrolyte level and charge		
All engine belts—check visually		
Hydraulic fluid level—check level		
Engine oil level—dipstick		
Transmission fluid level—dipstick		
Engine air cleaner—squeeze rubber dirt trap or check the restriction alarm (if equipped)		
Fuel sedimentor (diesel)		
Radiator coolant—check level		
Operator's manual—in container		
Nameplate—attached and information matches model, serial number, and attachments		
Seatbelt—functioning smoothly		

Hood latch—adjusted and securely fastened

Brake fluid—check level

Engine on inspection

Unusual noises? (investigated immediately)

Accelerator or direction control pedal—functioning smoothly

Service brake—functioning smoothly

Parking brake—functioning smoothly

Steering operation—functioning smoothly

Drive control—forward/reverse—functioning smoothly

Tilt control—forward and back—functioning smoothly

Hoist and lowering control—functioning smoothly

Attachment control—operation

Horn and lights—functioning

Cab (if equipped) —heater, defroster, wipers—functioning

Gauges: ammeter, engine oil pressure, hour meter, fuel level, temperature, instrument monitors—functioning

platform within easy reach of the operator. Lower controls shall provide for overriding the upper controls. Controls shall be plainly marked as to their function. Lower level controls shall not be operated unless permission has been obtained from the employee in the lift, except in case of emergency."

3.3 Before You Operate

It is important that the person operating a lift be authorized and properly trained to do so. The lift should be moved into position by lowering and cradling the lift and stowing

TABLE 7.6   Example daily preinspection form for electric PIV.

Driver/operator name:_____ Date:_____ Time:_____

Electric PIV inspection form	Okay? yes/no/NA	Maintenance required?
Engine off inspection		
Motor off checks		
Leaks—hydraulic oil, battery		
Tires—condition and pressure		
Forks, top clip retaining pin and heel—condition		
Load backrest extension—attached		
Hydraulic hoses, mast chains, cables and stops—check visually		
Finger guards—attached		
Overhead guard—attached		
Safety warnings—attached (refer to parts manual for location)		
Battery—water/electrolyte level and charge		
Hydraulic fluid level—dipstick		
Transmission fluid level—dipstick		
Operator's manual in container		
Capacity plate attached—information matches model, serial number and attachments		
Battery restraint system—adjust and fasten		
Operator protection		
Sitdown truck—seatbelt—functioning smoothly		
Man-up/stockpicker truck—fall protection/restraining means—functioning		
Brake fluid—check level		

Engine on inspection

Unusual noises? (investigated immediately)

Accelerator linkage—functioning smoothly

Parking brake—functioning smoothly

Service brake—functioning smoothly

Steering operation—functioning smoothly

Drive control—forward/reverse—functioning smoothly

Tilt control—forward and back—functioning smoothly

Hoist and lowering control—functioning smoothly

Attachment control—operation

Horn—functioning

Lights and alarms (where present) —functioning

Hour meter—functioning

Battery discharge indicator—functioning

Instrument monitors—functioning

---

the outriggers. Anticipated loads being put on the boom and basket should be compared to manufacturer's limits. Finally, the area should be assessed for any power lines, conductive objects, or any other objects that could pin, hit, or pull a person from the bucket.

3.4   Personal Protective Equipment

It is important to determine the type of PPE necessary while working from or on a boom. Standard equipment includes a hard hat, steel-toe boots, and a body harness attached to a lanyard, which is attached to the bucket.

3.5   Surface Conditions

Surface conditions should be assessed for stability and incline. Outriggers should be positioned on pads or a solid surface. If on an incline, wheel chocks should be installed. A lift should never be operated on ground that cannot be stabilized or that has been recently backfilled.

3.6   Fall Protection

Fall protection, such as a body harness or positioning device (not a body belt), should be used at all times when working from a boom bucket or basket. Attaching the harness to an adjacent pole, structure, or piece of equipment while working is not permitted. The fall protection lanyard should always be attached to the boom or to the basket to prevent it from being pulled from the bucket.

3.7   Electrical Safety

One of the most dangerous hazards associated with being lifted up on an aerial or boom lift are power lines. A minimum clearance of at least 3 m (10 ft) should be kept from any overhead power line or other conductive object (i.e., wires, transformers, ducts, and pipes). Regardless of whether or not the lines are believed to be "energized," power lines should always be treated as if they are.

3.8   Inspections

Boom lifts should be inspected before each shift and should be regularly maintained. At least once a year, all systems should be thoroughly inspected (i.e., electrically, mechanically, etc.) and repaired if necessary.

3.9   Ground Controls

Lifts have lower controls and upper controls. Lower controls are only used in emergency situations. They cannot control driving or steering the lift.

3.10 Refueling

When refueling the boom lift, it is important to always have the vehicle turned off and the boom lowered and stowed. The operator should make sure there are no open flames; additionally, he or she should not mistakenly put fuel into the hydraulic tank.

3.11 Checklists

Inspections are required by OSHA. Checklists should be created for both preshift/preworkplace inspections and annual inspections on boom lifts and should be kept on file in case they are requested by OSHA.

4.0 REFERENCES

American National Standards Act (2004) *Emergency Eye Wash and Shower Equipment;* ANSI Z358.1-2004; American National Standards Institute: Washington, D.C.

Federal Motor Carrier Safety Administration, A&I Online: Safety Measurement System. http://ai.fmcsa.dot.gov/SMS/ (accessed Aug 2011).

National Fire Protection Association (2011) NFPA 58: Liquefied Petroleum Gas Code, 2011 Edition; National Fire Protection Association: Quincy, Massachusetts.

National Response Center Online Reporting Tool. http://www.nrc.uscg.mil (accessed Aug 2011).

Occupational Safety and Health Administration (1998) *Powered Industrial Trucks; Code of Federal Regulations, Part 1910, Title 178,* Appendix A; Occupational Safety and Health Administration: Washington, D.C.

Occupational Safety and Health Administration (2008) *eTools Home: Powered Industrial Trucks.* http://www.osha.gov/dcsp/products/etools/pit/forklift/index.html (accessed Aug 2011).

5.0 SUGGESTED READINGS

American National Standards Institute; Industrial Truck Standards Development Foundation (2009) *Safety Standards for Low Lift and High Lift Trucks;* ANSI/ITSDF B56.1-2009; Washington, D.C.

Doherty, L. (2006) *How to Prevent Pallet Jacks from Causing Injury,* Safety Xchange, http://www.safetyxchange.org/health-safety/how-to-prevent-them-from-causing-injury (accessed Aug 2011).

Federal Motor Carrier Safety Administration (2011) National Consumer Complaint Database. https://nccdb.fmcsa.dot.gov/HomePage.asp (accessed Aug 2011).

Lab Safety EZ Facts®, Forklift Battery Changing Station Safety, Document Number 112. http://www.labsafety.com/refinfo/ezfacts/ezf112.htm (accessed Aug 2011).

Occupational Safety and Health Administration (1996) *Aerial Lifts*; *Code of Federal Regulations*, Part 1926, Title 453; Occupation Safety and Health Administration: Washington, D.C.

Occupational Safety and Health Administration (2006) *Powered Industrial Trucks*; *Code of Federal Regulations*, Part 1910, Title 178; Occupational Safety and Health Administration: Washington, D.C.

Occupational Safety and Health Administration (2011) *Using Aerial Lifts* Fact Sheet. http://www.osha.gov/OshDoc/data_Hurricane_Facts/aerial_lifts.pdf (accessed Aug 2011).

Occupational Safety and Health Administration (2011) *Safety and Health Topics, Powered Industrial Trucks*. http://www.osha.gov/SLTC/poweredindustrial-trucks/index.html (accessed Aug 2011).

Occupational Safety and Health Administration (2011) Sample Daily Checklists for Powered Industrial Trucks Web Site. http://www.osha.gov/dte/library/pit/daily_pit_checklist.html (accessed Sept 2011).

Railroad Commission of Texas (2011) Propane, Alternative Energy Division Web Site. http://www.propane.tx.gov/training/customersafetybulletin/documents/Changing%20forklift%20cylinders%2012–07.pdf (accessed Aug 2011).

U.S. Department of Transportation (2011) Pipeline and Hazardous Materials Safety Administration Web Site. http://phmsa.dot.gov/hazmat (accessed Aug 2011).

Chapter 8

Biological Hazards at Wastewater Treatment Facilities

1.0 TYPES OF HAZARDS

1.1 Bacteria

Unlike viruses, bacteria do not require a living host cell to reproduce. Pathogenic bacteria are microscopic and are extremely common in wastewater. Because bacteria can reproduce outside the body, microorganisms can be present in large quantities in the collection system. Bacterial infections, therefore, will result from their proliferation in an aqueous environment. Table 8.1 provides a summary of the various diseases associated with wastewater-contaminated environments.

Because of their daily exposure to wastewater-contaminate environments, wastewater personnel have a higher incidence of potential exposure to pathogens than the general public. For most workers, however, the risk of developing a disease is relatively low. Proper personal hygiene is critical, however, because infections may occur

TABLE 8.1   Diseases associated with wastewater-contaminated environments.

Disease	Organism	Mode of transmission
Bacillary dysentery	*Shigella spp.*	Ingestion[b]
Asiatic cholera	*Vibrio cholerae*	Ingestion
Typhoid fever	*Salmonella typhi*	Ingestion
Tuberculosis	*Mycobacterium tuberculosis*	Inhalation[c]
Tetanus	*Clostridium tetani*	Wound contact
Infectious hepatitis	Hapatitis A virus	Ingestion
Poliomyelitis	Poliovirus	Ingestion
Common cold[a]	Echovirus	Inhalation
Hookworm disease	*Necator americanus/Ancylostoma duodenale*	Skin contact
Histoplasmosis	*Histoplasma capsulatum*	Inhalation
Leptrospirosis	Leptospira	Wound contact/inhalation

[a]The common cold is typically associated with various rhinovirus types, several coronaviruses, and some unknown viruses.

[b]Inhalation is by way of mouth and nose and taken through the lungs and into the bloodstream.

[c]Ingestion is by way of mouth or nose and taken in through the stomach and intestine and into the bloodstream.

without symptoms and antibodies to bacteria and viruses may develop without illness symptoms (latent infection) being readily apparent.

The most common bacterial pathogens found in wastewater are *Salmonella* and *Shigella*. Other bacterial microorganisms include *Vibrio, clostridium, Yersinia, Campylobacter, and Leptospira*. *Escherichia coli (E. coli)*, which can cause gastroenteritis, is generally not considered a pathogen because it is a microorganism that naturally inhabits that gastrointestinal tract of humans. The most common bacterial pathogens found in wastewater are listed in Table 8.2.

1.1.1 Salmonella

Salmonella is a significant cause of food poisoning from improperly prepared products. *Salmonella* can cause infections of the stomach and intestinal tract (acute gastroenteritis), typhoid fever, and paratyphoid fever. *Salmonella* infection results from oral ingestion, although large numbers of these microorganisms are required to cause illness.

Salmonella are routinely isolated from wastewater treatment processes, compost operations, sludge handling facilities, and associated landfills. Isolation of *Salmonella* from treatment plant effluent and sludge varies from plant to plant and season to season (Ottolenghi and Hamparian, 1982). Infection is unlikely in the wastewater field without direct ingestion of waste (Niederinghaus, 1986). The risk of infection

TABLE 8.2 Bacterial pathogens found in wastewater.

Microorganism	Disease
Salmonella	Salmonellosis (gastroenteritis)
	Typhoid fever
Shigella	Shigellosis (gastroenteritis)
	Bacillary dysentery
Clostridium	Tetanus
	Gas gangrene
	Gastroenteritis
Vibrio	Asiatich cholera
Leptospira	Weil's disease (Leptospirosis)
Campylobacter	Acute bacterial enteritis
Yersinia	Acute gastroenteritis

from *Salmonella* and all other pathogens is significantly reduced with proper hygienic practices.

1.1.2   Shigella

Shigella infection (shigellosis) is responsible for bacillary dysentery and is the primary cause of infectious diarrhea in the United States (Niederinghaus, 1986). Like *Salmonella, Shigella* is typically transmitted through oral ingestion of contaminated food and water or through hand-to-mouth contact. Few organisms are required to cause infection, which makes this bacteria a common biological hazard to wastewater workers (Niederinghaus, 1986). *Shigella* survives for only a short time in the sewer system, however, and generally represents a greater potential hazard for collection system workers than treatment plant operators.

1.1.3   Vibrio

Asiatic cholera is caused by *Vibro cholerae*, which produce a poison or endotoxin that results in vomiting, diarrhea, and loss of body fluids. Cholera can be spread by the ingestion of fecal-contaminated water and is typically present in many developing countries and communities with inadequate sanitation practices. Control of this disease is achieved through proper measures such as water disinfection and wastewater treatment.

1.1.4   Clostridium

Tetanus results from a localized infection of a deep or puncture wound by *Clostridium tetani*. Symptoms of infection include contraction of the muscles controlling the jaw, body muscle spasms, and paralysis of the throat muscle, which can lead to death from respiratory failure. The organism is commonly found in fecal-contaminated environments and in soils. Infection may occur whenever a deep wound is contaminated with wastewater-contaminated material. The general public, including wastewater system personnel, should make sure that tetanus vaccines are taken every 10 years after initial doses and after wounds, unless it has been fewer than 5 years since the last dose. A booster tetanus toxoid given at the time of injury will also provide immunity to the disease.

1.1.5   Yersinia

Yersinia entercolitica is an enteric pathogen that causes acute gastroenteritis. The most common symptoms are fever and diarrhea, with moderate dehydration. The fecal-oral route is the most common mode of transmission.

1.1.6 Campylobacter

Campylobacter fetus and *C. jejuni* cause acute bacterial enteritis (Tortora et al., 1982). These organisms are transmitted by the fecal-oral route through contaminated water sources and other modes. Most outbreaks of enteritis caused by *Campylobacter* have been associated with surface and drinking water supplies (Carter et al., 1987).

1.1.7 Leptospira

Leptospira bacteria are responsible for leptospirosis, or Weil's disease, which infects the liver, kidneys, and central nervous system. This disease was known as "the illness of the wastewater worker" in England before the 1950s. Recent studies, however, have not verified this bacteria as a current problem for wastewater workers. Infection typically occurs by way of contact with mucous membranes or skin abrasions (Hunter et al., 1987). Although *Leptospira* are killed rapidly in wastewater carrying detergent byproducts, this may represent an infection risk to collection system workers in some instances.

1.2 Viruses

A virus is any of a group of ultramicroscopic agents that reproduce only in living cells. This characteristic of viruses is important because viruses cannot reproduce without a host cell and, therefore, will not reproduce in wastewater. The primary source of viruses that are infectious to man is from human waste that has been discharged to the sewer (Hunter et al., 1987).

More than 100 different types of viruses are found in human waste. Human viruses commonly found in wastewater are listed in Table 8.3 (WEF, 2001). These viruses multiply in the living cells of the intestinal tract and end up in human feces. Because millions of viruses can be produced by an infected cell, they are found in large quantities in wastewater (Niederinghaus, 1986). Characteristics of various wastewater viruses and their mode of transmission and communicability are found in Table 8.4 (WEF, 2001).

While there are many types of viruses present in wastewater, the general category that has received the most study is the enteric, or intestinal, virus. This group includes varieties that are responsible for diseases such as infectious hepatitis, meningitis, poliomyelitis, respiratory diseases, gastroenteritis, and the common cold. Along with these various diseases, almost all of the viruses produce latent infections, which can go undetected because no symptoms may be present.

TABLE 8.3   Human viruses found in wastewater.

Virus group	Disease
Norwalk	Acute gastroenteritis
Rotavirus	Acute gastroenteritis
Adenovirus	Acute respiratory disease, conjunctivitis, pharynoconjunctival fever
Coxsackie A	Upper respiratory tract infection
Coxsackie B	Upper respiratory tract infection, myocarditis, aspectic meningitis, Bornholm's disease
Echovirus	Common cold, aseptic meningitis, conjunctivitis, gastroenteritis
Hepatitis A	Infectious hepatitis
Poliovirus	Poliomyelitis
Reovirus	Upper respiratory tract infection

TABLE 8.4   Characteristics of various wastewater viruses.

Virus group	Mode of transmission	Incubation period	Period of communicability
Adenovirus	Inhalation	5–7 days	Short
Echovirus	Inhalation	1–2 days	Short
Hepatitis A	Ingestion	15–40 days	Long
Poliovirus	Ingestion	5–20 days	Long
Norwalk	Ingestion		
Rotavirus	Ingestion		
Coxsackie A	Ingestion or inhalation		
Coxsackie B	Ingestion or inhalation		

1.2.1   Hepatitis A

The main waterborne disease resulting from viral infection is hepatitis A. The hepatitis A virus is the causative agent of infectious hepatitis, a systemic disease primarily involving the liver. The virus is commonly associated with fecal-oral transmission through wastewater contamination and contaminated food. An infected person generally exhibits flu-like symptoms, cramps, vomiting, high fever, and jaundice.

The hepatitis A infectious agent is resistant to heat, acid, and chemical treatment, including low levels of chlorine (Kowal, 1986). Thus, wastewater personnel have a higher potential incidence of exposure to the hepatitis A virus because of their daily contact with wastewater.

1.2.2   Norwalk Virus

Another common type of virus that has been associated with inadequately treated wastewater is the Norwalk agent. The Norwalk agent produces an acute gastrointestinal disease consisting of vomiting, diarrhea, low-grade fever, and body aches. Symptoms generally last for a short period of time, typically 24 to 48 hours. During this time, the virus can be passed through the stool and has the potential to affect other members of the family if appropriate hygiene is not practiced in the home. Outbreaks of the illness have been associated with septage disposal, municipal water supplies, and recreational water contact.

1.2.3   Adenovirus

Adenoviruses have been associated with respiratory tract infections and conjunctivitis (eye infection). The virus has been isolated from wastewater and sludges and can cause acute diarrheal disease and viral gastroenteritis.

1.2.4   Rotavirus

Rotaviruses are a common cause of acute viral gastroenteritis. Outbreaks of this common illness have been associated with wastewater-contaminated water resources. Raw wastewater and chlorinated wastewater effluents from activated sludge plants treating domestic wastes have been shown to discharge high densities of these viruses each day (Hejkal et al., 1984).

1.2.5   Coxsackieviruses A and B

Coxsackievirus A causes aseptic meningitis and conjunctivitis and is one of the causes of the common cold (Jawetz et al., 1982). Coxsackievirus B causes several types of diseases, including heart disease (Jawetz et al., 1982). The primary modes of transmission for coxsackieviruses are through inhalation and ingestion of contaminated materials.

1.2.6   Poliovirus

The poliovirus is associated with poliomyelitis, which affects the central nervous system. The primary mode of transmission is ingestion of fecal-contaminated water containing the virus. The poliovirus is a more stable virus than most other viruses and can remain infectious for relatively long periods of time in contaminated food and water (Tortora et al., 1982).

Poliovirus vaccines have reduced the incidence of poliomyelitis and have contributed to the decline in reported cases of the disease. Outbreaks typically occur only in segments of the population lacking proper immunization.

1.2.7 *Acquired Immune Deficiency Syndrome*

Acquired immune deficiency syndrome (AIDS) is caused by the human immunodeficiency virus (HIV) that attacks the body's immune system, leaving the body susceptible to numerous diseases. The AIDS virus is a delicate virus that cannot survive for long periods of time outside of the human body. The virus exists in low concentrations in the blood of infected persons and after entering the wastewater sewer system, it is subjected to enormous dilution factors and harsh environments (low levels of heat, pH extremes, surfactants, and chemical agents) that are not conducive to AIDS virus survival (Gerardi et al., 1988).

Operators have been concerned with the possible transmission of AIDS from human wastes such as urine, excrement, and blood that are discharged to sewer lines serviced by municipal wastewater treatment facilities (Clark, 1987). Fears have been raised over the handling of raw wastewater during routine contact and during repairs and maintenance to lift station pumps, bar screens, broken sewer lines, and clogged laterals. Further contact with contaminated wastewater originating from prisons, hospitals, and institutions and uneasiness over the removal of hypodermic needles, condoms, feminine napkins, and aborted fetuses have added to the growing apprehension about disease transmission (Clark, 1987).

Acquired immune deficiency syndrome and hepatitis B are both blood-borne viruses and cannot reproduce outside the human body. To be transmitted, AIDS and hepatitis B must enter the bloodstream directly. A blood-borne virus from contaminated wastewater can gain direct access through an open wound or abrasion of the skin. Merely coming in contact with contaminated wastewater does not imply exposure to AIDS or hepatitis B.

The Centers for Disease Control and Prevention has stated that there is no scientific evidence that HIV is spread in wastewater or its aerosols. The virus has never been recovered from wastewater and it is believed that the pH, temperature, and other conditions of the collection system are not suitable to its survival. There have been no known cases of wastewater workers or plumbers who have contracted AIDS where the mode of transmission was judged to be from occupational exposure.

The scientific evidence to date indicates that AIDS cannot be contracted through occupational exposure associated with wastewater treatment. Generally, infected body fluids that are discharged to sewers are immediately diluted to the point where they do not represent a significant risk to wastewater workers. The AIDS virus, in particular, is not well suited to the collection system environment and is likely to become deactivated upon contact with wastewater. Wastewater workers should, however, pay close attention to personal hygiene and exercise caution and common sense whenever they are working in and around contaminated wastewater to minimize exposure to bacteria and viruses.

1.3 Parasites

A parasite lives on or in another organism of a different species, from which it derives its nourishment. The organism is called the parasite's *host*. Parasites typically do not kill their hosts because the life of the parasite would also be terminated.

In many instances, however, parasites will weaken the host or cause symptoms similar to disease caused by bacteria or viruses. Waterborne parasites found in wastewater consist of various types of protozoa and worms. These organisms often do not survive the journey through the wastewater collection system and treatment facilities. The cysts and eggs, in which the protozoa and worms reproduce, are often resistant to adverse conditions. These resistant cysts and eggs, therefore, may show up in wastewater or sludge samples.

The number and variety of parasitic forms present in wastewater or sludges depend heavily on the origin of wastes entering the treatment plant. The most commonly studied protozoa are *Entamoeba histolytica* and *Giardia lamblia*. *E. histolytica* is the agent that causes amoebic dysentery, a disease with symptoms that include varying degrees of abdominal cramps and diarrhea, alternated with constipation. *G. lamblia* is also contracted orally and can lead to a variety of intestinal symptoms. *Giardia* is hardy protozoa that exists in a cyst stage and can be resistant to chlorination. The most common parasites found in wastewater are listed in Table 8.5 (Clark, 1987; Niederinghaus, 1986).

The eggs of many varieties of roundworms, hookworms, and tapeworms have also been found in wastewater. Infestation of roundworms and tapeworms is typically transmitted orally and typically results in abdominal pain and weight loss. Hookworms are generally transmitted through cracks in bare skin (such as between the toes), although oral infestation is also possible. Hookworms cause a general loss of energy and anemia (Niederinghaus, 1986).

TABLE 8.5   Parasites found in wastewater.

Organism	Disease
Protozoa	
Entamoeba histolytica	Amoebic dysentery
Giardia lamblia	Giardiasis
Roundworms (nematodes)	Abdominal pain and weight loss
Hookworms (ancylostomatodes)	Anemia
Tapeworms (cestodes)	Abdominal pain and weight loss

Parasite survival rates are affected by the wastewater or sludge treatment processes to which they are subjected. In general, each process that exposes a parasite to a different or hostile environment may shorten its survival time.

In instances of parasitic infestation, it is possible that the host's symptoms may be nonexistent. Because hand-to-mouth contact is the principal cause of infection, it is important that hands are washed frequently.

1.4   Macroorganisms

There are numerous places where rodents can be attracted to wastewater facilities. The most common areas where this occurs are screening, grit collection, and sludge treatment and disposal areas. Screenings and grit should be collected and stored in containers that minimize rodents from entering and congregating. General good housekeeping practices should also minimize rodents from becoming a problem.

Insects can also become a problem at wastewater treatment plants. Any areas of standing water or ponding can become breeding grounds for insects such as mosquitoes. Standing water, therefore, should be eliminated. If possible, tanks that contain water or wastewater and are not being used should be drained. Good housekeeping practices should be followed to prevent attraction of insects.

2.0   HOW INFECTIONS CAN SPREAD

There are three basic routes that may lead to infection: ingestion through splashes, contaminated food, or cigarettes; inhalation of infectious agents or aerosols; and infection caused by an unprotected cut or abrasion. Wastewater workers often come in physical contact with raw wastewater and sludge during their daily activities. Even when direct physical contact is avoided, the worker may handle objects that are contaminated. Cuts and abrasions, including those that are minor, should be cared for properly. Open wounds invite infection from many of the viruses and bacteria present in wastewater. Table 8.6 summarizes significant routes of infection.

Ingestion is generally the primary route of wastewater worker infection. The common practice of touching the mouth with the hand will contribute to the possibility of infection. Workers who eat or smoke without washing their hands have a much higher risk of infection. Most surfaces near wastewater equipment are likely to be covered with bacteria or viruses. These potentially infectious agents may be deposited on surfaces in the form of an aerosol or may come from direct contact with the wastewater or sludge. A good rule of thumb for a worker to follow is to never touch oneself above the neck whenever there is contact with wastewater. Table 8.7 lists methods to prevent ingestion of pathogenic organisms.

At locations where wastewater or sludge is sprayed, the possibility of inhaling infectious agents will increase. Workers should avoid prolonged exposures at those areas where contact with such aerosols are likely. In instances where prolonged

TABLE 8.6   Routes of infection.

Ingestion	Eating, drinking, or accidentally swallowing a pathogenic organism (e.g., hepatitis A)
Inhalation	Breathing spray or mist containing pathogenic organisms (e.g., common cold)
Direct contact	Entry of pathogenic organism to body via cut or break in the skin (e.g., tetanus)

TABLE 8.7   Methods to prevent ingestion of pathogenic organisms.

Wash hands

  Never eat, drink, or use tobacco products before washing hands;

  Avoid touching face, mouth, eyes, or nose before washing hands; and

  Wash hands immediately after any contact with wastewater or sludge.

Control activities

  Eat only in designated areas of the plant and away from treatment facilities and

  Do not smoke or use chewing tobacco while working in direct contact with wastewater or sludge.

TABLE 8.8 Methods to prevent direct contact entry of pathogenic organisms.

Body

Wear protective clothing and equipment;

Shower and change clothes before going home;

Leave work clothes, gloves, and boots on-site to prevent possible disease transmission to family or friends;

Use separate lockers for street and work clothes to minimize contamination; and

If work clothes are washed at home, separate from the family wash and use chlorine bleach.

Hands

Wear gloves whenever there is contact with wastewater or sludge;

Use thin, disposable latex gloves for light work and reinforced rubber gloves for heavy activities, and discard gloves that become torn; and

Do not submerge hand below top of glove.

Face

Never touch face, mouth, eyes, ears, or nose while working with wastewater or sludge;

Wear goggles in the presence of heavy aerosols; and

Wear surgical-type masks or respirators in the presence of heavy aerosols.

exposure to aerosols is anticipated, use of surgical masks and goggles may help to minimize contact. Methods to prevent direct entry of pathogenic organisms by contact are included in Table 8.8.

3.0 HOW TO PREVENT INFECTIONS

3.1 Personal Protection Measures

The safety precautions required to significantly reduce the possibility of biological contamination by wastewater are outlined in Table 8.9. The most important consideration is the use of good common sense. If collection systems and treatment plant workers are aware of hazards, they can protect themselves simply by following correct personal hygiene habits. Laboratory workers also must be aware of the potential for infection because of the nature of the samples being handled.

Although there has been no evidence that wastewater workers have transmitted infection to their families, good personal hygiene is still important. Workers

TABLE 8.9   Workplace precautions and personal hygiene guidelines (Gerardi et al., 1998).

- Wash hands frequently with soap and water after contacting wastewater; visiting restrooms; before eating, drinking, or smoking; and at end of work shift.
- Promptly treat cuts and abrasions using appropriate first aid measures.
- Wear heavy duty gloves (or double gloving) and boots that are waterproof and puncture resistant.
- Wear surgical-type masks and goggles or face shields for prolonged exposure to wastewater aerosols.
- Change soiled uniforms or protective clothing as soon as the job is completed.
- Shower before changing into clean work clothes and shoes.
- Launder work clothes at work not at home.
- Handle sharp items with extra care to prevent accidental injuries.
- Clean contaminated tools after use.
- Follow good common sense and exercise extra caution whenever there is contact with contaminated water or sludge.
- Wherever possible, use dual lockers to separate work and street clothes.
- Promptly clean body parts that contact wastewater or sludges.

should thoroughly clean up at the end of the work day before going home. Ideally, soiled clothing should be laundered before it is taken home or it should be handled separately from domestic laundry and washed with hot water and disinfected. Dual locker systems are desirable for all wastewater workers, allowing one locker for work clothes and one for street clothes.

Another important key to preventing exposure is the proper use of personal protective equipment (PPE). Waterproof and puncture-resistant gloves should be worn whenever working with wastewater or sludge. If prolonged exposure to aerosols or dusts is anticipated, respiratory and eye protection should be worn. First aid kits should be readily available at the jobsite to allow for the immediate treatment of minor cuts. All tools contaminated with wastewater should be cleaned with a common cleaner or a mild solution of sodium hypochlorite.

3.2   Immunizations

The Centers for Disease Control and Prevention recommends that immunizations for diphtheria and tetanus be current for the general public, including all wastewater workers. Boosters are recommended every 10 years after the initial immunizations (typically during childhood years) are administered. The tetanus booster needs to be repeated if a wound or puncture becomes dirty and if boosters have not been given within 5 years.

Primary vaccinations for polio and typhoid are presently considered to be sufficient unless there is a regional outbreak. The preventive effect of the vaccine immune serum globulin for hepatitis A is short-lived (about 3 weeks) and is not routinely recommended for wastewater workers unless there has been direct exposure to wastewater splashed into an open wound or the mouth or a severe outbreak has occurred in the community. The vaccine for hepatitis B is also not routinely recommended for wastewater workers because the risk of transmission by wastewater is extremely remote. Vaccinations are available from physicians, health clinics, and county health departments.

Presently, no additional immunizations above those recommended by the U.S. Public Health Service for adults in the general population are advised for workers in contact with wastewater. Wastewater workers and all other adults should be adequately vaccinated against diphtheria and tetanus. Poliovirus and typhoid vaccines and immune globulin are not routinely recommended for wastewater workers. Table 8.10 summarizes immunizations recommended by the U.S. Public Health Service (CDC, 1984).

3.3 Work Procedures

As discussed previously, when working at wastewater treatment facilities, the most important practice is personal hygiene. Workers should avoid direct contact with wastewater as much as possible by wearing PPE such as gloves, boots, respirators, face shields, and so on. In short, workers should assess the risk of exposure to wastewater and wear the proper PPE. When a cut or abrasion does occur, the worker should seek medical attention as soon as possible to clean and dress the affected area.

4.0 HOW TO TREAT INFECTIONS

All injuries should be treated promptly to prevent infection or illness. Potential entry points will exist for microorganisms to cause infection if minor breaks in the skin or mucous membranes resulting from burns, rashes, cuts, and insect bites are left untreated. Soap and water are the best initial first aid measures that can be used for

TABLE 8.10 Immunizations recommended by the U.S. Public Health Service (CDC, 1984).

Disease	Who needs immunization	Immunization
Hepatitis A	Individuals with close personal contact with hepatitis A	Hepatitis A immune globulin treatment
Hepatitis B	Homosexual males, household and sexual contacts with carriers, and those who have had direct exposure to blood of a person known or suspected to be a carrier	Hepatitis A immune globulin treatment and hepatitis B vaccine
Influenza Measles	Adults 65 years or older Adults born in 1957 or later, unless they have evidence of vaccination on or after their first birthday, documentation of physician diagnosed disease, or laboratory evidence of disease	Annual influenza vaccine Combined measles, mumps, and rubella (MMR)
Mumps	Adults, especially males, who have not been previously infected	Mumps vaccine
Pneumococcal disease	Adults 65 years or older	Pneumococcal polysaccharide vaccine
Rubella	Women of childbearing age, unless proof of vaccination or laboratory evidence of immunity is available	Rubella vaccine
Tetanus and diphtheria	Adults every 10 years after initial doses and after wounds, unless it has been fewer than 5 years since last dose.	TD vaccine

minor cuts. Table 8.11 lists recommended contents of a standard first aid kit. The first aid kit should include a variety of antibacterial ointments or disinfectants, dressings, waterless soap, antiseptic wipes, and sterile eyewash solution. An antibiotic ointment or disinfectant should be applied to the wound after thorough washing. Adhesive bandages, tape, and sterile gauze should also be used to further protect the treated area and to keep the wound clean and dry. Generally, prompt medical attention is

TABLE 8.11   Suggested contents of a first aid kit.

Variety of bacterial ointments/disinfectants

Dressings

Waterless soap

Antiseptic wipes

Sterile eyewash solution

Adhesive bandages

Tape

Scissors

Sterile gauze

Splint

Aspirin

required if the skin or mucous membrane is severely injured and in contact with contaminated wastewater or sludge or if severe wounds or punctures do not respond to methods to control bleeding.

Because wastewater workers frequently expose their hands to water and wastewater, occasional skin problems such as fungal infections, rashes, chapping, and cracking may occur. Protective hand creams or lotions can typically be used to minimize such problems. If these medications are ineffective or if contact dermatitis becomes a problem, an occupational physician should be consulted. If wastewater gets splashed into the eyes, ears, or nose of a worker, they should be immediately flushed with fresh potable water or solution from the first aid kit.

5.0 WORKERS WHO ARE AT RISK

Several studies have been conducted on the actual infection rate of wastewater workers. During early years of employment, wastewater workers may be more prone to illness than more experienced workers. Newer employees may experience increased rates of gastrointestinal and upper respiratory illnesses, which are thought to be related to biological exposures (Clark, 1987). Table 8.12 shows the results of various studies of health effects of biological hazards to wastewater

TABLE 8.12   Summary of biological health risks to wastewater workers.

Type of hazard	Effects observed
Hepatitis A	Evidence of increased risk when working with raw wastewater and primary sludge.
Other viral infections	May indicate infection in the most exposed workers. Other factors contributing to infection should not be overlooked.
Leptospirosis	Formerly considered a problem; risks now appear minimal.
Gastrointestinal illness	Increased rates, especially among new workers. Other factors contributing to infection should not be overlooked.
Compost-related factors	Excess nasal, ear, and skin abnormalities and eye irritation.

workers (Clark, 1987). Although areas of higher risk exist, the risk of contamination is not overwhelming. Simple procedures involving personal hygiene and work methods, however, can reduce these risks to far below other common occupational hazards.

Most studies have indicated that areas with the greatest risk for infection involve routine and direct contact with untreated wastewater or sludge. Included in this category are workers involved in sewer maintenance and raw sludge handling. Various treatment processes designed for solids or biochemical oxygen demand (BOD) removal will provide varying degrees of disinfection, as shown in Table 8.13 (Metcalf and Eddy, 2003). Risk of infection will rapidly decline as wastewater undergoes various treatment steps.

5.1   Collection System Personnel

Because of their direct high exposure to raw wastewater, collection system workers have greater risks of infection than do treatment plant employees. Although various studies have indicated evidence of increased risk of viral infections (including hepatitis A), parasite infection, and gastrointestinal illness in these workers, improved and modern work practices can reduce these risks. Leptospirosis, transmitted through the urine of infected rats, was considered to be the British sewer worker's disease before the 1950s (see Section 1.1.7). Recent investigations have revealed that the risk of this particular bacterial infection is minimal. Present-day wastewater characteristics and probable lower infection rates in rats may have contributed to the reduced prevalence of this disease.

TABLE 8.13   Percent removal of bacterial pathogens by individual different treatment processes.

Process	Percent removal
Course screens	0–5
Fine screens	10–20
Grit chambers	10–25
Plain sedimentation	25–75
Chemical precipitation	40–80
Trickling filters	90–95
Activated sludge	90–98

5.2 Treatment Plant and Laboratory Personnel

All operators at wastewater treatment facilities do not necessarily fall into the high-exposure group. Studies have shown increased risk for those operators involved with raw sludge handling or in enclosed areas where wastes are aerated or agitated. While all operators have the opportunity to come in contact with various infectious agents, those handling digested sludge or outdoor wet processes appear to have lower risk of infection.

Laboratory personnel are required to perform analyses on a variety of wastewater and sludge samples. Although the risk of infection from wastewater samples is not as high in the laboratory environment as in sewers or outside facilities, infectious agents that are commonly found in such samples are nevertheless a biological hazard.

The risk of laboratory-acquired infection results from any procedure that releases infective organisms to the environment or affords access for such organisms to the human body (Hurrell, 1982). The most widespread mechanism for laboratory-acquired infection is typically by airborne contamination of the infective agent. The laboratory environment, therefore, should be properly ventilated by a plenum and exhaust air system to minimize exposure to chemical or biological risks. Exhaust air should be routed from the laboratory to the outside of the building and discharged to the atmosphere.

Laboratory workers must be provided with adequate training in proper micro-biological techniques and safety. Workers should be familiar with aseptic handling techniques and the biology of the organisms under evaluation to fully appreciate the potential hazard. An emergency procedure should also be developed to deal with accidental contamination of personnel and work areas and appropriate vaccinations should be administered if known pathogens are being evaluated. All laboratory apparatuses and waste should also be decontaminated by disinfection or sterilization to keep the environment free from microorganisms. Table 8.14 lists recommended safe laboratory practices.

5.3   Biosolids Personnel

Specific studies have been conducted on workers who deal with wastewater sludge composting. The heat generated in a properly managed composting operation is sufficient to significantly reduce levels of all pathogens of concern in the wastewater industry. The conditions created in composting, however, allow for the proliferation of many thermophilic microorganisms such as *Aspergillus fumagatus*. *A. fumagatus* grows well at 45 °C (113 °F) and higher, which makes it prevalent at composting sites. The mode of infection is by way of inhalation of *A. fumagatus* spores in the dust at the site. Symptoms that have been reported by workers include abnormal skin, ear, and nose infections. Higher rates of eye and skin irritations have also been noted (Clark et al., 1984). Although it is unknown whether these symptoms were attributable to the composting operation, appropriate eye and respiratory protective measures should be used.

TABLE 8.14   Safe laboratory practices.

- Do not eat, drink, or smoke while handling wastewater or sludge samples.

- Wash hands before and often while working in the laboratory.

- Wear protective clothing, laboratory coats, eye protection, and latex gloves, as required.

- Do not place hands on face, eyes, nose, or mouth while working in the laboratory; always keep your hands below the collar.

- Use bulb to pipette samples; do not pipette by mouth.

- Wipe up spills immediately.

- Discard all unused samples immediately.

- Store non-compatible or highly reactive chemicals separately. Acids, alkalies, and chlorine should not be stored next to each other.

- Take extra precautions when handling glassware to prevent breakage injury.

Extensive studies pertaining to health effects associated with long-term exposure to sludge compost have not been conducted. Studies of these workers that have been conducted show a susceptibility to fungal infection from microorganisms grown in the composting process. However, these studies are of groups of compost workers in only four areas and may not be universally representative of the composting process. Further studies will be needed (e.g., some varieties of *Nocardia* are pathogenic to man) to determine if there are any significant biological hazards associated with long-term use of the sludge composting process.

6.0 SUMMARY

A number of occupational hazards confront treatment plant and wastewater collection system workers. The danger of infection to these workers through contact with wastewater is real if proper safety precautions are not observed. Although the possibility of infection is greatest for workers in high-exposure areas, such as collection systems and raw sludge processing, all workers who handle or come in contact with wastewater are susceptible to infection.

The incidence of occupational illness or disease among experienced wastewater workers is comparable to other non-wastewater-related professions. Wastewater workers, however, must be alert to the potential for illness and should use common sense and follow safe work procedures. The implementation of strong safety programs, good personal hygiene practices, and PPE and clothing will minimize the risk of exposure to infectious agents commonly found in wastewater and sludge.

7.0 REFERENCES

Carter, A. M.; Pacha, R. E.; Clark, G. W.; Williams, E. A. (1987) Seasonal Occurrence of Campylobacter spp. in Surface Waters and Their Correlation with Standard Indicator Bacteria. *Appl. Environ. Microbiol.*, **53**, 523.

Centers for Disease Control and Prevention (1984) Adult Immunizations, Recommendations of the Immunizations Practice Advisory Committee (ACIP). *Morbid. Mortal. Wkly. Rep.*, **33**, 15.

Clark, C. S. (1987) Potential and Actual Biological Related Health Risks of Wastewater Industry Employment. *J.—Water Pollut. Control Fed.*, **59**, 999.

Clark, C. S.; Bjornson, H. S.; Schwartz-Fulton, J. (1984) Biological Health Risks Associated with the Composting of Wastewater Treatment Plant Sludge. *J. Water Pollut. Control Fed.*, **56**, 1269.

Gerardi, M. H.; Maczuga, A. P.; Zimmerman, M. C. (1988) An Operator's Guide to Wastewater Viruses. *Public Works*, **50**.

Hejkal, T. W.; Wellings, F. M.; LaRock, P. A.; Lewis, A. L. (1984) Seasonal Occurrence of Rotavirus in Sewage. *Appl. Environ. Microbiol.*, **47**, 558.

Hunter, R. M., et al. (1987) Operator Exposure to the AIDS Virus. *Proceedings of the American Water Works Association/Water Pollution Control Federation Joint Conference*; Montana Section.

Hurrell, D. J. (1982) *High Risk Safety Technology: Biological Hazards*; Green, A. E., Ed.; Wiley & Sons: London, England.

Jawetz, E.; Melnick, J. L.; Adelberg, E. A. (1982) *Review of Medical Microbiology*, 15th ed.; Lange Medical Publications: Los Altos, California.

Kowal, N. E. (1986) *Health Effects of Land Application of Municipal Sludge*; EPA-600/52-85-142; U.S. Environmental Protection Agency: Washington, D.C.

Metcalf and Eddy, Inc. (2003) *Wastewater Engineering: Treatment and Reuse*, 4th ed.; McGraw-Hill: New York.

Niederinghaus, L. (1986) Biological Hazards at Treatment Plants. *Oper. Forum*, **3** (2), 16.

Ottolenghi, A. C.; Hamparian, V. V. (1982) Multiyear Study of Sludge Application to Farm Land: Prevalence of Bacterial Enteric Pathogens and Antibody Status of Farm Families. *Appl. Environ. Microbiol.*, **53**, 1118.

Tortora, G. J.; Funke, B. R.; Case, C. L. (Eds.) (1982) *Microbiology: An Introduction*; Benjamin/Cummings Publishing: Menlo Park, California.

Water Environment Federation (2001) *Wastewater Biology: The Microlife*, 2nd ed.; Water Environment Federation: Alexandria, Virginia.

8.0   SUGGESTED READINGS

Centers for Disease Control and Prevention Home Page. http://www.cdc.gov/ (accessed Jan 2012).

Hadeed, S. J. (1990) 1989 Safety Survey Injury Rates Drop to 15-Year Low. *Oper. Forum*, **7** (4), 24.

National Institutes of Health Home Page. http://www.nih.gov/ (accessed Jan 2012).

National Institute for Occupational Safety and Health Home Page. http://www.cdc.gov/NIOSH/ (accessed Jan 2012).

Occupational Safety and Health Administration Home Page. http://www.osha.gov/ (accessed Jan 2012).

Pahren, H.; Jakubowski, W. (Eds.) (1980) Wastewater Aerosols and Disease; EPA-600/9–80-028; U.S. Environmental Protection Agency: Cincinnati, Ohio.

Water Environment Federation (2007) *Operation of Municipal Wastewater Treatment Plants;* 6th ed.; Manual of Practice No. 11; McGraw-Hill: New York.

Chapter 9

Hazardous Materials and Waste Management

(continued)

1.0   OVERVIEW

Defining and handling hazardous waste are not easy tasks. Compliance with environmental laws is important and is directly related to how that facility generates, handles, stores, and disposes of chemicals and hazardous materials no longer being used for the purposes in which they were manufactured. Many wastes from treatment facility processes can be identified as hazardous through past knowledge, laboratory testing, or information derived from the U.S. Environmental Protection Agency (U.S. EPA), Title 40, *Code of Federal Regulations* (CFR).

Environmental laws and regulations governing waste management overlap multiple enforcement agencies at the federal, state, and local levels (see Table 9.1). This chapter will discuss proper storage, safe handling practices, and disposal procedures of hazardous wastes. For specific information regarding safe handling practices, the reader is referred to Chapters 4, 5, and 10.

This chapter will also explain how to determine when materials become a waste; characteristics determining a waste as hazardous; basic hazardous waste classification; regulatory agencies enforcing applicable laws and regulations; responsibilities and liabilities related to a generator's "cradle to grave" concept; basic recordkeeping requirements; and where to find information regarding hazardous waste determination.

TABLE 9.1   List of applicable laws.

Federal	State	Local
29 CFR OSHA -Part 1910	Title 27 CUPA -Solid wastes management	Air Rules -Local air district
49 CFR USDOT -§171.3	Title 26 Toxics -Compilation of the toxic regulations	Hazardous Waste -CUPA -Household hazardous waste -POTW environmental control
40 CFR U.S. EPA -RCRA	Title 22 hazardous waste -Hazardous waste law	Hazardous materials -CUPA -Fire department
	Title 8 California/OSHA -Division of Industrial Safety	

2.0   HAZARDOUS MATERIALS

2.1   What are Hazardous Materials?

A *hazardous material* is any item or agent (biological, chemical, or physical) that has the potential to cause harm to humans, animals, or the environment, either by itself or through interaction with other factors (i.e., other materials or processes).

Hazardous materials in the United States are defined and regulated primarily by laws and regulations administered by U.S. EPA, the Occupational Safety and Health Administration (OSHA), the U.S. Department of Transportation (USDOT), and the U.S. Nuclear Regulatory Commission (NRC). Each agency defines a *hazardous material* according to the scope and purpose of the governing law.

The Occupational Safety and Health Administration defines a hazardous material to include any substance or chemical that is a health or physical hazard. These include chemicals that are carcinogens, toxic agents, irritants, corrosives, and sensitizers; chemicals that are combustible, explosive, flammable, oxidizers, pyrophorics (i.e., substances that will ignite spontaneously in air), and unstable-reactive or water-reactive; and chemicals that, during the course of normal handling, use, or storage, may produce or release dusts, gases, fumes, vapors, mists, or smoke. These also include agents that act on the hematopoietic system (i.e., the formation of blood cellular components) and agents that damage the lungs, skin, eyes, or mucous membranes (full definitions can be found in 29 CFR 1910.1200).

The U.S. EPA incorporates OSHA's definition, adding, "any item or chemical which can cause harm to people, plants, or animals when released by spilling, leaking, pumping, pouring, emitting, emptying, discharging, injecting, escaping, leaching, dumping or disposing into the environment" (40 CFR 355 contains a list of over 350 hazardous and extremely hazardous substances [EHSs]).

The U.S. Department of Transportation defines a hazardous material as any item or chemical which, when being transported or moved, is a risk to public safety or the environment. The hazardous material must also be regulated under the following: Hazardous Materials Regulations (49 CFR 100–180); International Maritime Dangerous Goods Code; Dangerous Goods Regulations of the International Air Transport Association; Technical Instructions of the International Civil Aviation Organization; and the U.S. Air Force Joint Manual, *Preparing Hazardous Materials for Military Air Shipments*.

The NRC regulates items or chemicals that are "special nuclear source" or byproduct materials or radioactive substances (see 10 CFR 20).

2.2   Laws and Regulations Preventing Pollution

The Pollution Prevention Act of 1990 established a national policy that pollution should be prevented or reduced at the source. The act further established that pollution that cannot be prevented should be recycled in an environmentally safe manner and, if it cannot be prevented or recycled, should be treated in an environmentally safe manner. Disposal or other release into the environment should only be used as a last resort and should be conducted in an environmentally safe manner. The Clean Air Act (CAA) of 1970 resulted in a significant shift in the federal government's role in air pollution control. This legislation authorized development of comprehensive federal and state regulations that limit emissions from both stationary (industrial) sources and mobile sources. The 1990 CAA Amendment (CAAA) substantially increased the authority and responsibility of the federal government.

National Emission Standards for Hazardous Air Pollutants (NESHAP) was developed from CAA and expanded into CAAA for controlling 187 originally identified toxic air pollutants. Examples of toxic air pollutants include benzene, which is found in gasoline; perchlorethylene, which is emitted from some dry cleaning facilities and can be found in some equipment parts cleaners; and methylene chloride, which is used as a solvent and paint stripper. Examples of other listed air toxics include dioxin; asbestos (found in building materials and thermal system insulations); toluene (found in paints and solvents); and metals such as cadmium, mercury, chromium, and lead compounds.

The Clean Water Act (CWA), enacted in 1948, was initially called the *Federal Water Pollution Control Act*. The act was significantly reorganized and expanded in 1972 and 1977 to establish the basic structure for regulating discharges of pollutants into U.S. waters and regulating quality standards for surface waters. The CWA set water quality standards for all contaminants in surface waters.

Under CWA, U.S. EPA implemented pollution control programs setting wastewater standards for industries. The CWA made it unlawful to discharge any pollutant from a point source into navigable waters, unless a permit was obtained. The U.S. EPA's National Pollutant Discharge Elimination System (NPDES) permit program controls such discharges. Municipalities rely on assistance from other partners (such as industry, developers, and, in some permit applications, homeowners) to ensure that they can meet the requirements contained in their municipal NPDES permits.

The Emergency Planning and Community Right-to-Know Act (EPCRA) was authorized by Title III of the Superfund Amendments and Reauthorization Act (SARA) as national legislation on community safety. The EPCRA was passed in response to concerns regarding environmental and safety hazards posed by the storage and handling of toxic chemicals. These concerns were triggered by the disaster in Bhopal, India, in which more than 2,000 people suffered death or serious injury from the accidental release of methyl isocyanate. To reduce the likelihood of such a disaster in the United States, Congress imposed requirements on both states and regulated facilities.

To implement EPCRA, Congress requires each state to appoint a State Emergency Response Commission (SERC). The SERCs are required to divide their states into emergency planning districts and to name a local emergency planning committee for each district.

Facilities must report the storage, use, and release of certain hazardous chemicals. Facilities with any EHS on-site greater than the threshold planning quantities are subject to EPCRA emergency planning requirements. Table 9.2 is a partial listing of the SARA Title III EHS list.

The Federal Insecticide, Fungicide, and Rodenticide Act (FIFRA) provides for federal regulation of pesticide distribution, sale, and use. All pesticides distributed or sold in the United States must be registered (licensed) by U.S. EPA. Before U.S. EPA may register a pesticide under FIFRA, the applicant must show that using the

TABLE 9.2 Superfund Amendments and Reauthorization Act Title III, Extremely Hazardous Substances.

CAS	EHS NAME	TPQ*	CAS	EHS NAME	TPQ*
7782505	Chlorine	100	143339	Sodium cyanide (Na(CN))	100
7664393	Hydrofluoric acid	100	62748	Sodium fluoroacetate	10/10 000
7647010	Hydrogen chloride (gas only)	500	13410010	Sodium selenate	100/10 000
74908	Hydrogen cyanide	100	10102188	Sodium selenite	100/10 000
7664393	Hydrogen fluoride	100	10102202	Sodium tellurite	500/10 000
7722841	Hydrogen peroxide (Conc.> 52%)	1 000	7446095	Sulfur dioxide	500
7783075	Hydrogen selenide	10	7783600	Sulfur fluoride (SF4), (T-4)-	100
7783064	Hydrogen sulfide	500	7664939	Sulfuric acid	1 000
107302	Methane, chloromethoxy-	100	7783600	Sulfur tetrafluoride	100
624839	Methane, isocyanato-	500	7446119	Sulfur trioxide	100
542881	Methane, oxybis[chloro-	100	78002	Tetraethyl lead	100
594423	Methanesulfenyl chloride, trichloro-	500	6533739	Thallium(I) carbonate	100/10 000
558258	Methanesulfonyl fluoride	1 000	7791120	Thallium chloride TlCl	100/10 000
509148	Methane, tetranitro-	500	7446186	Thallium(I) sulfate	100/10 000
74931	Methanethiol	500	10031591	Thallium sulfate	100/10 000
67663	Methane, trichloro-	10 000	6533739	Thallous carbonate	100/10 000
7697372	Nitric acid	1 000	7791120	Thallous chloride	100/10 000

10102439	Nitric oxide	100	100/10 000
7631892	Sodium arsenate	1 000/10 000	744618€ Thallous sulfate
7784465	Sodium arsenite	500/10 000	2231574 Thiocarbazide 1 000/10 000
			556649 Thiocyanic acid, methyl 10 000
			ester
26628228	Sodium azide (Na(N3))	500	76028 Trichloroacetyl chloride 500
124652	Sodium cacodylate	100/10 000	

*TPQ = Threshold Planning Quantity in pounds. For some solid chemicals, there are two TPQs (e.g., 500/10 000). The lower TPQ applies to solids in powder form, in solution, or in molten form

**Partial Listing Only - Not A Complete Listing

pesticide according to manufacturer's specifications "will not generally cause unreasonable adverse effects on the environment."

The FIFRA defines the term, *unreasonable adverse effects on the environment*, to mean "(1) any unreasonable risk to man or the environment, taking into account the economic, social, and environmental costs and benefits of the use of any pesticide, or (2) a human dietary risk from residues that result from a use of a pesticide in or on any food inconsistent with the standard under section 408 of the Federal Food, Drug, and Cosmetic Act."

The FIFRA may be applicable to water and wastewater facilities applying restricted-use pesticides. In some circumstances, use of a registered pesticide may be restricted to pesticide applicators with special training. A product, or its uses, classified as "restricted use" may only be applied by a certified pesticide applicator or under the direct supervision of a certified applicator. Information on restricted use of a pesticide is found in CFR Part 152.160-175, Chapter 40.

3.0 MANAGING HAZARDOUS MATERIALS

3.1 Emissions from Incineration

Section 129 of CAA specifically addresses emissions from solid waste combustion. Sections 111 and 129 require U.S. EPA to establish new source performance standards (NSPS) for new units, while Sections 111(d) and 129 require the agency to establish emission guidelines for existing units. Both NSPS and the emission guidelines under Section 129 use a maximum achievable control technology-type approach as used under Section 112. The NSPS are direct federal regulations that apply to new sources. Emission guidelines do not directly regulate solid waste combustion units, rather, they establish requirements for state plans that are the vehicle by which states implement the guidelines. Once approved, these state plans become federally enforceable. The U.S. EPA has promulgated NSPS and emission guidelines for large municipal waste combustors (MWCs), small MWCs, and commercial and industrial solid waste incinerators. The agency plans to promulgate NSPS and emission guidelines for "other" solid waste incinerators.

On March 21, 2011, U.S. EPA promulgated "Standards of performance for New Stationary Sources and Emission Guidelines for Existing Sources: Sewage Sludge Incineration Units" for wastewater treatment facilities designed to treat domestic wastewater sludge. The final rule sets limits for 9 pollutants under Section 129 of CAA. These 9 pollutants are cadmium, carbon monoxide, hydrogen chloride, lead, mercury, nitrogen oxides, particulate matter, polychlorinated dibenzo-p-dioxins and polychlorinated dibenzolfurans, and sulfur dioxide. The rule became effective May 20, 2011.

Categories and entities potentially affected by the final action are those that operate wastewater sludge incinerators. Although there is no specific North American Industry Classification System (NAICS) code for wastewater sludge incinerators, these units may be operated by wastewater treatment facilities designed to treat domestic wastewater sludge. Table 9.3 includes examples of NAICS codes that could apply.

Compliance with emission guidelines is required 3 years from the date of the facility's state plan approval or March 21, 2016, under the federal plan if no state or tribal plan has been approved. All wastewater sludge incinerator units are subject to implementing the emission guidelines and obtaining a Title V operating permit. There are requirements for wastewater sludge incinerators constructed after October 14, 2010, or modified after September 21, 2011. For complete rule information, the reader is referred to U.S. EPA's Air Toxics Web site, Sewage Sludge Incinerators at http://www.epa.gov/ttn/atw/129/ssi/ssipg.html#IMP.

3.2 Handling Hazardous Materials

Engineering controls must be used to reduce employee exposures to hazardous materials whenever feasible. The two most common engineering controls are the use of local exhaust and general ventilation. These measures limit an employee's exposure to airborne contaminants. When engineering controls are not available or fail to adequately reduce hazards, other personal protective equipment (PPE) is required. Examples of PPE include safety glasses, hearing protection, gloves, respirators, and so on. Personal protection devices must be provided and worn in accordance with the manufacturer's recommendations indicated on the label or material safety data

TABLE 9.3   Example Naics codes.

Category	NAICS code	Examples of potentially regulated entities
Solid waste combustors and incinerators	562213	Municipalities with wastewater sludge incinerators
Wastewater treatment facilities	221320	

sheet (MSDS) of the product (see Chapter 10, "Personal Protective Equipment," for specific details on chemical PPE).

Shipments of hazardous materials should always be inspected for evidence of leakage prior to accepting the shipment. In the event of damage to the container or packaging and leakage, the shipper should be notified and the materials returned to the supplier for replacement. Most shipping companies will not accept leaking hazardous materials. In this instance, it may be necessary to "overpack" (meaning oversized containers designed for encapsulating hazardous waste and material for disposal) to prevent leaking materials from continuing to contaminate and/or damage the shipping vehicle. If overpacking is unavailable, the leaking container or package should be placed in a larger container for secondary containment until the item can be properly contained in a suitable USDOT shipping device. Regardless, notification to the supplier should include steps that were taken to prevent continued hazardous materials contamination.

Deliveries of bulk chemicals by tanker trucks must follow precautionary measures when dispensing the hazardous materials so that materials are not spilled onto the facility ground. If catch basins or other storm water drainage systems are located nearby to the point of delivery, it is important to verify that the system returns to the treatment plant and does not discharge to surface waters. The delivery driver should be protected and have the necessary PPE for personal safety (see Chapter 10 for specific details on chemical PPE).

The following guidelines are precautions that may be imposed on transportation of hazardous materials to wastewater treatment plants:

- All hazardous materials shall be transported in secondary containment of sufficient size to hold the entire content in the event of a spill or leakage;

- Routes for transport of hazardous materials should be planned to minimize exposure to personnel in the event of a spill. When transporting hazardous materials, areas that are not readily accessible to the public should be used, if possible;

- Spill prevention kits should be placed at strategic locations along the transportation route in the event of a hazardous material spill. These kits might include

  o Neutralizing agents such as sodium carbonate, sodium bicarbonate, or sodium bisulfite;

- o Absorbents such as vermiculite, "super sorb," or absorbant pillows or dikes (paper towels, rags, and sponges may be used, but caution should be exercised because some chemicals may ignite upon contact with them); and

- o Plastic scoops and shovels, disposable mops, disposable protective clothing, and containers to receive the spilled material and all items used in the cleanup;

- Only personnel trained in spill response should be allowed to clean up small chemical spills. Larger chemical spills (greater than the capacity of the spill kits or beyond treatment plant personnel training) should be contracted with emergency response companies who specialize in hazardous material cleanup; and

- Hazardous materials shall not be transported by treatment plant personnel.

3.3 Storage of Hazardous Materials

All hazardous materials must be properly labeled with their exact contents, hazardous properties, date of receipt, and, if appropriate, date of expiration. Hazardous substances should be stored in the original containers in which they were packaged at the manufacturing plant. If this is not practical, these products should be transferred into containers that are constructed to withstand the effects of the product over the maximum storage time according to manufacturers' recommendations.

Hazardous materials must be stored based on their compatibility, not by their alphabetical order. Hazardous substances should be stored in an orderly manner, with older products most accessible and the newer products least accessible. Good housekeeping must be practiced in areas where hazardous products are stored.

Incompatible materials must not be stored such that they may come in contact with each other. Combining incompatible materials in the same storage location may result in the following:

- Heat or pressure;

- Fire or explosion;

- Violent reaction;

- Toxic dusts, mists, vapors, or gases; and

- Flammable vapors or gases.

Flammable materials in containers larger than 3.8 L (1 gal) should be stored in a ventilated National Fire Protection Association-approved flammable storage cabinet. To ensure integrity and electrical bonding, the cabinet should be installed per the manufacturer's instructions.

Because of their corrosive nature, acids and bases should not be stored in flammable storage cabinets or other areas that are next to combustible, flammable, or other hazardous materials that could violently react with acid or base. In addition, acids and bases must be segregated from each other.

It is important to carefully read the label of a hazardous chemical before it is stored. The chemical's MSDS will provide any special storage information and incompatibilities, which must be followed by the user. Information regarding incompatible materials is summarized in U.S. EPA's Chemical Compatibility Chart, which is available at http://www.uos.harvard.edu/ehs/environmental/ EPAChemicalCompatibilityChart.pdf.

3.4 Hazardous Materials and Employee Health and Safety

Federal OSHA defines *hazardous and toxic substances* as those chemicals present in the workplace that are capable of causing harm. In OSHA's definition, the term, *chemicals,* includes dusts, mixtures, and common materials such as paints, fuels, and solvents. The Occupational Safety and Health Administration currently regulates exposure to approximately 400 substances. Twenty-five states, Puerto Rico, and the Virgin Islands have OSHA-approved state plans and have adopted their own standards and enforcement policies. Most states adopt standards that are identical to federal OSHA; however, some states have adopted different standards applicable to this topic or may have different enforcement policies.

Many workers are unaware of chemicals that create potential hazards in their work environment, making them more vulnerable to exposure and injury. Training employees about hazards in the workplace is critical to establishing comprehension and safe work practices. Table 9.4 provides recommended minimum training for workers handling hazardous materials and hazardous wastes.

3.5 First Aid Procedures

Chemicals splashed into the eye can lead to injuries that cause loss of vision. Therefore, it is imperative that chemicals are immediately flushed from the eye. To do so, tilt the head down toward the affected eye and apply a gentle stream of water to the bridge of the nose. The runoff water will then cross the eye and flush out the

TABLE 9.4   Recommended training for personnel handling hazardous materials.

Hazard communication

- Acetylene fuel and gas safety

- Emergency action plan

- Fire extinguisher and fire fighting equipment

- Fire prevention plan

- Flammable liquids/gasses/vapors

- Pesticide safety

- Process safety management

Asbestos/asbestos awareness (to include nonasbestos building materials)

- Actinolite (Nonasbestos)

- Anthophyllite (Nonasbestos)

- Tremolite (Nonasbestos)

First aid and CPR

Hazardous waste operations and emergency response

Personal protective equipment

Respiratory protection

Welding and cutting safety—hot work

chemical. The affected eye should be kept lower than the unaffected eye to avoid flushing the chemical into the unaffected eye. The eye should be flushed with copious amounts of water for at least 20 minutes, keeping the eye open as widely as possible. If contact lenses are worn by the affected person, they should be removed. It is important to ensure that runoff water does not come into contact with other rescuers, but goes directly down a drain or is contained.

If ingestion occurs, management should consult a MSDS or chemical first aid manual or call the Poison Control Information Center at 1-800-282-3171. It is important to follow directions and to seek medical attention immediately. In the event of minor skin contact, the affected area should be promptly flushed with water and any contaminated clothing should be removed. If symptoms persist after washing, medical attention should be sought.

Inhalation hazards include pesticides, fumigants, chemical fumes, vapors, and gases. Signs and symptoms vary with each type of exposure. Some cause eye irritation while others cause irritation of the respiratory tract. Additional symptoms may include pale or bluish skin color, chest pain or tightness, dizziness, headache, confusion, irritability, nausea, or vomiting. It is important to get the victim into fresh air right away. If the victim is breathing without difficulty, call the Poison Control Center. If the victim is having trouble breathing or has other signs or symptoms of poisoning, medical attention should be sought immediately.

Chemical burns require large amounts of water to flush the chemicals from the skin. Powered chemicals should be brushed from the skin, followed by flushing for 20 minutes. Do not use bare hands to brush off the chemicals. Ensure run-off water does not flow over unaffected skin or onto the rescuer. Follow the first aid directions on the label of the chemical container; locate the MSDS, contact the Poison Control Center, and obtain medical care as quickly as possible.

For some chemicals, such as hydrofluoric acid, effects resulting from exposure may not become apparent until hours or days later. The MSDS should be consulted for any chemical to which someone has been exposed, even if no immediate injury is apparent.

If clothing is on fire, the flames should be extinguished ("stop, drop, and roll"). The victim should be removed from the environment, if possible. If a drenching shower is immediately available, cool water will help stop the spread of the burn. If the victim begins to shiver, discontinue the cooling process. Hypothermia may occur because extensive burns reduce the body's ability to retain heat. Further heat loss can be prevented by covering the victim with a clean white sheet, blanket, or other clean large cover. Any clothing or jewelry that does not stick to the burned skin should be removed. It is important to call for medical assistance as quickly as possible. It is also important to not use butter, oil, salve, or petroleum-based creams for the initial treatment of burns because these retain heat and allow the burning process to continue. Fire blankets are primarily used as a first aid measure for prevention of shock rather than against smoldering or burning clothing because a fire blanket may direct flames toward the face.

4.0   DEFINING HAZARDOUS WASTE

Daily operation of a wastewater treatment facility generates a wide variety of wastes each month. Chemicals used in the processes and maintenance work (such as parts cleaners) and spent oils, paints, and solvents are a few of the more common wastes. Some wastes generated will be classified as nonhazardous, while others are hazardous, and a small portion may fit into extremely hazardous waste.

Correctly determining whether a waste meets the Resource Conservation Recovery Act (RCRA) definition of hazardous waste is essential to determining how to manage the waste. Responsibility for proper identification rests with the generator of the waste. Hazardous waste is waste that is dangerous or potentially harmful to human health or the environment. The Federal Hazardous Substance Act defines hazardous substance as

- Any substance or mixture of substances that (1) is toxic, (2) is corrosive, (3) is an irritant, (4) is a strong sensitizer, (5) is flammable or combustible, or (5) generates pressure through decomposition, heat, or other means if such substance or mixture of substances may cause substantial personal injury or substantial illness during or as a proximate result of any customary or reasonably foreseeable handling or use, including reasonably foreseeable ingestion by children;

- Any radioactive substance that has been determined to be sufficiently hazardous to require labeling in accordance with this act to protect the public health.

Hazardous substances (materials) that meet the aforementioned definition would inherently generate a waste that is classified as a hazardous waste.

5.0 GENERATOR INFORMATION

5.1 Large Quantity Generator

In a given single month, large quantity generators (LQGs) generate

- One thousand kilograms (2200 lb or 1.1 tons) or more of hazardous waste or

- One kilogram (2.2 lb) or more of acutely hazardous waste (i.e., waste codes denoted with the hazard code "H" and all P-listed wastes; see Section 5.1).

A generator will also fit the definition of a LQG if more than 100 kg (220 lb) of waste materials were generated during a spill cleanup when contaminated with RCRA acutely hazardous waste.

5.2 Small Quantity Generator

This category most likely describes wastewater treatment facilities. Small quantity generators (SQGs) produce between 100 and 1000 kg of hazardous waste within a single month and are subject to modified regulations found in 40 CFR Part 262. Generally, SQGs must comply with some but not all of the regulations that apply to LQGs.

5.3 Conditionally Exempt Small Quantity Generator

Conditionally exempt small quantity generators (CESQGs) produce 100 kg or less of hazardous waste within a single month. As mentioned in Section 5.2, generators who produce 1 kg or less of acutely hazardous waste, or 100 kg or less of contaminated soil, waste, or debris resulting from the cleanup of an acute hazardous waste spill are CESQGs. Conditionally exempt small quantity generators are exempt from 40 CFR Parts 262 through 270 if they comply with the requirements in 40 CFR Part 261.5.

5.4 Episodic Generators

In any single month, generators may exceed or fall below their normal generation limits. If the amount of waste generated in a single month places the generator in a different category, the generator is responsible for complying with all applicable requirements of that category for all waste generated during that calendar month. For instance, if a generator produces 300 kg (660 lb) of hazardous waste in March, that waste must be managed in accordance with SQG regulations. If the same generator produces 1500 kg (3300 lb) of hazardous waste in April, that waste must be managed in accordance with LQG regulations.

6.0 RESOURCE CONSERVATION AND RECOVERY ACT

The generator must determine how the waste is defined under RCRA before the hazardous waste can be classified. The waste can be liquid, solid, gas, or sludge; discarded commercial products (e.g., pesticides, aerosol cans, and cleaning fluids) or byproducts of processes. A helpful interactive tool is available on U.S. EPA's *Definition of Solid Waste Decision Tool v2* Web site (http://www.epa.gov/osw/hazard/dsw/too.htm). The tool is designed to simplify the waste classification process and enable the user to conclude whether the waste is considered hazardous. Figure 9.1 is a replication of the flow chart used in the interactive process. Specific types of waste are detailed in the following sections.

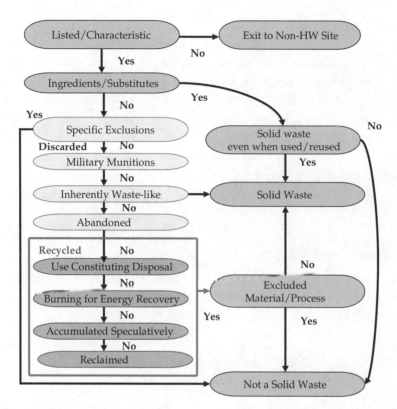

Figure 9.1   Definition of solid waste process flow chart (courtesy of U.S. EPA).

6.1 Listed Wastes

The U.S. EPA has established lists of wastes, which are organized into the following three categories:

- The F-list (nonspecific source wastes)—this category identifies wastes generated from common processes (manufacturing and industrial) that have been used in cleaning and/or degreasing operations. The subcategory, *nonspecific source wastes*, indicates that the processes producing these wastes can occur in different sectors of industry.

- The K-list (source-specific wastes)—this category includes certain wastes from specific industries, petroleum refining or pesticide manufacturing, and certain sludges and wastewaters from treatment and production processes.

- The P-list and the U-list (discarded commercial chemical products)—these two lists are similar in that both list certain commercial chemical products as hazardous when the materials are discarded or intended to be discarded (the reader should note that the California Health and Safety Code, Chapter 6.5, states, "A discarded material is one that is relinquished, reclaimed, or recycled"). The listing consists of commercial chemical products having the generic names listed, off-specification species, container residues, and spill residues. The difference between the two lists is that chemicals on the P-list are identified as acutely hazardous wastes and those listed on the U-list are identified as toxic wastes. Wastes included in all categories can be found in 40 CFR §261.31.

6.2 Characteristic Wastes

This type of waste is not listed on any other waste list and demonstrates the characteristics defined as a hazardous waste, namely, ignitability, corrosivity, radioactivity, or toxicity. Characteristic wastes are as follows:

- Ignitable wastes—these create fires under certain conditions, are spontaneously combustible, or have a flash point less than 60 °C (140 °F). Examples include waste oils and used solvents.

- Corrosive wastes—are acids or bases (pH less than or equal to 2 or greater than or equal to 12.5) that are capable of corroding metal containers, such as storage tanks, drums, and barrels. Battery acid is an example of this type of corrosive waste.

- Reactive wastes—are unstable under normal or ambient conditions. They can cause explosions and generate toxic fumes, gases, or vapors when heated or compressed or mixed with water. Examples include lithium-sulfur batteries and explosives (ordinates).

- Toxic wastes—are harmful or fatal when ingested or absorbed (e.g., mercury or lead). These constituents are likely to affect discharges to waterways and or wastes that are placed into landfills for disposal. Toxicity is defined through a laboratory procedure called the toxicity characteristic leaching procedure (TCLP) (Method 1311). The TCLP helps identify wastes likely to leach concentrations of contaminants that may be harmful to human health or the environment (for more details, the reader is referred to 40 CFR §261.24).

6.3 Universal Wastes

The U.S. EPA's universal waste regulations streamline hazardous waste management standards for federally designated "universal wastes." The universal waste regulations were developed to govern proper collection and management of these ubiquitously generated wastes. The intent of the law is to facilitate environmentally sound collection, proper recycling, or treatment. In addition, the regulations also ensure that these wastes will go to appropriate treatment or recycling facilities. These wastes are identified as

- Batteries,
- Pesticides,
- Mercury-containing equipment (e.g., thermostats), and
- Bulbs (fluorescent lamps).

Federal universal waste regulations are set forth in 40 CFR Part 273; however, some individual state regulations can modify the universal waste rule or add additional universal waste(s). Therefore, it is important to check with a particular state for applicable regulations.

6.4 Used Oil Waste

EPA's regulatory definition of used oil is as follows: used oil is any oil that has been refined from crude oil or any synthetic oil that has been used and, as a result of such use, is contaminated by physical or chemical impurities. Characteristics of used motor oil are that it is insoluble and environmentally persistent and that it can contain toxic chemicals and heavy metals.

7.0 NON-RESOURCE CONSERVATION RECOVERY ACT OR CALIFORNIA-ONLY WASTE

In California, hazardous wastes are classified as either RCRA or non-RCRA. This is important because the appropriate waste code numbers must be used for various legal purposes such as filling out transportation papers (manifest), disposal fees, and treatment determinations. California has determined that some wastes, although not classified as hazardous at the federal level, are classified hazardous at the state level. California is authorized by U.S. EPA to oversee the RCRA program to ensure that generators of hazardous waste are managing the waste lawfully.

7.1 Treated Wood Waste

Wood treated with preserving chemicals that protect it from insect attack and fungal decay during use (e.g., fence posts, landscape timbers, or railroad ties) is classified as treated wood waste in California. The treated wood waste (it is important to remember that product becomes a waste when it is no longer used for the purpose in which it was designed) is subject to California's hazardous waste control law because chemical treatment of the wood contains hazardous chemicals posing a risk to human health and the environment.

7.2 Universal and Electronic Wastes

Universal wastes may not be discarded in solid waste landfills and are classified as a hazardous waste. These include batteries, fluorescent tubes, and some electronic devices. California Universal Waste Rule regulations (Chapter 23 of Title 22) define an *electronic device* as "any electronic device that is identified as hazardous waste." An electronic device that meets this definition can be managed under simple requirements as a universal waste. The following are examples of some common electronic devices:

- Cardiac resynchronization therapy (CRT) devices, including older televisions and computer monitors;
- Liquid crystal display (LCD) desktop computer monitors and laptop computers;
- Liquid crystal display televisions;
- Plasma televisions;
- Portable digital video disc (DVD) players with LCD screens;
- Cash registers and oscilloscopes containing CRTs;
- Computers;
- Computer keyboards and other peripherals;
- Telephones, cell phones, and answering machines;
- Stereo equipment, radios, tape, compact disc players/recorders, and phonographs;
- Video cassette recorders and calculators; and
- Microwaves.

7.3 Mercury Wastes

The unique properties of mercury inspired manufacturers to use this liquid metal in many common consumer products. Once these products are no longer used and become waste, many of the items are managed under the California Universal Waste Rule (California Code of Regulations 22, Chapter 23). The following are common sources of mercury at wastewater treatment facilities:

- Thermometers,
- Thermostats,
- Manometers,
- Barometers,
- Fluorescent light bulbs and ballasts,
- Batteries,
- Switches,
- Dental amalgam (discharges from dental sources to publicly owned treatment works [POTWs]),
- Pesticides, and
- Fungicides in some paints (mold suppression).

7.4 Used Oil Waste

Section 25250.1 of the California Health and Safety Code defines used oil as "any oil that has been refined from crude oil, or any synthetic oil, that has been used." Wastewater treatment facilities generate used oil via maintenance (draining oil from pumps) and through the use of synthetic oils for equipment lubrication. The California definition continues to describe the use "as a consequence of extended storage, or spillage, [that] has been contaminated with physical or chemical impurities." Essentially, any time the oil product is no longer used in the manner in which it was intended or designed, the material becomes a waste. Table 9.5 lists spent oils that California classifies as hazardous waste. Used oil does not include

- Antifreeze,
- Brake fluid,

- Other automotive wastes,

- Fuels, and

- Solvents.

TABLE 9.5   Used oils by definition, health and safety code §26250.1 (California Department of Toxic Substances Control, Endnote ii).

Used Motor Oils	Used Industrial Oils	Other Used Oils
Vehicle crankcase oils	Hydraulic oils	Transformer oils
Engine lubricating oils	Compressor oils	Refrigeration oils
Transmission fluids	Turbine oils	Metal working oils
Gearbox and differential oils	Bearing oils	Railroad oils
Gear oils	Vegetable oils used for lubrication	

Waste Synthetic Oils (May be Managed as Used Oil)

Oil derived from coal, oil shale, or polymers

Water-soluble petroleum-based oils

Vegetable or animal oil used as a lubricant

Hydraulic fluid

Heat transfer fluid

Substances Not Regulated As Used Oils

Oils with a flashpoint below 100 °F

Oils mixed with hazardous waste

Wastewater containing small amounts of used oil

Oily wastes are not used oil

Oily wastewaters that are not used oil

Tank bottoms

Used oil processing bottoms

Used oil re-refining distillation bottoms

Cooking oils (edible)

Grease

Oils containing 5 ppm polychlorinate

7.5   Agencies That Enforce the Law

A certified unified program agency (CUPA) is an agency certified to implement the unified program within a jurisdiction. This is the lead agency that will oversee that hazardous waste management is properly accomplished at the generator level. The CUPA also has legal authority to enforce regulations through written citations and violations. The CUPA can collect state and local fees, minimizing the payment of fees via multiple statements.

A participating agency is a state or local agency that has a written agreement with a CUPA pursuant to the California Health and Safety Code to implement or enforce one or more of the following unified program elements:

- Hazardous Materials Business Plan Program,
- Hazardous Waste Generator Program,
- California Accidental Release Prevention Program,
- Underground Storage Tank Program, and
- Aboveground Petroleum Storage Act Program.

In some CUPA jurisdictions, the participating agency may be more than one agency equipped to inspect and enforce the law (e.g., fire departments).

8.0   HAZARDOUS WASTE MANAGEMENT

8.1   U.S. Environmental Protection Agency Identification Numbers

A U.S. EPA identification number is used to track hazardous wastes from the point of generation to the final disposal site; this process is also known as the *cradle-to-grave cycle*. The Resource Conservation and Recovery Act requires the hazardous waste handler generating or transporting hazardous waste or operating a facility for recycling, treating, storing, or disposing of hazardous waste to notify U.S. EPA or their authorized state waste management authority and obtain a U.S. EPA identification number (also known as a RCRA identification number). Generators of certain universal waste, used oil, and boilers or industrial furnaces may require a U.S. EPA identification number. Failure to comply with RCRA notification requirements may result in civil and criminal penalties.

The Notification of Regulated Waste Activity (U.S. EPA Form 8700-12) is used to determine if one is subject to requirements under RCRA for notifying U.S. EPA or an authorized state of the regulated waste activities.

A U.S. EPA identification number is site-specific, except when issued to a transporter. The identification number is used to track waste through its route of transport and is assigned specifically to a physical location; the identification belongs to any owners or operators at that location. The U.S. EPA issues federal (RCRA) identification numbers. However, certain states, such as Arizona and Nevada, are authorized to issue federal RCRA identification numbers.

The California Department of Toxic Substances Control issues California identification numbers for generators and transporters and treatment, storage, and disposal facilities that handle hazardous wastes not regulated under federal RCRA. As stated previously, this depends on the type of waste and rate of monthly accumulation that is generated.

8.2   Uniform Hazardous Waste Manifest

A significant component of the Uniform Hazardous Waste Manifest is identification of the generator of the waste and the transporter picking up the hazardous waste and taking it off-site for treatment, recycling, storage, or disposal. The manifest identifies the specific waste codes regarding the type and quantity of the waste being transported, instructions for waste handling, and signatures for all the parties involved in the disposal process.

Responsible safe and legal handling of all hazardous wastes from generation through accumulation, recycling, transportation, storage, treatment, and disposal is dependent on compliance with all applicable regulations. Table 9.6 includes the basic generator requirements explained in this chapter.

The Hazardous Waste Manifest is used to track hazardous waste from a waste generator's site to the site of its disposal. It is required by USDOT and U.S. EPA and the manifest allows the waste generator to verify delivery of the waste, ensuring no waste has been lost or unaccounted for during the process (hence the preceding cradle-to-grave reference). Information documented on the manifest form regarding the generation, management, and final disposition of hazardous wastes is reported biennially by U.S. EPA in partnership with participating states. The 2009 National Hazardous Waste Biennial Report (U.S. EPA, 2009) consists of the following three volumes of data: *The National Analysis*, the *State Detail Analysis*, and the *List of Reported RCRA Sites*.

As of January 2010, certain states have additional requirements pertaining to the use of the new Uniform Hazardous Waste Manifest. Handlers of waste (i.e., generators or treatment, storage, or disposal facilities) must obtain the new forms from any

TABLE 9.6 Generator quantities and applicable regulations.

	CESQGs	SQGs	LQGs
Quantity limits	≤100 kg/month	Between 100–1000 kg/month	≥1000 kg/month
	≤1 kg/month of acute hazardous waste	§262.34(d)	>1 kg/month of acute hazardous waste
	≤100 kg/month of acute spill residue or soil		>100 kg/month of acute spill residue or soil
	§§261.5(a) and (e)		Part 262 and §261.5(e)
U.S. EPA identification number	Not required	Required	Required
	§261.5	§262.12	§262.12
On-site accumulation quantity	≤1000 kg	≤6000 kg	No limit
	≤1 kg acute	§262.34(d)(1)	
	≤100 kg of acute spill residue or soil		
	§§261.5(f)(2) and (g)(2)		
Accumulation time limits	None	≤180 days or	≤90 days
	§261.5	≤270 days (if greater than 200 miles)	§262.34(a)
		§§262.34(d)(2) and (3)	
Storage requirements	None	Basic requirements with technical standards for tanks or containers	Full compliance for management of tanks, containers, drip pads, or containment buildings
	§261.5	§§262.34(d)(2) and (3)	§262.34(a)

(*continued*)

TABLE 9.6   Continued

	Generator quantities and applicable regulations		
	CESQGs	SQGs	LQGs
Sent to:	State approved or RCRA permitted/ interim status facility	RCRA permitted/ interim status facility	RCRA permitted/ interim status facility
	§§261.5(f)(3) and (g)(3)	§262.20(b)	§262.20(b)
Manifest	Not required	Required	Required
	§261.5	§262.20	§262.20
Biennial report	Not required	Not required	Required
	§261.5	§262.44	§262.41
Personnel training	Not required	Basic training required	Required
	§261.5	§262.34(d)(5)(iii)	§262.34(a)(4)
Contingency plan	Not required	Basic plan	Full plan required
	§261.5	§262.34(d)(5)(i)	§262.34(a)(4)
Emergency procedures	Not required	Required	Full plan required
	§261.5	§262.34(d)(5)(iv)	§262.34(a)(4)
USDOT transport requirements	Yes (if required by USDOT)	Yes §§262.30–262.33	Yes §§262.30–262.33

source that has been approved by the U.S. EPA Manifest Registry to print and distribute the form. Specific requirements for each state can be found at http://www.epa.gov/osw/hazard/transportation/states.htm.

A training video for the new manifest form is available at http://www.pneac.org/hazwastemanifest. The training video provides instruction to generators, transporters, and treatment/storage/disposal facilities for completing the new manifest.

8.3   Container Management

8.3.1   Labeling and Marking

A compliant program monitors the waste accumulation time, condition of the storage containers and their location, above and below ground tanks and their secondary

TABLE 9.7   Generator requirements checklist.

To do list	Regulation reference
Determine whether any generated waste is a hazardous waste.	22 CFR, Ch. 12 §66264.11
Obtain a U.S. EPA identification number from the California Department of Toxic Substances Control.	22 CFR, Ch. 12, 66262.12
Keep accurate and appropriate records of hazardous waste management and maintain records for at least 3 years.	22 CFR, Ch. 12, Article 4, §66262.40
Provide appropriate emergency and decontamination training to employees.	29 CFR 40 CFR, §262.34(d)
Label and handle all hazardous waste as specified in the regulations, including not exceeding accumulation times.	Title 22, Ch. 12, §66262.34
Inspect all containers weekly and tanks daily	22 CCR §66265.174 & §66262.195
Arrange transportation of all wastes in compliance with USDOT standards and use the manifest for cradle-to-grave tracking.	22 CCR, Article 2, §66262.23 (a-e)
Use only qualified transporters who have in their possession a registration and inspection report.	49 CFR, Part 396
Submit fees as required.	22 CCR, §25205
Complete and submit all required reports, including biennial reports, in a timely manner.	22 CCR, Article 4, §66262.40-47
Send hazardous waste to permitted treatment storage and disposal facility or obtain proper permits to treat the waste onsite.	22 CCR §25201 (a)

containment, and labeling of all containers; the program also performs regular inspections and maintains records of the inspections.

Container labels must have the waste's accumulation start date (e.g., the date the waste was first introduced into the container), a label or stenciled lettering with the words "hazardous waste"; the physical state of the waste and its content and composition (e.g., solid, liquid, or sludge); hazardous properties of the waste's characteristics (e.g., ignitable or corrosive); and name and address of the generator. Table 9.7 presents a suggested checklist to assist generators in their hazardous waste inspections.

8.3.2   Verification Questionnaire and Manifest Fees Assessment

Annually, the California Department of Toxic Substances Control sends generators holding an active U.S. EPA identification number a verification questionnaire and fees assessment form for the previous fiscal year (July 1 through June 30). The generator's U.S. EPA identification number is tracked via the Uniform Hazardous Waste Manifest; completion of the verification questionnaire and fee assessment forms are required by California law.

9.0   REFERENCES

California Health and Safety Code, Chapter 6.5, Division 20, Article 13 (commencing with section 25250), and *California Code of Regulations Title 22*, Division 4.5 (Cal. Code Regs.), including Chapter 29 ("Used Oil") (commencing with section 66279.1).

California Code, *California Health and Safety Code*, Chapter 6.11, *Unified Hazardous Waste and Hazardous Materials Management Regulatory Program*, Section 25404.3, Subdivision(d).

U.S. Environmental Protection Agency (2007) *Hazardous Waste Generator Regulations: A User-Friendly Reference Document*.

U.S. Environmental Protection Agency, *Title 40, Code of Federal Regulations (CFR), Protection of Environment*, Chapter 1, Subchapter Solid Wastes, Part 261, §261.1–261.151.

U.S. Environmental Protection Agency, Title 40 CFR Part 273.

U.S. Environmental Protection Agency, Title 40 CFR Part 279.

U.S. Environmental Protection Agency Home Page, *Definition of Solid Waste Decision Tool v2*. http://www.epa.gov/osw/hazard/dsw/too.htm (accessed March 2011).

U.S. Environmental Protection Agency, *The Notification of Regulated Waste Activity*; U.S. EPA Form 8700–12.

U.S. Environmental Protection Agency Technology Transfer Network Air Toxics Web Site. http://www.epa.gov/ttn/atw/129/ssi/ssipg.html#IMP (accessed July 2011).

10.0 SUGGESTED READINGS

California Department of Toxic Substances Control (1997) *California Compliance School Student Workbook.*

California Department of Toxic Substances Control (2008) *Fact Sheet: Requirements for Generators of Treated Wood Waste (TWW).*

California Department of Toxic Substances Control (2008) *Regulatory Assistance Guidance Document: Used Oil Generator Requirements.*

California Department of Toxic Substances Control (2010) *Fact Sheet: Senate Bill 546 (Stats: 2009): An Overview.*

California Department of Toxic Substances Control (2010) *Fact Sheet: Universal Waste Fact Sheet.*

Florida State University, Environmental Health and Safety, Hazardous Materials Handling and Storage Home Page. http://www.safety.fsu.edu/hazmatmanual (accessed Aug 2011).

Institute of Hazardous Materials Management Home Page. http://www.ihmm.org (accessed July 2011).

Printers' National Environmental Assistance Center Home Page. *Hazardous Waste Manifest Training Video.* http://www.pneac.org/hazwastemanifest (accessed March 2011).

United States Code (1960) Title 15, Sections 1261–1278, *Federal Hazardous Substances Act*, July 12, 1960.

U.S. Environmental Protection Agency (2009) *National Hazardous Waste Biennial Report.* http://www.epa.gov/epawaste/inforesources/data/br09/index.htm (accessed June 2012).

U.S. Environmental Protection Agency, Hazardous Waste Home Page. http://www.epa.gov/osw/hazard (accessed July 2011).

U.S. Environmental Protection Agency, Hazardous Waste Transporters Home Page. http://www.epa.gov/epawaste/hazard/transporttion/manifest (accessed July 2011).

U. S. Environmental Protection Agency Pollution Prevention Home Page. http://www.epa.gov/p2/pubs/p2policy/act1990 (accessed July 2011).

Wikipedia, Haematoppoiesis Web Site. http://en.wikipedia.org/wiki/Haematopoiesis (accessed July 2011).

Chapter 10

Personal Protective Equipment

(continued)

1.0   INTRODUCTION

In Chapter 3, there were many references covering identifying and predicting hazards. Most of the time, it is simply too difficult to remove all hazardous conditions. Additionally, following the hierarchy of controls might introduce the use of procedures and potentially a job hazard analysis (JHA). Within most JHAs, personal protective equipment (PPE) is likely to be recommended. The last line of defense is PPE. It is important to consider PPE the only barrier between an employee and the many hazards they face in a workday.

While it is important to recognize the importance of PPE, it is also important to recognize that the use of PPE is in the hands of the employee. This chapter will outline the many common practices and standards that are followed to ensure a successful PPE program. Personal protective equipment should not be considered the only practice an employer implements. The hierarchy of controls, as introduced in Chapter 3, should be the first stage in any PPE program development. Material safety data sheets (MSDSs) can be integral in deciding which level of PPE might be appropriate for specific hazards. Eliminating the hazard during the construction phase, engineering controls, and administrative work practices are always the first steps before deciding to use PPE.

2.0   HEAD PROTECTION

2.1   American National Standards Institute Standard

The Occupational Safety and Health Administration (OSHA) and the American National Standards Institute (ANSI) have established standards and guidelines for employers to follow. For the most part, employers are required to follow OSHA regulations and OSHA will recommend following ANSI standards to meet compliance requirements within the regulations. The ANSI standard for head protection (ANSI Z89.1-2003) is a guideline and a consensus standard. It can be downloaded for a nominal fee at the ANSI Web site (http://www.ansi.org/). The makeup of the ANSI standard is set up into classes and types of hard hats and head protection. The classes will be identified in Section 2.2 of this chapter.

Hard hats must contain user information under the older ANSI 1997 standard. In addition to the manufacturer's name, ANSI legend, and class designation, Z89.1-1997-compliant helmets must be marked with the date of manufacture. Instructions pertaining to sizing, care, and service life guidelines must also accompany the hard hat.

Helmets marked with a "reverse donning arrow" ⟳ can be worn frontward or backward in accordance with the manufacturer's wearing instructions. They pass all testing requirements, whether worn frontward or backward.

Helmets marked with "LT" for "lower temperature" indicate that the hard hat meets all testing requirements of the standard when preconditioned at a temperature of -30 °C (-22 °F).

Helmets marked with an "HV" for "high visibility" indicate that the hard hat meets all testing requirements of the standard for high visibility colors. This includes tests for chromaticity and luminescence.

One common misconception is that hard hats have a predetermined service life; however, this is not the case. Both the 1986 and 1997 ANSI standards address service life under maintenance and care of the hard hat. The standards state that all hard hat components should be inspected daily for signs of dents, cracks, penetration, and any damage caused by impact, rough treatment, or wear. Although it is not considered a "shelf life," Mine Safety Appliances-brand hard hats do have useful service life guidelines. These guidelines suggest replacing the suspension every 12 months and the hard hat after 5 years of use. Any hard hat that fails visual inspection should be removed from service until the problem is corrected.

In addition to everyday wear and tear, UV radiation can pose a problem for hats constructed of plastic materials. Damage caused by UV radiation is easy to spot: the hat will lose its glossy finish and eventually take on a chalky appearance. Further degradation could cause the shell to actually start flaking away. Once the effects of UV radiation are detected, the hard hat shell should be replaced immediately.

2.2 Occupational Safety and Health Administration Requirements

Occupational Safety and Health Administration 29 CFR 1910.135(a)(1) states, "Each affected employee shall wear protective helmets when working in areas where there is a potential for injury to the head from falling objects." The standard also covers conditions where electrical hazards are present. Occupational Safety and Health Administration 1910.135(a)(2) states, "Protective helmets designed to reduce electrical shock hazard shall be worn by each such affected employee when near exposed electrical conductors which could contact the head."

Although the OSHA standards themselves do not identify specific occupations or applications where head protection is required, Appendix B to Subpart I Part 9 lists some examples. It states, "Some examples of occupations for which head protection should be routinely considered are carpenters, electricians, linemen, mechanics and repairers, plumbers and pipe fitters, assemblers, packers, wrappers, sawyers, welders, laborers, freight handlers, timber cutting and logging, stock handlers, and warehouse laborers." The appendix also provides examples of general applications where head protection should be worn. In the wastewater industry, collections, maintenance, construction activities, and many others would fall into this category.

In terms of what constitutes a "protective helmet," 29 CFR 1910.135 makes a distinction between hard hats purchased prior to July 5, 1994, and hats purchased after that date. Helmets purchased after July 5, 2003, must comply with the performance guidelines in ANSI Z89.1-2003, *American National Standard for Personal Protection—Protective Headwear for Industrial Workers Requirements*. Hats obtained before that date must comply with the 1997 version of the ANSI standard (ANSI Z89.1-1997).

The older ANSI Z89.1-1986 separates protective helmets into different types and classes. The standard identifies Type 1 and Type 2 helmets. Type 1 helmets incorporate a full brim (the brim fully encircles the dome of the hat); Type 2 helmets have no encircling brim, but may include a short bill on the front (similar to a baseball cap).

In terms of electrical performance, ANSI Z89.1-1986 recognizes the following three classes:

- Class A helmets—intended to reduce the force of impact of falling objects and to reduce the danger of contact with exposed low-voltage electrical conductors. For certification, sample shells are proof-tested at 2200 V of electrical charge;

- Class B helmets—intended to reduce the force of impact of falling objects and to reduce the danger of contact with exposed high-voltage electrical conductors. Sample shells are proof-tested at 20 000 V; and

- Class C helmets—intended to reduce the force of impact of falling objects, but offer no electrical protection.

It is important to note that the voltages stated in Classes A and B are not intended to be an indication of the voltage at which the headgear protects the wearer.

In 1997 ANSI published a revision to its Z89.1 head protection standard. ANSI Z89.1 contains some notable changes. The revision eliminated the old Type 1 and Type 2 design designations. In the revised standard, the term, *type,* is used to designate whether a helmet provides protection strictly from blows to the top of the head (Type I) or protection from blows to both the top and sides of the head

(Type II). Additionally, Z89.1-1997 also changed the alpha designations for the classes of electrical performance. Under Z89.1-1997, the following three classes are recognized:

- Class G (general) helmets—this is equivalent to the old Class A. Class G helmets are proof tested at 2200 V;

- Class E (electrical) helmets—this is equivalent to the old Class B. Class E helmets are proof tested at 20 000 V; and

- Class C (conductive) helmets—this class provides no electrical insulation; the alpha designation did not change from the old standard.

Hard hats must also contain user information under the 1997 standard. In addition to the manufacturer's name, ANSI legend, and class designation, Z89.1-1997-compliant helmets must be marked with the date of manufacture. Instructions pertaining to sizing, care, and service life guidelines must also accompany the hard hat (see Table 10.1 for a description of hard hat options under the ANSI Z89.1-1997 class designations.

TABLE 10.1 Hard hat selection chart (ANSI Z89.1-1997).

	Class A/G	Class B/E	Class C
Description	General service, limited voltage protection	Utility service, high voltage protection	General service, metallic, no voltage protection
Material	Water resistant, slow burning	Water resistant, slow burning	Water resistant, slow burning
Insulation resistance	2200 V, 60 Hz for 1 minute, with 3 mA maximum leakage	20 000 V, 60 Hz for 3 minutes, with 9 mA maximum leakage	N/A
Flammability (burn rate)	3 in./minute maximum	3 in./minute maximum	N/A
Impact resistance (transmitted force)	385 kg (850 lb) average, 453 kg (1000 lb) maximum	385 kg (850 lb) average, 453 kg (1000 lb) maximum	385 kg (850 lb) average, 453 kg (1000 lb) maximum
Penetration resistance	9.5 mm (3/8 in.) maximum	9.5 mm (3/8 in.) maximum	11 mm (7/16 in.) maximum
Standard	Z89.1-1997	Z89.2-1997	Z89.1-1997

3.0   HAND AND FOOT PROTECTION

3.1   Hand Protection

The hand is one of the most complex parts of the body. Movement of the tendons, bones, tissues, and nerves allow one to grip and do a wide variety of complex jobs. Without hands, it would be extremely difficult to do routine, simple tasks such as opening doors, using a fork, work, or tying shoes. Nearly 205,000 injuries and illnesses to the wrists/hands/fingers involving days away from work in 2009 represent 27% of the total injuries for that year (Bureau of Labor Statistics; http://www.bls. gov/news.release/cfoi.nr0.htm).

There are several jobs that require the use of gloves stemming from steel work, knife handling, ice picking, and simple jobs like using a screwdriver, rigging a wire rope, cutting with a box cutter, and so on. Some jobs may include chemical handling and/or chemical mixing. In the wastewater industry, typical glove use could include sewer system collections, confined space entry, laboratory work, sampling, and other miscellaneous jobs that require handling of chemicals and/or wastewater.

The manufacturing process of glove making may result in slight variations in performance. The user is warned to exercise care and to check the glove regularly for breakthrough and diminished physical performance.

In some instances, physical performance may be a more critical factor than chemical resistance. If a job application involves handling heavy, rough, or sharp objects, then the glove must have high resistance to abrasion, cuts, snags, and so on. A hole in a glove can provide much greater chemical exposure potential than molecular permeation.

The thicker the glove material, the greater the chemical resistance. However, thick gloves can impair grip, dexterity, and safety. Sensitivity and the ability to grip are important factors. Indeed, proper glove design and fit contribute to comfort, productivity, and safety. Curved-finger glove design fits the natural hand contour for working comfort. Gloves that are too small bind and cause undue hand fatigue. However, gloves that are too large are uncomfortable, hard to work in, and can be dangerous if they get caught in moving machinery.

The following steps should be followed when selecting the proper gloves for handling chemicals:

- Refer to the manufacturer's chemical resistance guide and physical performance chart and select the glove type with the highest rating for the chemical and physical conditions;

- Refer to the chemical label and MSDS, which may recommend a specific glove type;
- Select unsupported gloves for extra dexterity and sense of touch. An unlined glove is recommended to minimize exposure from contamination;
- Select a palm finish to provide the grip needed for the job (i.e., smooth, dipped, or embossed);
- Choose the glove length by the depth to which the arm will be immersed and by allowing for protection against chemical splash;
- Select thin-gauge gloves for jobs demanding sensitive touch and high flexibility. If greater protection or durability is desired, choose a heavy-duty style; and
- Choose the glove size that will ensure optimum wear, dexterity, working ease, and comfort.

Selection of the proper chemical-resistant glove begins with an evaluation of the job application. Factors that influence this selection are

- The type of chemicals to be handled (or used);
- Frequency and duration of chemical contact;
- Nature of contact (total immersion or splash only);
- Concentration of chemicals;
- Temperature of chemicals;
- Abrasion and resistance requirements;
- Puncture-, snag-, tear-, and cut-resistance requirements;
- Length to be protected (hand only, forearm, or arm);
- Dexterity requirements;
- Grip requirements (dry grip, wet grip, or oily);
- Cuff edge (safety cuff, knit wrist, or gauntlet);
- Color requirements (to show contamination);
- Thermal protection (e.g., when handling anhydrous ammonia); and
- Size and comfort requirements.

The type of chemical being used is a key factor in choosing what material the glove should be made of. With emulsifiable concentrates, volatile solvents (like toluene and xylene), and nonvolatile solvents (like alkylated napthalenes and petroleum oil) correct glove selection is critical. Some of the more common glove materials are:

- Butyl—a synthetic rubber with good resistance to weathering and a wide variety of chemicals;

- Rubber—a highly flexible and conforming material made from a liquid tapped from rubber plants;

- Neoprene—a synthetic rubber having chemical and wear-resistance properties superior to those of natural rubber;

- Nitrile—a copolymer available in a wide range of acrylonitrile (propane nitrile) content; chemical resistance and stiffness increase with higher acrylonitrile content;

- Polyethylene—a fairly chemical-resistant material used as a freestanding film or a fabric coating;

- Polyvinyl alcohol—a water-soluble polymer that exhibits exceptional resistance to many organic solvents that rapidly permeate most rubbers;

- Polyvinyl chloride—a stiff polymer that is made softer and more suitable for protective clothing applications by the addition of plasticizers;

- Polyurethane—an abrasion-resistant rubber that is either coated into fabrics or formed into gloves or boots;

- Server shield—a registered trademark of North Hand Protection (Clover, South Carolina), it is highly chemical-resistant to many different classes of chemicals; and

- Viton®—a registered trademark of DuPont (Wilmington, Delaware), it is a highly chemical-resistant but expensive synthetic elastomer.

For a given thickness, the type of polymer selected has the greatest influence on the level of chemical protection. For a given polymer, an increase in thickness will result in a higher level of protection. A rule of thumb is that double the thickness will quadruple the breakthrough time

The OSHA regulation for hand protection is short. Following the required elements in 29 CFR 1910.132 would achieve compliance in any wastewater categories. Two paragraphs were recently added to 29 CFR 1910.138, which requires employers to provide hand protection and to select the hand protection appropriately. Selection of hand protection is outlined in the introduction of Section 3.0 of this chapter. Further resources for selection, maintenance, use, and disposal can be found in 29 CFR 1910.132 and 40 CFR 172. Chapter 9 of this manual of practice also provides further information on disposal of potentially hazardous wastes. The reader is also referred to Chapter 3 to gain more information on how to perform a JHA.

3.2 Foot Protection

3.2.1 *American Society for Testing and Materials F-2412-2005 (Standards for Testing)*

The American Society for Testing and Materials (ASTM) has set this standard for testing and setting materials for hazards around foot protection. The standard tests effectiveness on impact, resistance, compressive force, conductivity, static dissipativeness, puncture resistance, saw-cut resistance, insulation, and metatarsal protection.

3.2.2 *American Society for Testing and Materials F-2413-2005 (Standards for Performance)*

This specification covers minimum design, performance, testing, and classification requirements and prescribes fit, function, and performance criteria for footwear designed to be worn to provide protection against a variety of workplace hazards that can potentially result in injury. Although it is not the intention of this specification to serve as a detailed manufacturing or purchasing specification, it can be referenced in purchase contracts to ensure that minimum performance requirements are met. Footwear conforming to this specification should meet performance requirements for the following: impact resistance for the toe area of footwear; compression resistance for the toe area of footwear; metatarsal protection that reduces the chance of injury to the metatarsal bones at the top of the foot; conductive properties that reduce hazards that may result from static electricity buildup and reduce the possibility of ignition of explosives and volatile chemicals; electric shock resistance; static dissipative properties to reduce hazards caused by excessively low footwear resistance that may exist where static dissipative footwear is required; puncture resistance of footwear bottoms; chain saw cut resistance; and dielectric insulation.

3.2.3 *Occupational Safety and Health Administration 29 CFR 1910.136*

The OSHA standard for foot protection is limited in information, and references ASTM and ANSI standards. There is one statement in paragraph (a) that stipulates that employers "shall ensure that each affected employee uses protective footwear when working in areas where there is a danger of foot injuries to falling or rolling objects or piercing the sole."

3.2.4   Should an Employer Provide Foot Protection?

An employer is required to provide protection to all employees meeting the definition in 29 CFR 1910.136 (a).

4.0   EYE AND FACE PROTECTION

Thousands of people are blinded each year from work-related eye injuries that could have been prevented with proper selection and use of eye and face protection. According to OSHA, eye injuries alone cost more than $300 million per year in lost production time, medical expenses, and worker compensation (http://www.OSHA. gov/). The Occupational Safety and Health Administration requires eye and face protective equipment where there is a reasonable probability of preventing injury when such equipment is used. Employers must provide a type of protector suitable for work to be performed, and employees must use the protectors. These stipulations also apply to supervisors, management personnel, and to visitors while they are in hazardous areas. Suitable eye protectors must be provided where there is a potential for injury to the eyes or face from flying particles, molten metal, liquid chemicals, acids or caustic liquids, chemical gases or vapors, potentially injurious light/UV radiation, or a combination of these. Protectors must meet the following minimum requirements:

- Provide adequate protection against the particular hazards for which they are designed,
- Be reasonably comfortable when worn under designated conditions,
- Fit snugly without interfering with the movements or vision of the wearer,
- Be durable,
- Be capable of being disinfected,
- Be easily cleanable, and
- Be kept clean and in good repair.

Every protector should be distinctly marked to facilitate identification of the manufacturer. Each affected employee should use equipment with filter lenses that have a shade number (issued by the manufacturer) appropriate for the work being performed for protection from injurious light radiation. The following sections provide a listing of appropriate shade numbers for various operations.

4.1   American National Standards Institute Standard

The ANSI Z87.1 standard sets forth requirements for the design, construction, testing, and use of eye protection devices, including standards for impact and penetration resistance. All safety glasses, goggles, and face shields used by employees under OSHA jurisdiction must meet the ANSI Z87.1 standard.

4.2   Occupational Safety and Health Administration Requirements

The OSHA standard has the following two requirements: (1) Employers are to provide eye and face protection when hazards are present that pose a significant health risk to employees and (2) eye and face protection should be provided to employees who have prescription eyeglasses.

5.0   RESPIRATORY PROTECTION

5.1   Medical Evaluation

Every employee who will be required to wear respiratory protection should have a physical examination to determine his or her fitness to wear a respirator. The examining physician or licensed health care professional (PLHCP) determines whether or not the individual will be restricted from wearing respiratory protective equipment. Specific medical tests and procedures will be in accordance with OSHA and the PLHCP's requirements.

All employees who are required to wear respirators must have an annual exam by a PLHCP to review their continued fitness to wear a respirator and to monitor for effectiveness of the respirator program in protecting the employee against hazards. At the discretion of the physician, a more frequent schedule of physical exams may be needed. The OSHA regulation 29 CFR 1910.134, Appendix C, requires a medical evaluation to be filled out prior to being evaluated by a PLHCP.

5.2   Written Program Requirements

A written program is required by OSHA when employees are engaged in operations that require the use of a respirator. The written program requirements can be found in 29 CFR 1910.134. Elements of a written program include, but are not limited to, selection, maintenance, proper fit, types of respirators worn, medical evaluations, and identifying the program administrator. The program should also define training outlines, types of fit testing approved by an employer, and which respirators are required for specific tasks.

5.3   Fit Testing

A quantitative fit test should be performed to determine the ability of each individual respirator wearer to obtain a satisfactory fit with any respirator. Personnel must successfully pass the fit test before being issued a respirator. No employee is permitted to wear a respirator in a work situation until he or she has demonstrated that an acceptable fit can be obtained. Respirator fitting is conducted initially upon assignment to a task requiring use of a respirator. Refitting is conducted annually.

5.3.1   Qualitative Fit Testing

Qualitative fit tests of respirators are required, and the step-by-step procedures are listed under the respiratory protection standard. This test checks the employee's response to a chemical introduced outside the respirator face piece. This response is either voluntary or involuntary depending on the chemical test agent used. Several methods may be used.

5.3.2   Quantitative Fit Testing

Quantitative fit testing, using the Portacount Plus fit test system, is generally performed on both full-face and half-face negative-pressure respirators. Fit factors are determined by comparing the particle concentration outside the respirator with the concentration inside the respirator face piece. An acceptable fit is achieved when the respirator wearer successfully completes a series of six programmed exercises. These exercises include normal breathing, deep breathing, moving the head up and down, moving the head side to side, reading, and normal breathing with the appropriate fit factor (100 or more for a half-mask respirator, 500 for a full-face respirator, and 10 000 for supplied-air respirators [SARs] and self-contained breathing apparatuses [SCBAs]).

5.3.3   Special Conditions

No attempt should be made to fit a respirator on an employee who has facial hair that comes between the sealing periphery of the face piece and the face or if facial hair interferes with normal functioning of the exhalation valve of the respirator.

5.4   Occupational Safety and Health Administration Requirements

Respiratory protection is the largest regulation in the PPE subsection. Requirements in the regulation include a written program, medical surveillance, fit testing, training, and voluntary use.

5.5   Storage and Maintenance

All respirators should be stored to protect them from damage, contamination, dust, sunlight, extreme temperatures, excessive moisture, and damaging chemicals; they should also be packed or stored to prevent deformation of the face piece and exhalation valve. The employer should ensure that respirators are cleaned and disinfected using the procedures in Appendix B-2 of 29 CFR 1910.134 or procedures recommended by the respirator manufacturer, provided that such procedures are of equivalent effectiveness. The respirators should be cleaned and disinfected with warm water and detergent. Alcohol-based wipes should not be used because these elements will break down the rubber in the face piece and cause it to crack.

5.6   Types of Respirators

5.6.1   Atmosphere Supplying

An atmosphere-supplying respirator is a respirator that supplies the respirator user with breathing air from a source independent of the ambient atmosphere and includes SARs and SCBA units. Typical applications in wastewater include emergency response to chemicals and escape for hazardous areas.

5.6.2   Negative Pressure (Air Purifying)

A negative pressure respirator is a respirator in which the air pressure inside the face piece is negative during inhalation with respect to the ambient air pressure outside the respirator. Typical applications in the wastewater industry include collections maintenance, standby for chlorine/sulfur dioxide transfers and connections, and several others.

6.0   FALL PROTECTION

6.1   Fall Prevention First

Fall prevention is a technique that prevents falls from occurring in the first place. Fall-arrest systems are secondary to not falling at all. Preventing falls is always the first strategy when deploying employees to work at heights. Fall prevention can come in many forms and design; for the most part, however, prevention comes with employee behavior. As stated in Chapter 1, behavior-based safety is a great start, but can only be successful if the employee is willing. Although there are many engineered designs that may prevent falls, it still comes down to employee behavior when working at heights. Following instructions, procedures, and doing the right thing might be hard, especially if the employee doesn't know the prescribed procedure(s).

6.1.1   Designing Prevention

In Chapter 9 of *Design of Municipal Wastewater Treatment Plants* (WEF et al., 2009) there is a brief discussion on designing areas that are 122 cm (4 ft) or higher. In construction, the fall applicability statute is 183 cm (6 ft). Using guardrails, covers, and other design prevention strategies is always the best step in preventing falls after the design is over.

6.1.2   Walking and Working Surfaces

The Occupational Safety and Health Administration has two distinct regulations for industry and construction. The bulk of the regulations that pertain to fall protection are strictly for the construction sector. However, during most activities for treatment plants, fall protection may be needed outside of areas that have zero construction. Cross applicability may apply to both sectors (industry and construction alike). The industry regulation to follow is the walking/working surfaces regulation, which is Subpart D of 29 CFR 1910.20–30.

6.1.3   Occupational Safety and Health Administration Standards

The OSHA standards that have applicability to the wastewater sector include the aforementioned walking–working surfaces standard Subpart D of 29 CFR 1910. This regulation has many requirements including hole covers, guardrails, and stairs and ladders. Railing on stairways is also a part of this regulation.

The regulation that is most referred to is the construction standard in 29 CFR 1926 Subpart M. This is the regulation that has specifications on fall-arrest equipment including lanyards, connectors, anchorage points, and the synonymous full body harness. When most employees speak in terms of fall protection, perception is always the harness and lanyard. This is a misnomer that has plagued the construction industry for years. Fall protection has many meanings. Mostly, protection and behavior are the meanings that typically get overlooked. Fall protection means more than just a harness and lanyard. As mentioned previously, prevention and design is always the first step in fall protection, *then* adding fall-arrest harnesses. Fall prevention prevents the fall and fall-arrest harnesses do not.

6.2 Prevention Strategies

6.2.1 Guardrails

Often, the nature and location of work will dictate the form that fall protection takes. If the employer chooses to use a guardrail system, he or she must comply with the following provisions:

- Top edge height of top rails, or equivalent guardrail system members, must be between 99 and 114 cm (39 and 45 in.) above the walking/working level, except when conditions warrant otherwise and all other criteria are met (e.g., when employees are using stilts, the top edge height of the top rail must be increased by an amount equal to the height of the stilts);

- Midrails, screens, mesh, intermediate vertical members, or equivalent intermediate structures must be installed between the top edge and the walking/working surface when there is no wall or other structure at least 53-cm (21-in.) high;

- Midrails must be midway between the top edge of the guardrail system and the walking/working level;

- Screens and mesh must extend from the top rail to the walking/working level and along the entire opening between rail supports;

- Intermediate members (such as balasters) between posts must be no more than 48 cm (19 in.) apart;

- Other structural members (such as additional midrails or architectural panels) must be installed to leave no openings wider than 48 cm (19 in.);

- Guardrail systems must be capable of withstanding at least 91 kg (200 lb) of force applied within 5 cm (2 in.) of the top edge in any direction and at any point along the edge, and without causing the top edge of the guardrail to deflect downward to a height less than 99 cm (39 in.) above the walking/working level; and

- Midrails, screens, mesh, and other intermediate members must be capable of withstanding at least 68 kg (150 lb) of force applied in any direction at any point along the midrail or other member.

6.2.2   Covers

Covers are typical when there is a permanent hole in a walking/working surface. Streets, pipe galleys, and vaults are the most familiar in the wastewater industry. According to the OSHA standard, any hole cover must be capable of withstanding twice the maximum weight that can cross the cover. The cover must also display the reason or name of the utility it covers. For example, a sewer manhole cover must display the word, *sewer*, on the cover.

6.2.3   Monitors

Safety monitors represent the last line of defense. Safety monitors are employees who could be used to monitor the area for unauthorized employees and can always keep employees informed of the potential for a fall hazard. Safety monitors can only be deployed when other means cannot be used or it is impractical for their application. An example of impractical application is residential construction. The framers cannot deploy fall-arrest systems for lack of anchorage points; instead, they use a controlled access zone and perimeter with a safety monitor.

6.2.4   Controlled Access Zones

Controlled access zones are for authorized site employees only. Typically, when there is a leading edge, the area is controlled by posters, signs, and/or markings. Caution tape, security guards, and other means may be used as well. Near the leading edge, a 0.9-m (3-ft) perimeter can be controlled with any of the aforementioned items.

6.3   Fall-Arrest Systems

Personal fall-arrest systems catch workers after they have fallen. A personal fall-arrest system consists of a harness, lanyard, and secure anchorage. The harness is worn around the upper body, while the lanyard is secured to an anchorage. An anchorage may be any of the following:

- An I-beam;
- A pipe or beam approximately 150 mm (6 in.) or more thick;
- A tower strut or cross-member; or
- A manufactured anchorage device (it is important to never anchor onto electrical conduit, sag rods, unistruts, or scaffolds unless they are specifically designed for use as anchorages).

6.3.1 Lanyards

There are generally two types of lanyards. One is a single length of material that stops a fall suddenly at a distance of 1.8 m (6 ft) from the anchorage. The other type, known as a *decelerating lanyard,* uses friction or other means to slow the fall, starting at 1.8 m (6 ft) from the anchorage and ending after another 1 m (3 ft, 6 in.).

Deceleration devices may not always be used because they need more vertical distance to operate. They are, however, safer because they do not bring the body to a sudden stop. Decelerating lanyards also expose the fall victim to potential danger after arresting the fall because there is a much greater wing distance. This can be especially dangerous in enclosed work areas or near power lines.

6.3.2 Harness

An employee should always inspect a harness before putting it on. Frayed or burned areas, loose webbing, broken fibers, cuts, cracks, and/or worn or rough edges on metal fittings can cause the harness to fail when it is stressed in a fall. In addition, the harness must be worn properly for it to work. The following steps should be followed when putting on a harness:

- Hold harness by the back of the D-rings and shake straps into place;
- Release buckled straps and slip them over your shoulders, locating the D-ring in the middle of your back between your shoulder blades;
- Pull the leg straps between your legs and connect it to the opposite end;
- Make sure the waist strap is tight but not binding;
- Connect the chest strap and position it in the middle of your chest;
- Be sure the harness is snug but allows full movement; and
- Remember that body belts can no longer be used for personal fall arrest; they may be used for positioning only.

6.3.3 Anchorage Connection

The best location for an anchorage is directly above where an employee is working. The higher the anchorage, the less distance an employee will fall before a lanyard stops him or her. It is also important to keep the anchorage directly overhead to prevent "swing falls." In a swing fall, the body will not only fall downward, but also sideways until it is under the anchorage. The greater the sideways distance an individual travels, the more he or she will swing and possibly collide with objects.

Finally, it is important for employees to check the drop zone to make sure they will not hit anything before the fall protection stops them.

Employees should ensure any anchorage is strong enough to withstand the fall-arrest force it may sustain should they fall. All anchorage points need to be approved by the on-site competent person. Employees have the responsibility to

- Inspect the anchorage for damage before hooking up;

- Use an anchor that has no obstacles under it that he or she could fall into;

- Allow for free-fall distance, the deceleration distance of equipment, and any distance the lifeline stretches when selecting an anchor;

- Check for the manufacturer's labels stating equipment stretch and deceleration distance;

- Allow a maximum deceleration distance of 1 m (3 ft 6 in.) as a rule of thumb; and

- Remember that the farther one's attachment to the lifeline is from the line's anchor, the more the line can stretch.

6.4 Positioning Systems

Positioning devices help prevent falls by supporting employees in a working position. Positioning devices do not have to be as strong as fall-arrest systems because they are not designed to catch a falling worker. Examples of positioning devices include

- Window cleaner's positioning system,

- Lineman's belts and pole straps, and

- Restraint lines.

These devices use a short lanyard that allows a fall no greater than 61 cm (2 ft).

7.0 PROTECTIVE CLOTHING

Table 10.2 displays a matrix of PPE options and their uses.

7.1 U.S. Environmental Protection Agency Level A

7.1.1 Use

Level A suits have had their time in the wastewater field. It is apparent that the minimization of chlorine use as a disinfectant has taken hold and been replaced by other chemicals like sodium hypochlorite, ozone, and UV disinfection.

Recently, the Chlorine Institute recommended the use of Level B when responding to chlorine emergencies. With respect to firefighters and outside emergency agencies, Level B ensembles were the industry directive; however, firefighters and emergency responders have always responded in Level A, which is the highest level of protection. This manual of practice does not take a position and does not recommend any levels of protection.

7.1.2   Selection

Selecting the Level A ensemble is typically not a difficult decision. However, wearing the Level A suit adds additional strain and hazard to the responder. The decision to wear Level A must be pre-arranged and written in procedure. There are no chemicals at wastewater treatment facilities that should warrant the use of Level A unless directed by the local fire service/district.

7.1.3   Maintenance

Because the Level A suit is fully encapsulating and requires an SCBA, it typically is the most expensive suit purchased. Therefore, it is recommended to maintain Level A suits as long as possible. To do this, a strict maintenance program must be required. It is important to follow all manufacturer requirements for maintenance and ensure that suits have been pressure-tested each year. Additionally, all Level A suits should be stored in a cool dry location.

7.2   U.S. Environmental Protection Agency Level B

7.2.1   Use

Level B protection requires a garment (including SCBA) that provides protection against splashes from a hazardous chemical. Because the breathing apparatus is worn on the outside of the garment, Level B protection is not vapor-protective. It is worn when vapor-protective clothing (Level A) is not required. The wrists, ankles, face piece and hood, and waist are secured to prevent any entry of splashed liquid. Depending on the chemical being handled, specific types of gloves and boots are donned. These may or may not be attached to the garment. The garment itself may be one piece or a two-piece hooded suit. Level B protection also requires wearing chemical-resistant boots with steel toes and shanks on the outside of the garment. As with Level A, chemical-resistant gloves and two-way radio communications are also required.

7.2.2   Selection

The use of a Level B ensemble requires the addition of a SCBA. The use of Level B would require highly hazardous acute gaseous materials that have little effect on the

TABLE 10.2   Personal protective equipment matrix and use

	Eyes					Hands						Ears	
	Glasses with side shields	Goggles	Laser goggles	Face shield	Tinted face shield	Leather	Rubber	Neoprene	Latex/nitrile	Chemical resistant	Voltage rated	Plugs	Muffs
Band saw		●		●									
Belt sander	●			●									
Buffers	●	●		●		●							
Drain cleaning machine	●							●					
Drill press	●			●									
Ducting	●					●			●				
Electric hand-held eq.	●												
Former	●												
Fume hoods	●								●				
Grinder	●			●								●	
Hydraulic press	●			●									
Jointer	●												
Key cutting machine	●											●	
Laser driller	●	●											
Lathe	●												
Liner	●	●											
Metal brake	●			●		●							
Milling machine	●												
Miter saw	●												
Mortise and tenon machine	●												
Notching machine	●					●							
Panel saw	●												

Body		Respiratory		Head	Foot		Other Protective Equipment/procedures						PPE references	
Protective clothing	Harness	Dust mask	Respirator	Hard hat	Safety shoes	Metatarsal	Insulated blanket	Proper lifting	Load live locator	Guarding	Shoring	MSDS	Manufacturer guidelines	Permit
		●		●	●					●			●	
		●		●	●					●			●	
		●		●	●					●			●	
				●	●								●	
				●	●								●	
		●		●	●								●	
				●	●								●	
				●	●								●	
				●	●								●	
●		●		●	●					●			●	
				●	●								●	
		●		●	●					●			●	
				●	●					●			●	
				●	●					●			●	
				●	●					●			●	
				●	●								●	
				●	●							●	●	
				●	●					●			●	
		●		●	●					●			●	
		●		●									●	
		●		●	●					●			●	
		●		●	●					●			●	

(continued)

TABLE 10.2   Continued

	Eyes					Hands						Ears	
	Glasses with side shields	Goggles	Laser goggles	Face shield	Tinted face shield	Leather	Rubber	Neoprene	Latex/nitrile	Chemical resistant	Voltage rated	Plugs	Muffs
Parts cleaner	●	●		●				●					
Pipe threading machine	●							●		●			
Pittsburgh seamer	●					●							
Planner	●			●		●						●	
Plasma cutter	●			●		●							
Press brake	●												
Pullmax cutter	●					●							
Radial arm saw	●												
Rolling machine	●					●							
Sand blaster	●			●									
Shaper	●			●		●							
Shear	●												
Soldering equipment	●					●				●			
Spot welder	●	●											
Surface planer	●											●	
Table saw	●												
Threading equipment	●							●					
Vacuum pumps	●								●				
Welding equipment	●			●	●					●	●		
Tampers	●					●							
Lawn mowers	●					●						●	●
Weed cutters	●			●		●				●	●		
Chain saws	●			●		●				●	●		
Leaf blowers	●											●	●
Powder actuated tools	●			●								●	●

Body		Respiratory		Head	Foot		Other Protective Equipment/procedures					PPE references		
Protective clothing	Harness	Dust mask	Respirator	Hard hat	Safety shoes	Metatarsal	Insulated blanket	Proper lifting	Load live locator	Guarding	Shoring	MSDS	Manufacturer guidelines	Permit
●		●		●	●							●		
				●	●								●	
				●	●								●	
				●	●					●			●	
●				●	●								●	
				●	●							●	●	
				●	●					●			●	
		●		●	●					●			●	
				●	●								●	
				●	●							●	●	
				●	●					●			●	
				●	●								●	
				●	●							●	●	
				●	●							●	●	
				●	●					●			●	
		●		●	●					●			●	
				●	●								●	
●		●		●	●							●	●	
●				●	●							●	●	
				●	●					●			●	
				●	●					●			●	
				●	●					●			●	
				●	●					●			●	
				●	●									
				●	●					●			●	

skin. Emergencies typically dictate the use of Level B. However, if an employee is working at a hazardous waste site, a Level B ensemble must be selected through the appropriate JHA as mentioned in Chapter 3.

7.2.3   Maintenance

Secured breathing apparatuses must be maintained as required by the manufacturer. Hydrostatic testing of SCBA tanks is required every 5 years. Suits for Level B are typically disposable and are not as expensive as Level A ensembles. Level B splash suits are typically thrown away after use. Storage of unused suits must be in a cool, dry location. If suits are intended to be kept after use, a thorough decontamination system must be used.

7.3   U.S. Environmental Protection Agency Level C

7.3.1   Use

Level C protection differs from Level B in the area of equipment needed for respiratory protection. The same type of garment used for Level B protection is worn for Level C. Level C protection allows for the use of respiratory protection equipment other than SCBA. This protection includes any of the various types of air-purifying respirators. Employees should not use this level of protection unless the specific hazardous material is known and its concentration can be measured. Level C equipment does not offer the protection needed in an oxygen-deficient atmosphere.

7.3.2   Selection

Level C is worn only when concentrations are known. Respiratory protection drops in Level C from SCBA to an air-purifying respirator. The splash suit is the same that is used in a Level B suit.

7.3.3   Maintenance

Air-purifying respirators require more detailed maintenance than an SCBA. Cleaning also requires more attention to detail. A SCBA has required inspections throughout intervals and after each use. An air-purifying respirator (APR) requires inspections frequently and before and after each use. It is imperative that cartridges attached to the APR are stored in an area that meets the cleanliness standard for OSHA housekeeping regulation and is also cool and dry. It is important to check manufacturers' specifications for removal/replacement of chemical cartridges and the storage of those cartridges.

7.4   U.S. Environmental Protection Agency Level D

7.4.1   Use

Level D protection does not protect the employee from chemical exposure. Therefore, this level of protection can only be used in situations where a crew member has no possibility of contact with chemicals. A pair of coveralls or other work-type garment along with chemical-resistant footwear with steel toes and shanks are all that is required to qualify as Level D protection. Most firefighter turnout gear is considered to be Level D.

7.4.2   Selection

Level D is used for nonchemical exposure jobs only.

7.4.3   Maintenance

There are typically no requirements for Level D ensembles. It is recommended that uniforms not be laundered by employees themselves.

7.5   Other Types of Protective Clothing

7.5.1   Uniforms

Uniforms allow employees who are working at wastewater treatment plants the opportunity to not spread any potential contamination to their personal home or retreat.

7.5.2   Arc Flash Uniforms

Arc flash suits are designed to protect employees from serious workplace injuries or illnesses resulting from contact with electrical hazards. Many different types of safety clothing are available, including aprons, smocks, coveralls, footwear, gloves, jackets, leggings, pants, vests, and hoods. The importance of arc flash suits cannot be underestimated to greatly reduce human exposure to dangerous and harmful environments. Cotton work clothes can be easily ignited by electric arc flash. Employees are now required by the National Fire Protection Association standard 70E to wear flame-resistant protective clothing that meets ASTM Standard Performance Specification F1506 requirements wherever employees are exposed to the possibility of electric arc flash.

8.0 REFERENCES

American National Standards Institute, ANSI Z89.1-2003.

American National Standards Institute, ANSI Z87.1-2003.

American Society for Testing and Materials, *Standards for Testing of Steel Toed Boots,* ASTM F-2412-2005.

American Society for Testing and Materials, *Standards for Performance of Steel Toed Boots,* ASTM F-2413-2005.

Occupational Safety and Health Administration, 29 Code of Federal Regulations 1910.132; 1910.132 (d), (2).

Occupational Safety and Health Administration 29 *Code of Federal Regulations* 1926.28 (Subpart C).

Occupational Safety and Health Administration 29 *Code of Federal Regulations* 1904.39.

Water Environment Federation; American Society of Civil Engineers; Environmental and Water Resources Institute (2009) *Design of Municipal Wastewater Treatment Plants,* 5th ed.; WEF Manual of Practice No. 8; ASCE Manual and Report on Engineering Practice No. 76; McGraw-Hill: New York.

Chapter 11

Coordination with Other Agencies and Officials

(continued)

1.0   IDENTIFYING AGENCIES FOR COORDINATION

1.1 Job Hazard Analysis Data

Data developed when performing job hazard analysis (JHA) is useful in identifying agencies and organizations, which require coordination. While the JHA is typically associated with selection of personal protective equipment (PPE) and work procedures, it may also identify wide-ranging coordination issues for assistance from agencies outside an organization. This section focuses on use of JHA data to identify hazards and related procedures requiring outside assistance or support. Development of JHA is covered in Chapter 3 and PPE is covered in detail in Chapter 10.

While many examples are available, use of the results of a JHA for workers performing confined space rescues is a good example of required coordination. When rescue team members must perform entries or rescues without non-entry rescue equipment, they must have a backup plan for their safety in addition to a wide range of training. Generally, professional rescuers must be on-site or immediately available and the coordination and evaluation of these activities must be documented. At a minimum, the backup team must be available in a timeframe that can perform a rescue, not just recovery. Additional areas requiring coordination for confined spaces are discussed in depth in both Chapters 4 and 5 (29 CFR 1910.146).

In addition to JHA data developed for emergency action plans, fire prevention plans, security plans, and continuity of service plans all have coordination requirements and are covered in detail in Chapters 2 and 9.

Job hazard analysis results for workers performing work using hazardous materials or working with hazardous wastes will identify coordination issues and PPE needed by workers. Coordination of lockout activities is commonly a direct result of a JHA, but identification and coordination of a backup plan for the work requiring the lockout may require special coordination if outside agencies or organizations are working under that lockout protection.

1.2 Evaluating Risk

To reduce or control risks, many utilities perform evaluations using failure mode analysis to identify potentially unwelcome or unacceptable consequences. During development of the procedures or approaches to reduce the identified risk to an acceptable level, additional coordination issues are commonly encountered. The additional coordination may take the form of enhanced notification of the public through such means as "reverse 911" or be as simple as providing updated information to the local emergency planning committee. Knowing whom to call to efficiently incorporate a utility's changes into community response plans is a critical component of effective coordination.

In some instances, such as with a risk management plan (RMP), an update of the hazard analysis must be filed with the U.S. Environmental Protection Agency (U.S. EPA) every 3 years taking into account additional population and public receptors within the immediate zone of concern for the facility. This information includes both worst-case and most likely scenarios and is a required activity. An RMP is covered in detail in Sections 2.4 and 8.0 of this chapter.

In addition to being required, it simply makes good business sense to perform these types of evaluations. Coordination with outside agencies and officials who will assist a utility in dealing with the consequences of unwelcome, undesirable, or simply unacceptable events that may affect the utility or community require preparation in advance of the event.

For example, if part of a utility's emergency plan is to use local pumper trucks to maintain lift stations during significant storm outages, that activity must be coordinated in advance to ensure availability of the trucks and personnel needed to operate them. That information must be coordinated with the company performing the service, the operations staff who will use the services, and the staff who will pay the bills. The water/wastewater agency response network (WARN) agencies discussed in Section 5.0 are examples of this type of coordination activity in which agreements are put in place in advance of storm or unwanted incidents, allowing agencies to help each other because they already coordinated all the details of how they will help each other. The water/wastewater agency response network members simply need to communicate what type of help they need because all of the other issues have been coordinated in advance. Preparing in advance allows a utility to focus on the issues at hand.

1.3   Emergency Plans To Identify Coordination Needs

Every emergency plan includes preparation of a list of phone numbers, e-mails, Web sites, and contact information. Those lists and contacts are the basis for coordination issues related to emergency response plans. Much of the coordination work for mature plans is simply verifying that the numbers work and the correct person is accessible. Although modern technology offers a wide range of powerful communication tools when operational, experience has shown that during the initial phases of many severe weather events, communications are limited. An old ally of emergency response is amateur radio, or ham radio, which is the licensed and private use of designated radio bands for purposes of private recreation and noncommercial exchange of messages. However, ham radio has proven itself to be an important tool for emergency communication. While considered ancient and almost forgotten compared to modern technology, access to a ham radio network following a catastrophic event may be the only form of communication available if cell towers and phone systems are down. Communication between plants may also be as basic as runners, drivers, or simple routes where information must be physically conveyed. During a significant storm, lift stations may go down but drinking water may continue to flow causing lift stations to overflow. Coordination of pump-around and fueling of generators become critical issues for public health and must be preplanned and coordinated to avoid widespread public health issues. Communication with water treatment and distribution system operators may provide valuable options in reducing overflows.

While each utility must evaluate its specific plans, a basic list of common agencies considered for coordination should include, but not be limited to, the following:

- Local law enforcement (see Section 1.4),
- County law enforcement (see Section 1.5),
- State law enforcement (see Section 1.6),
- Federal law enforcement (Section 1.7),
- Local emergency planning committee (see Section 4.0),
- Water/wastewater agency response network coordination activities (see Section 5.0),
- Local environmental agencies (see Section 6.0),
- State environmental protection agency (see Section 7.0), and
- Federal environmental protection agency (see Section 8.0).

1.4 Local Law Enforcement

A wide range of law enforcement agencies enforce environmental safety and health rules. Some states participate in combining agencies and empowering them to levy fines and fees. This section focuses on methods to establish lines of communication with support agencies and officials who a utility may have to rely on during any unwanted event in which internal resources are simply beyond their ability. Plant security and emergency response both require communication and coordination with all first response organizations listed in a utility's plan. Chapter 12 covers security and emergency preparedness. The ability to work on a basis of mutual respect and previous experience is invaluable during emergency operations; indeed, just knowing the officials who you will be working with is a valuable communication and coordination tool. Where plant managers and officials representing law enforcement have worked together previously, the communications are credible and the response or mitigation is greatly enhanced.

Participation in cooperative law enforcement programs provides wastewater managers real opportunities to improve communication with first responders in their service area.

A wide range of benefits are possible for both the utility and the law enforcement agency by participating in mutual projects. In terms of public safety, any action that encourages interaction between industry and law enforcement is desirable. Cooperative efforts range from hosting training at a wastewater treatment plant, participating in local emergency management expositions for the public, sharing a skid pad for driver training, or providing the local K-9 team a secure place to practice. The roles and relationships local law enforcement play during security-related events may be the long-term payoff for a utility's efforts, but the most basic benefit of enhanced patrols and improved communication between operations and enforcement is almost immediate and is priceless in its value to a utility.

Most law enforcement agencies and wastewater treatment plants operate continuously so both have a challenge communicating to everyone on every shift. Therefore, it may be necessary to meet with three different shift supervisors at three different times.

Local law enforcement is generally the first to put up roadblocks and isolate areas that pose a threat to public health. An important part of any emergency plan includes getting in-plant responders to the plant by coordinating the issue with local law enforcement controlling that access. Once again, the range of options is wide, but simple solutions such as picture identification for all workers who may participate in public safety issues is an important first step in coordination. Official government picture identification with designations of "Emergency Response Team Member" or "First Responder Technician Level" is generally an accepted incident command description for plant responder identification badges.

1.5 County Law Enforcement

For many plants, county law enforcement is considered their local agency and the agency providing service to the plant is where coordination activities should be directed. However, it is also possible to have lift stations and other equipment in areas patrolled by county law enforcement even though the plant is in another area. Most city and county law enforcement agencies work closely together and some share common facilities and joint communication centers. Those same centers may coordinate ambulance, fire, hazardous materials, or rescue out of the same building.

Often, that same building also houses the emergency operations center (EOC) and hosts a wide range of first responder activities. Those utilities that have emergency plans that include use of any of the county's first response capabilities should visit the center and communicate and coordinate with it. Where logical, coordinating actions and activities to enhance plans can then take place. Many of the technology improvements being used today by county law enforcement agencies can also be valuable resources for treatment plants and collection systems. Many utilities actually have a seat at the county EOC and participate directly during emergency situations, which may affect the public. The time to prepare a utility's chair and coordinate a plan is before an event.

1.6 State Law Enforcement

A wide range of law enforcement agencies exist at the state level and a working understanding of these agencies is an integral part of response planning and everyday operations. State law enforcement is most visibly represented by the highway patrol and includes control of the issuance of commercial driver's licenses and some form of commercial vehicle enforcement. Most states also have some form of capitol police, but the division of law enforcement is the state division most likely referenced in emergency response plans.

While much of the work of a wastewater utility is restricted to local plants and systems, state law enforcement can quickly become a utility's new best friend when large weather events cause catastrophic damage. During restoration events, state law enforcement can assist in a wide range of activities as part of the state emergency response team. They control the roads and enforce the peace during a time of desperation for many people.

Generally, these agencies are going to participate in several regional activities that pertain to emergency response programs, driver awareness and safety belt programs, and general public safety-type activities. Participation by a utility in promoting these activities can be large or small, but can be helpful in establishing lines of communication. State law enforcement may participate in local emergency planning committee (LEPC) meetings, emergency response expositions, or even sponsor walks or drives for other charity organizations. In many instances, it has been state law enforcement officers escorting wastewater workers participating in WARN organizations as they responded to devastated plants in regions far from home that had simply been washed away by tides and winds that flooded the tanks with seawater. It was state law enforcement that led the first response teams in to help.

In a worst-case situation, the National Guard, which is a dual state–federal force, may also provide a wide range of assistance and is accessed through state law enforcement agencies.

1.7 Federal Law Enforcement

Federal law enforcement includes the Central Intelligence Agency; Federal Bureau of Investigation (FBI); security screeners, customs, and border patrols, and Internal Revenue Service agents. The Department of Homeland Security (DHS) was formed in 2001, consolidating 22 agencies and employing more than 150,000 federal workers; it is dedicated to protecting the nation against terrorism. The Department of Homeland Security transferred functions from the Departments of the Treasury, Justice, Health and Human Services, Defense, Energy, Agriculture, and Transportation and the FBI, U.S. Secret Service, General Services Administration, and the U.S. Coast Guard. For many treatment plants, the potential for terrorist acts is the catalyst for having one or several federal law enforcement numbers on their list. In the event of a terrorist attack, natural disaster, or other large-scale emergency, DHS will provide a coordinated, comprehensive federal response and mount a swift and effective recovery effort. Coordination activities for security events are covered in detail in Chapter 12 ("Security").

2.0 IDENTIFYING PLANS REQUIRING COORDINATION

2.1 Emergency Action Plans

The unique circumstances of each water reclamation facility drive the complexity and components of its emergency response plan. The ultimate plan should reflect the actions and activities that will be taken by workers during an unwanted event. The most effective plans are practiced and exercised often enough to keep the plan effective, just as an athlete takes repetitive steps to stay in shape. Coordination considerations need to start with a utility's industry partners. In some instances, a hazardous materials ordinance may require coordination for both customers and facilities. Many water reclamation facilities have had informal agreements of assistance for years, but wastewater utilities are facing new challenges. An example of effective modern innovation is WARN. While each state WARN has subtle differences, improvements to existing emergency preparedness and security are the focus of the efforts (the reader is referred to Section 5.0 for more information). Joining a WARN organization is a cost-effective opportunity to increase a facility's response and recovery capability. Even the simplest coordination issue of feeding responders can make a significant difference in the overall outcome to any emergency response. Additional information on the development of emergency action plans is listed in Chapter 9.

2.2 Fire Prevention Plan

Fire prevention plans are covered in several other chapters of this manual; they generally consist of good housekeeping, maintenance, and control of electrical hazards, portable heaters, hot work, and proper control and storage of flammable materials. However, if data developed during a JHA identifies a special or unique hazard, then a plan must be developed and coordinated to ensure its viability. Treatment plant communication and coordination with fire services personnel is critical to the successful outcome of many emergency responses, whether they are public or worker safety issues.

Strategies to improve coordination with fire services include knowing the public information officer for the fire services who support your plant. Participation and support for fire service activities for public safety is another way to improve communication. Inviting fire services personnel to visit a plant and evaluate the spaces and places they may have to assist with in the future is a good idea. Their assistance may be related to confined spaces, elevated towers, dangerous pits, tanks, or process areas. When special projects develop, utility management may have to meet three different shift commanders at three different times; interaction with them leads to improved communication and smoother responses. To be effective, fire prevention plans must be exercised and reviewed on a regular basis.

2.3 Process Safety Management

For those operations using hazardous chemicals in their process, CFR 1910.119, *Process Safety Management of Highly Hazardous Chemicals*, requires that the employer provide employees involved in operating the process with the ability to identify and understand the hazards posed by those processes. Safety information should include information pertaining to hazards of highly hazardous chemicals used or produced by the process, information pertaining to the technology of the process, and information pertaining to equipment in the process.

Employers are also required to develop emergency response plans. The employer should establish and implement an emergency action plan for the entire plant in accordance with provisions of *Emergency Action Plans,* 29 CFR 1910.38. Employers covered under this standard may also be subject to the hazardous waste and emergency response provisions contained in *Hazardous Waste Operations and Emergency Response,* 29 CFR 1910. Each of these programs has several components requiring coordination of efforts.

2.4   Risk Management Plan

Under the authority of Section 112(r) of the Clean Air Act (CAA), the Chemical Accident Prevention Provisions require water reclamation facilities that produce, handle, process, distribute, or store certain chemicals to develop, prepare, and submit an RMP to U.S. EPA. Because the focus of the RMP is public protection, a wide range of requirements requiring communications and coordination exist. Mentioned several times in this chapter, coordination with other agencies is the common activity available to plant managers to better position themselves and their plant to work more closely with a first responder. Participation with an LEPC or local fire services will prove enhanced communication abilities for many parts of an RMP. In many instances, officials who respond during emergencies are the same ones who will assist in RMP audits and sit across the table from utility management at the EOC. Participation in any of these events will be a positive step in maintaining an effective RMP.

2.5   Hazardous Waste Operations

Many elements of hazardous waste operations require communication and coordination. Pre-emergency planning is required, including emergency treatment and first aid, emergency alerting procedures, evacuation routes, muster points, and notification procedures for local, state, and federal government agencies. Many of the communication components of hazardous waste operations are required and most must be supported by written documentation. Ultimately, effective coordination is often based on good communication skills, but the reality is that not everybody communicates effectively. In many organizations, a system is developed to ensure activities that encourage and promote coordination and behavior-based safety functions. The front line of effective communication begins with workers performing daily tasks associated with proper handling and care of the hazardous processes. While training can teach workers skills, behavioral-based actions and attitudes are more difficult to quantify. Managers, supervisors, and lead personnel must lead by example and clearly demonstrate real importance for the proper handling of hazardous materials. It is critical to ensure that the workers handling hazardous materials have been well trained and that training is documented and updated. It is also important to coordinate all activities that may affect hazardous waste operations with workers and to communicate with outside agencies that may be needed to respond to unwanted events.

2.6 Permit Required Confined Space

Coordination of permit required confined space activities is addressed in several chapters of this manual of practice. The written permit itself is a tool of communication in which the hazards of the space are clearly identified and specific mitigations for each hazard are listed and inspected prior to use. Coordination is required in all confined space activities to ensure a safe entry; however, identified directly for coordination in the standard are safety issues related to surge flow and flooding, rescue teams, non-entry rescues, and contingency plans. Other safety regulations such as lockout/tagout and entering tanks that previously held a hazardous chemical are also coordination issues.

2.7 Security Plans

Security plans require advance planning, resources, training, and points of contact. Coordination of security plan components may range from local law enforcement for simple vandalism to the FBI and DHS if public safety is threatened. Utility management should work with their local law enforcement to develop a communication network to ensure the quickest possible response for unwanted activities. Security plans are covered in more detail in Chapter 12.

2.8 Continuity of Service Plan

Continuity of services begins with effective planning and evaluation of a system. Depending on the results of an evaluation and historical information concerning operation of a wastewater utility, many plans may be put in place prior to unwanted events. A common occurrence during the loss of electrical power is that water may still be on, resulting in overflows at lift stations. Advance installation of bypass pumps or emergency generators at critical lift stations are common approaches taken by wastewater providers to ensure continuity of service. Overflows may also be prevented by having preplanned resources such as pump truck services available during storms. Front line supervisors must have working contact numbers and emergency phone numbers for each of the resources used in the plan. Information necessary to identify additional resources for coordination may be found in RMPs, process safety, JHAs, or by the history or experience of the location of the plant. A simple, but effective example is an area where heavy winds uproot large trees and interrupt water services for large areas. Coordination and publication of alternate locations of safe water may be an interim solution. Lift stations may be put on a "pump-around" route where a portable pump is used at multiple stations on a designated route until power is restored. Routes may also have to be set up to have emergency generators fueled and serviced to provide continuity of service until power can be restored. Even re-use water may be offered for free or at various locations during times of severe drought or high fire potential. Although not every organization has physical connections to alternative treatment sites, the possibility of being able to divert flows to an alternative treatment or storage site is a valuable tool when available.

3.0   LOCAL FIRE SERVICE COORDINATION

3.1   Incident Command

The Incident Command System is a systematic approach used for the command, control, and coordination of emergency response. Policies, procedures, and equipment are integrated into a common organizational structure designed to improve response operations. An incident command approach is based on a flexible, scalable response organization providing a common framework within which people can work together effectively. These people may be drawn from multiple agencies that do not routinely work together. Incident command training is available through a wide range of sources including the LEPC, fire departments, and county EOCs. When utility management does not know first responders personally, use of incident command becomes key to effective communication with police and fire personnel.

3.2   Coordination of Emergency Response Activities

The coordination required depends on the type of challenges faced. Where high uncertainty exists and sudden unexpected events could occur, coordination needs are for communication, real-time monitoring, and timely alert notification. As events unfold, existing plans may need to be modified to reflect the current situation. Having a utility representative at an EOC prior to a storm event is a common practice. Having a group of workers scheduled to rotate shifts at the EOC with the ability to communicate effectively with both groups is a good practice.

3.3   National Fire Protection Association 101 Life Safety Code

The National Fire Protection Association (NFPA) 101 Life Safety Code is the benchmark for safety in all types of structures, including wastewater treatment plants. The NFPA recommendations establish minimum levels of safety for virtually every wastewater plant. The National Fire Protection Association uses the latest research, technology, and existing industry standards to provide the most advanced rules for sprinklers, alarms, egress, emergency lighting, smoke barriers, and special hazard protection equipment. Special hazard protection might include scrubbers, containment buildings, automatic valve closers, containment vessels, or special fire suppression

A key agency official in the design of any hazardous materials building will be the local fire official. This official will base many decisions on NFPA-recommended rules. It is important to communicate and coordinate any hazardous materials storage, design, or maintenance activities with a local fire service provider.

3.4   Coordination of Training Activities

Coordination of training activities may include use of self-contained breathing apparatuses, assistance with emergency response safety equipment, use of specialized training areas, and coordination of resources. Driver training facilities can be shared between utilities, fire, and police. Utility workers may serve as a decontamination team if resources are exhausted by fire services. Tanker trucks and heavy equipment may be needed by fire services in unusual situations. Plants may need special protection during fire conditions to protect reclamation facilities and the treatment process.

3.5   Coordination of Hazardous Materials Facilities

The hazardous communication standard is based on communicating information about the hazards of chemicals so that workers can take precautions when working with them and, if exposed, will know what to do to avoid serious injury. Coordination begins with training all workers exposed to chemicals and even those who do not work with chemicals if they are exposed to hazards simply by being on-site. Every worker must be aware of the hazards and be able to notify plant responders if any problem is suspected. Additional details concerning coordination of hazardous materials are reflected in almost every chapter in this manual of practice. Emergency response plans are written reflections of the communication and activities that will take place to prevent or respond to hazardous materials incidents.

4.0   LOCAL EMERGENCY PLANNING COMMITTEE

4.1   Coordination of Activities for Spill Prevention

Local emergency planning committees work to understand chemical hazards in the community, develop emergency plans in case of an accidental release, and look for ways to prevent chemical accidents. Local emergency planning committees must develop an emergency response plan, review it at least annually, and provide information about chemicals in the community to citizens. Plans are developed by LEPCs with stakeholder participation. The LEPC membership includes elected state and local officials; police, fire, civil defense, and public health professionals; environment, transportation, and hospital officials; representatives from community groups and the media; and reclamation facility representatives.

Participation in LEPC activities exposes plant representatives to the entire community of first responders and is a good way to begin improved coordination of all emergency plans. Table-top exercises and full-scale responses should be coordinated with the assistance of LEPC staff and volunteers.

4.2   Coordination of Activities for a Hazardous Materials Release

An important responsibility of the LEPC is to establish procedures for receiving and processing public requests for information collected under the Emergency Planning and Community Right-to-Know Act (EPCRA). The LEPC also maintains identification of facilities using extremely hazardous materials and maintains copies of emergency response procedures and plans. The LEPC may also work with facility emergency coordinators during implementation of the plan. The LEPC could coordinate emergency notification procedures, assist in determining the probable affected area and population of a release, and, in some instances, coordinate additional emergency equipment. The utility's local LEPC is also a good source for training emergency responders and scheduling exercises for emergency response plans.

4.3 Audits of Risk Management Plans

Depending on a utility's location, a representative of the LEPC will typically be part of the team performing the RMP Audit. The audit team will compare written plans to physical inspections of the facility and incorporate interviews with workers to ensure the written programs are in place. Details concerning the RMP and audit information are covered in Chapter 9.

5.0 WATER/WASTEWATER AGENCY RESPONSE NETWORK COORDINATION ACTIVITIES

5.1 Weather Events Such as Hurricanes, Tornados, and Storm Events

The water/wastewater agency response network is a mutual aid network designed to provide mutual aid and assistance based on established agreements between water and wastewater agencies. In general, WARN members build and strengthen relationships between each other, but also define responsibilities and roles including involvement of the utility, state, and permitting agencies; state and local emergency management and response agencies; and federal or supporting professional organizations. Additional information about WARN is provided in Chapter 12.

5.2 Catastrophic System Outage That May Affect the Public

In addition to weather related events, many WARNs also provide a method whereby water or wastewater utilities that have sustained or anticipate damages from any incidents that have caused a catastrophic outage that may affect the public can provide and receive emergency aid and assistance in the form of personnel, equipment, materials, and other associated services as necessary from other water or wastewater utilities. Water/ wastewater agency response networks can be accessed through the World Wide Web by performing a simple search for "water/wastewater agency response network."

6.0 LOCAL ENVIRONMENTAL AGENCIES

6.1 Water Quality Issues Concerning Public Health

Local environmental agencies are comprised of a wide range of staff from elected officials to professional staff. Environmental agencies may be from cities, counties, or special districts. The staff in those agencies may be engineers, environmental managers, planners, regional planning councils, water management districts, or state agencies. It is important to establish communication with agency representatives that would assist a utility in water quality issues that can affect the public. Spending the time now to identify which agency and representative will represent public health issues relating to the operation of a facility is critical to ensuring a positive and coordinated outcome.

6.2   Coordination of Information Released to the Public

Communicating risk to the public needs to be done professionally and must be coordinated with those agencies that represent local public health and public safety. Generally, a trained professional such as a public information officer will deliver the information based on the facts that are available at the time. In some instances, the specific timing of the release of information and the credibility of the person presenting the information will have a significant effect on how the information is received and how the public will respond to it. Facts and details are important to disseminate, but, when providing risk communication, the way in which it is presented to the public can be the difference between public panic and public cooperation. It is important to coordinate information and cooperate with local environmental agencies to develop information releases based on consensus of all parties.

6.3   Coordination with Local Departments of Health

Local health departments are generally associated with county government in most states and provide a wide range of services based on their location. In addition to clinics and family health services, county health departments are also involved in identifying community-wide health issues and communicable disease potentials. Generally, environmental permits and inspections are also related activities and, in some instances, are under the same administrative group or in the same physical location. The most effective approach to the improvement of communications to ensure coordinated responses is shared activities, which promote positive health and environmental outcomes. Participation by utilities in environmental expositions, environmental cleanup efforts, plant tours, and support of projects sponsored by or for local health departments sets the stage for effective communication for the future. Having established credibility with the group or agency that will describe public risk issues an organization is involved in is the best chance an organization has in getting a positive message out to the public. Time should be taken in advance to support a local department of health and environmental groups. It is also important to make a special effort to be on the same team and to eliminate barriers that limit positive communication.

7.0 STATE ENVIRONMENTAL PROTECTION AGENCY

7.1 Audits of Risk Management Plans

Owners or operators of a stationary source with more than a threshold quantity of a regulated substance in a process must submit an RMP. The risk management program contains three elements: a hazard assessment, a prevention program, and an emergency response program. The entire program is described and documented in an RMP, which is submitted to U.S. EPA. Audits of the RMP help ensure compliance with the risk management program to ensure that the RMP meets the requirements of the regulation. A wide range of agencies perform these audits; however, in most instances a state environmental protection agency will perform the actual audit. Each implementing agency has flexibility in identifying facilities for RMP audits, but common selection criteria include previous accident history of the facility, accident history for other facilities in the same industry, quantity of RMP-regulated substance on-site, or close proximity to public and environmental receptors. Auditors will prepare an audit report summarizing their observations and conclusions. A copy of this report will be sent to the facility, the state emergency response commission, the LEPC, and, upon request, to any other federal, state, or local agency. Generally, these audits include representatives from your local fire department, LEPC, and other environmental professionals so the coordination at the local level can provide additional creditability during the audit process.

7.2 Coordination of Reporting of Hazardous Materials Releases

Reporting a hazardous materials leak or spill is required by law. Whether a utility's management calls or submits in writing the required report, data collected is essential to the appropriate investigation of future hazardous materials incidents and patterns. No detail is too small. Each incident reported may help alleviate future problems and may serve as the basis for program and regulatory changes. Choosing the appropriate reporting method and knowing whom to call must be determined in advance for any issue that poses a threat to the public or the environment.

Generally, an immediate telephonic notification within 15 minutes is required if, as a direct result of hazardous materials release, the threshold quantity is met or exceeded, a person is killed or hospitalized, or evacuation of the general public occurs lasting 1 or more hours. A detailed written report may also be required for all large hazardous materials releases, especially if it is capable of posing an unreasonable risk to public health and safety. In some instances, multiple calls may also be required such as calling a state warning point, but then also calling the National Response Center. It is important to take the time now to review a JHA, inventory of hazardous chemicals, and emergency response plans to verify the organization has the right contact list to ensure the right people are called at the right time.

During training or review of emergency response plans, it is also important to be up-to-date on communications issues such as phone contact lists and current phone numbers and to verify contact information.

8.0   FEDERAL ENVIRONMENTAL PROTECTION AGENCY

8.1   Five-Year Submittal of Risk Management Plan

Under the authority of Section 112(r) of CAA, the Chemical Accident Prevention Provisions require facilities that produce, handle, process, distribute, or store certain chemicals to develop a risk management program, prepare an RMP, and submit the RMP to U.S. EPA. Many wastewater facilities were initially required to comply with the rule in 1999 because of the disinfection chemicals in use at the time. The rule has been amended on several occasions since then.

While the industry has sought safer disinfection chemicals, the effectiveness of some of the RMP chemicals combined with their ability to successfully treat high flow levels has many organizations willing to comply with the RMP requirements and simply handle their chemicals responsibly. Wastewater treatment plants using containers of elemental chlorine must comply with the requirements for Program 2 or 3, which includes a wide range of activities.

For owners or operators of an RMP facility, U.S. EPA's Chemical Accident Prevention regulations, 40 CFR Part 68, require that an RMP be fully updated and resubmitted at least once every 5 years. If certain process changes described in 40 CFR §68.190 occur at a facility prior to the 5-year anniversary of the RMP, the RMP must be updated and resubmitted. Coordination of all phases of the organization, from engineering to operations, is needed to identify when changes have happened. Simple changes in the chemicals used in the process may reduce or even eliminate reporting requirements, but the 5-year anniversary date is reset whenever the RMP is fully updated and resubmitted.

8.2   Three-Year Update of Hazard Analysis

For treatment plants using elemental chlorine in ton containers, several aspects of such programs must be periodically reviewed and documented. These reviews include training, operating procedures, documentation, and a documented review and update of the plant's hazard analysis. For both Program 2 and 3, plant management is required to provide refresher training in operating procedures at least every 3 years and to perform a review and update of the facility's hazard analysis and process chemicals. Coordination may be required determining new considerations for the facility's hazard assessment or updates related to a process change.

8.3   Toxics Release Inventory Reporting

In 1986, the Emergency Planning and Community Right-to-Know Act (EPCRA) was enacted to inform communities and citizens of chemical hazards in their areas. Section 313 of EPCRA requires U.S. EPA and the states to collect data annually on releases and transfers of certain toxic chemicals from industrial facilities and to make the data available to the public in the Toxics Release Inventory (TRI).

In 1990, Congress passed the Pollution Prevention Act, which requires facilities to report additional data on waste management and source reduction activities to U.S. EPA under TRI. The goal of the Toxics Release Inventory Program is to provide communities with information about toxic chemical releases and waste management activities and to support informed decision-making at all levels by industry, government, and non-governmental organizations. The Toxics Release Inventory Program compiles data on toxic chemical releases and waste management activities and makes it available through data files and database tools.

The TRI requires coordination, and many of the chapters in this manual of practice deal directly with rules, requirements, and procedures related to hazardous materials used or stored at a facility. The selection of safety equipment is, in many instances, driven by information contained in a TRI report; PPE is covered extensively in Chapter 10. In Chapter 9, detailed sections describe how hazardous materials and waste require treatment plant managers to go beyond their gates and fences and reach out to those they may need to call in the time of an emergency. Many examples of required communication and coordination carry with them requirements that pose legal responsibilities and personal liabilities. Working closely with the local community, first response agencies, and planning committees is as basic to hazardous materials as understanding a facility's hazardous chemicals and dealing with them professionally.

9.0 REFERENCES

National Fire Protection Association, Life Safety Code 101; http://www.nfpa.org (accessed Nov 2011).

Occupational Safety and Health Administration; CFR 1910.38, Emergency Action Plans.

Occupational Safety and Health Administration; CFR 1910.119, Process Safety Management of Highly Hazardous Chemicals.

Occupational Safety and Health Administration; CFR 1910.120, Hazardous Waste Operations and Emergency Response.

Occupational Safety and Health Administration; CFR 1910.146, Permit-required Confined Spaces.

Occupational Safety and Health Administration; CFR 1910.147, Control of Hazardous Energy.

Occupational Safety and Health Administration; CFR 1910.1200, Hazard Communication Standard.

U.S. Environmental Protection Agency Clean Air Act Section 112(r). Risk Management Plan.

10.0 SUGGESTED READINGS

National Institute of Occupational Safety and Health Home Page. http://www.cdc.gov/niosh (accessed Nov 2011).

National Fire Protection Association Home Page http://www.nfpa.org (accessed Nov 2011).

Occupational Safety and Health Administration Home Page. http://www.osha.gov/ (accessed Nov 2011).

U.S. Chemical Safety and Hazard Board Home Page. http://www.csb.gov (accessed Nov 2011).

U.S. Environmental Protection Agency Home Page. http://www.epa.gov (accessed Nov 2011).

Water Environment Federation (2010) *Information Technology in Water and Wastewater Utilities;* Manual of Practice No. 33; McGraw-Hill: New York.

Water Environment Federation; American Society of Civil Engineers; Environmental & Water Resources Institute (2009) *Design of Municipal Wastewater Treatment Plants,* 5th ed.; WEF Manual of Practice No. 8; ASCE Manuals and Reports on Engineering Practice No. 76; McGraw-Hill: New York.

Water Environment Federation; American Water Works Association; International Water Association (2011) *International Standard Units for Water and Wastewater Processes;* WEF Manual of Practice No. 6; Water Environment Federation: Alexandria, Virginia

Chapter 12

Security and Emergency Preparedness

(continued)

1.0 INTRODUCTION AND OBJECTIVES

On September 11, 2001, the possibility of an international terrorist attack within the continental United States became a reality. The most recent terrorist attacks targeting the United States have been directed at constructed facilities and infrastructure (e.g., the World Trade Center in New York City, the Pentagon, select postal facilities, and congressional offices). Although these attacks seemed to initiate terrorism in the continental United States, numerous domestic terrorism attacks and incidents have occurred in the United States since the early 1950s. In addition to intentional attacks, the effects of hurricane Katrina on the Gulf Coast highlighted the risks and safety issues associated with remediation and recovery of infrastructure systems following a significant disaster. Thus, the current focus in safety and emergency preparedness is preparing for *all hazards* instead of focusing on intentional attacks or accidental discharges.

2.0   SECURITY ISSUES FOR THE 21ST CENTURY

2.1   Safety, Security, and Sustainability

To address preparing for all hazards, the "3-S design guidance" was developed in response to this paradigm shift. The 3-S design guidance consists of the following:

- Safety
  - Public health protection through regulatory compliance and
  - Workers and surrounding community protection;
- Security—All hazards
  - Vulnerability/resilience assessments and
  - Emergency response/operation plans; and
- Sustainability
  - Design and decision support systems and
  - Environmental considerations.

2.2   Risk, Resilience, and Resilience Management

In January 2010, the American Society of Civil Engineers (ASCE) conducted a series of workshops to address problems with infrastructure deficiencies in the United States. The outcomes associated with these workshops were discussed in Powell (2010). Based on these outcomes, a consensus was reached that the water and wastewater infrastructure in the United States is in a state of crisis and that the following recommendations may provide a roadmap to ease that crisis and a vision for improvement:

- Increase federal leadership in infrastructure;

- Promote sustainability and resilience;

- Develop federal, regional, and state infrastructure plans;

- Address life-cycle costs and ongoing maintenance; and

- Increase and improve investment from all stakeholders.

In the United States, the majority of water and wastewater infrastructure components were built in the 30 years following the end of World War II as required by an increase in urban populations. In 1996, there were 16 024 publicly owned wastewater treatment facilities in operation in the United States treating approximately 121 120 ML (32 000 mil. gal) of wastewater per day. These facilities served approximately 190 million people, representing approximately 72% of the United States population (U.S. EPA, 1996).

The U.S. Environmental Protection Agency (U.S. EPA) released the Clean Water and Drinking Water Gap Analysis Report in 2002 (U.S. EPA, 2002). This peer reviewed gap analysis was performed for both drinking water and wastewater infrastructure systems for a 20-year period from 2000 to 2019 and included estimates of the funding gap for both capital costs and operations and maintenance. Using the most conservative estimates, the total funding gap for the drinking water infrastructure was estimated to be 45 billion dollars and, for the wastewater collection and treatment infrastructure, 21 billion dollars.

The aforementioned information and the predicted infrastructure rehabilitation and replacement needs expected in the next decade prompted U.S. EPA to commit to promoting sustainable infrastructure practices. If successfully implemented, these practices would help reduce the predicted gap between infrastructure needs and infrastructure spending (U.S. EPA, 2006).

Utility resilience is defined as the ability of a utility to absorb and/or cope with an incident (intentional attack or natural hazard) with interruption of function or, if interrupted, return to normal operations as quickly as possible (ANSI, 2010). Once determined, utility resilience can be an additional metric to help utilities prepare for, respond to, remediate, and effectively manage an incident in an effort to return to normal operations as soon as possible.

2.2.1 Resilience

The water sector has recently developed a series of metrics based on the goals and objectives outlined in the Water Sector Specific Plan (SSP) under the National

Infrastructure Protection Plan (DHS, 2008). These indicators provide a foundation for the development of a measure for utility resilience. In addition, the water sector has actively encouraged and recognized excellence in utility management that is based on a performance framework commonly referred to as *effective utility management* (EUM) (U.S. EPA et al., 2008).

Effective utility management is an effort by U.S. EPA and professional water organizations to formalize a collaborative effort to promote effective utility management. The 10 attributes of an effectively managed water sector utility are as follows (U.S. EPA et al., 2008):

1. Product quality,
2. Employee and leadership development,
3. Financial viability,
4. Community sustainability,
5. Stakeholder understanding and support,
6. Customer satisfaction,
7. Operation optimization,
8. Operational resiliency,
9. Infrastructure stability, and
10. Water resource adequacy.

As a compliment to the aforementioned attributes, the following five keys to management success were also identified (U.S. EPA et al., 2008):

1. Leadership,
2. Strategic business planning,
3. Organizational approaches,
4. Measurement, and
5. Continual improvement management framework.

Many of the indicators in the EUM literature complement those from the Water SSP and/or have been adapted for purposes of developing a measure of utility resilience.

2.2.2   Utility Resilience Index

The utility resilience index (URI) is a numeric assessment of a utility's ability to absorb and/or cope with an incident and return to normal operations as quickly as possible. The URI is 100-point scale consisting of the following two sub-indices:

- Operational resilience index (ORI)—these indicators reflect the tactical capacity of the utility to react quickly and/or cope with various incidents that have the potential to disrupt services; and

- Financial resilience index (FRI)—these indicators reflect the fiscal capacity of the utility and supporting community to react quickly and/or cope with various incidents that have the potential to disrupt revenue.

The indicators in both sub-indices are arrayed on a scale that is based on a targeted performance level or utility or community condition. The utility will select the highest level and/or condition for each indicator. The assigned numeric value for each indicator is then multiplied by the respective weighting factor and then summed for each sub-index. The URI may be calculated using the following equations:

$$\text{URI} = (\text{ORI} \times w_1) + (\text{FRI} \times w_2) \tag{12.1}$$

Where
  URI = utility resilience index and
  w_n = weight for a given subindex (presently set at 50%).

$$\text{ORI} = \Sigma\ (O_1\ o_1 + O_2\ o_2 + \cdots O_n o_n) \tag{12.2}$$

Where
  ORI = operational resilience index,
  o_n = weight for a given indicator,
  O_n = operational indicator,
  n = number of indicators.

$$\text{FRI} = \Sigma\ (F_1\ f_1 + F_2 f_2 + \cdots F_n f_n) \tag{12.3}$$

Where
  FRI = financial resilience index,
  f_n = weight for a given indicator,
  F_n = financial indicator, and
  n = number of indicators.

Operational and FRI parameters are presented in the following sections.

2.2.2.1 Operational Resilience Index Parameters

The following are ORI parameters:

- Emergency response plan,

- National Incident Management System (NIMS) compliance,

- Mutual aid and assistance,

- Emergency power for critical operations,

- Ability to meet minimum daily treatment when treatment plant is nonfunctional,

- Critical parts and equipment, and

- Critical staff resilience.

2.2.2.2 Financial Resilience Index Parameters

The following are FRI parameters:
- Business continuity plan;

- Utility bond rating;

- Governmental Accounting Standards Board Statement No. 34 Assessment (GASB 34);

- Unemployment; and

- Median household income.

2.2.3 Asset Resilience

The same metrics, discussed previously, for utility resilience can also be applied to a single asset within a wastewater collection and treatment system (e.g., disinfection). *Asset resilience* can be defined as the ability of an asset to survive an incident without interruption of function or to restore function rapidly. Asset resilience can be explained using the following equation:

$$\text{Asset resilience} = f(\text{SD}, V, T) \tag{12.4}$$

Where
  SD = service denial = (Severity) × (Duration of denial of service);
  V = vulnerability or likelihood that the estimated consequences will result from a specific event, given that it occurs; and
  T = threat likelihood, or frequency, that the incident will occur over a given time span (typically 1 year).

3.0   NATURAL, ACCIDENTAL, AND INTENTIONAL THREATS TO WASTEWATER COLLECTION AND TREATMENT SYSTEMS

Emergency preparedness is no longer the sole concern of earthquake-prone Californians and those who live in the part of the country known as "Tornado Alley." For Americans, preparedness must now account for man-made disasters as well as natural ones. Knowing what to do during an emergency is an important part of being prepared and may make all the difference when seconds count (FEMA, http://www.ready.gov/america/index.html).

The threat from terrorism remains real and serious. An attack could take place at any time and any organization could be directly or indirectly affected. Acts of terrorism vary in scale and purpose. Some aim merely to inflict superficial damage or cause public distress to draw attention to a particular cause. Others can be more violent and indiscriminate with far-reaching consequences.

The most significant threat may come from international terrorism with its ambitions to mount high-impact attacks combining mass casualties with substantial disruption to vital services such as energy, transport, and communications. This is a threat that is different in scale and intent to any that the country has faced before. While the United States has faced a variety of terrorist threats in the past, a unique combination of factors (namely, the global reach, capability, resilience, sophistication, and ambition of international terrorist groups) means the United States currently faces a threat on a scale not previously encountered.

Many of these networks are loose-knit and operate without a conventional structure and with connections across the world, bound by shared extremist views or experiences. Some of these networks are centrally guided, while others are autonomous. However, both work to carry out terrorist attacks.

Terrorist groups and their associated networks remain capable of carrying out significant terrorist attacks such as those in London in July 2005. The threat from these groups and their associated networks is, therefore, likely to persist for some time.

In terms of physical attacks, most terrorist bombs are known as *improvised explosive devices* and can be categorized either by their means of delivery (vehicle-, person-borne, etc.) or by their content (chemical, biological, radiological, etc.) as follows:

- Vehicle (car, lorry [truck], and bike);
- Delivered item (parcel or packet); or

- Person-borne (rucksack [backpack], briefcase, handbag, or concealed on the body) (UK Centre for the Protection of National Infrastructure, http://www.cpni.gov.uk/).

Water and wastewater systems are particular targets because loss of their services would provide a psychological boost to terrorists. Other threats include disasters such as

- Chemical emergencies (http://www.fema.gov/hazard/chemical/index.shtm);
- Dam failures (http://www.fema.gov/hazard/damfailure/index.shtm);
- Earthquakes (http://www.fema.gov/hazard/earthquake/index.shtm);
- Fires (http://www.fema.gov/hazard/fire/index.shtm) or wildfire (http://www.fema.gov/hazard/wildfire/index.shtm);
- Floods (http://www.fema.gov/hazard/flood/index.shtm);
- Hazardous material releases (http://www.fema.gov/hazard/hazmat/index.shtm);
- Heat (http://www.fema.gov/hazard/heat/index.shtm);
- Hurricanes (http://www.fema.gov/hazard/hurricane/index.shtm);
- Landslides (http://www.fema.gov/hazard/landslide/index.shtm);
- Nuclear power plant emergencies (http://www.fema.gov/hazard/nuclear/index.shtm);
- Thunderstorms (http://www.fema.gov/hazard/thunderstorm/index.shtm);
- Tornadoes (http://www.fema.gov/hazard/tornado/index.shtm);
- Tsunamis (http://www.fema.gov/hazard/tsunami/index.shtm);
- Volcanoes (http://www.fema.gov/hazard/volcano/index.shtm);
- Wildfire (http://www.fema.gov/hazard/wildfire/index.shtm); and
- Winter storms (http://www.fema.gov/hazard/winter/index.shtm).

Internal threats include vandalism caused by outsiders or disgruntled current or former employees that the wastewater system needs to be protected against. The following are additional recommended resources:

- *Water Terrorism: An Overview of Water & Wastewater Security Problems and Solutions* by Richard Lancaster-Brooks, Khafra Engineering Consultants, at http://www.homelandsecurity.org/newjournal/articles/lancaster-brooks. htm and

- *Securing U.S. Water Supplies* by David Isenberg, independent consultant, at http://www.cdi.org/terrorism/water-pr.cfm.

Both publications provide details for protection of water and wastewater systems.

4.0 DOCUMENTED INCIDENTS IN WASTEWATER COLLECTION AND TREATMENT SYSTEMS

While not resulting from a security breach, the following narrative demonstrates what might happen if a security breach occurred at a wastewater collection and treatment facility. An event occurred in Louisville, Kentucky, shortly after 5:15 a.m. on Friday, February 13, 1981, when two women going to work at a hospital drove under the railroad overpass on Hill Street near 12th Street. There was a gigantic blast, and their car was hurled into the air and onto its side. At the same time, a police helicopter was heading toward the downtown area when the officers saw an unforgettable sight: a series of explosions, "like a bombing run," erupting along the streets of Old Louisville and through the University of Louisville campus (see Figure 12.1).

More than 3.2 km (2 miles) of Louisville streets were pockmarked with craters where manholes had been. Several blocks of Hill Street had fallen into the collapsed, 3.7-m (12-ft) diameter sewer line. Miraculously, no one was hurt seriously, but homes and businesses were extensively damaged and some families had to be evacuated.

FIGURE 12.1 Louisville, Kentucky, sewer explosions started at a railroad underpass on Hill Street (courtesy of *Courier-Journal* and *Louisville Times*; Photo by Larry Spitzer and Jon Seals).

Louisville was in the headlines and on broadcast news throughout the country for several days.

The cause of the explosion was traced to the Ralston-Purina soybean processing plant southeast of the university campus, where thousands of gallons of a highly flammable solvent, hexane, had spilled into the sewer lines. The fumes from hexane created an explosive mixture, which lay in wait in the larger sewer lines. As the women drove under the overpass, a spark from their car apparently ignited the gases (Louisville/Jefferson County Metropolitan Sewer District (http://www.msdlouky.org/aboutmsd/history20.htm).

Similarly, in Guadalajara, Mexico, a disastrous series of sewer gasoline explosions in Guadalajara on Wednesday, April 22, 1992, though not caused by a terrorist attack, demonstrate the potential impact of a well-planned and executed terrorist attack using a city's sewer lines (http://www.semp.us/publications/biot_reader.php?BiotID=356). The multiple blasts over a period of about 4 hours tore apart more than 9.7 km (6 miles) of sewer lines and, in the worst-hit places, left heavily trafficked streets in a pile of

Guadalajara street ravine following 1992 sewer explosions. Source: http://www.guadalajarareporter.com/fullbooks.cfm?section=books&id=115; accessed May 5, 2006.

Rubble in center of street destroyed by sewer explosions in Guadalajara, 1992. Photo credit, with permission (Jon Seals): Disaster Recovery Journal at: http://www.drj.com/drworld/content/w2_028.htm; accessed May 5, 2006.

FIGURE 12.2   Photographs of the Guadalajara, Mexico, disaster (courtesy of Jon Seals, *Disaster Recovery Journal* and http://www.guadalajarreporter.com).

rubble sitting in 7.6-m (25-ft) deep sewer trenches (see Figure 12.2). The explosions crushed to death 206 people, injured 1 460, damaged 1 148 buildings, and destroyed 350 businesses and 505 vehicles, according to one source (the numbers vary slightly from source to source). In addition, the disaster left about 15 000 people homeless. The political fallout rocked Mexico for years because local authorities knew of a gas leak problem for days, but chose not to evacuate the population (Suburban Emergency Management Project, http://www.semp.us/publications/biot_reader.php?BiotID=356).

The blasts measured 7.1 and 7.0 on the Richter scale at the University of Mexico in Mexico City some hundreds of miles away, according to one report. The number of explosions is controversial (Suburban Emergency Management Project, http://www.semp.us/publications/biot_reader.php?BiotID=356).

5.0 LEGISLATION REGARDING WASTEWATER UTILITY, VULNERABILITY ASSESSMENT, SECURITY, AND EMERGENCY PREPAREDNESS

As of September 2011, no specific statutory mandate has been issued for wastewater security outside the requirements for the Clean Air Act Risk Management Plan. However, legislative requirements may change for wastewater collection and treatment systems. Additional current information may be found in the American National Standards Institute (ANSI)/American Water Works Association (AWWA) G430: Security Practices for Operations and Management (2009) regarding the establishment of a minimum update cycle for vulnerability assessments, emergency response plans, and other preparedness requirements.

6.0 THE WATER SECTOR-SPECIFIC PLAN

The water sector, as defined by the National Infrastructure Protection Plan (NIPP) under the Homeland Security Presidential Directive (HSPD) 7, includes both drinking water and wastewater systems. The NIPP includes a partnership model for *collaborating* with sector asset owners and operators in recognition of the expertise and knowledge they can provide to DHS and ensure that appropriate policies are developed. As one of the 18 critical infrastructure sectors, water (including wastewater) is represented by the following nine associations and one affiliate:

- American Water Works Association (AWWA);
- Association of Metropolitan Water Agencies;

- National Association of Clean Water Agencies;

- National Association of Water Companies;

- National Rural Water Association;

- Water Environment Federation;

- Water Environment Federation Research Foundation,

- Water Research Foundation (formerly AWWA Research Foundation); and

- WaterISAC.

Each association has two voting members that make up the Water Sector Coordinating Council (WSCC). The WaterISAC is a nonvoting member. The WSCC was formed in 2004 and has worked closely with both U.S. EPA and DHS to advance the level of security and preparedness in the water sector. One critical and early action was development of the Water SSP that applies the overarching NIPP framework on the water sector.

Early in the process, WSCC recognized that a traditional security-only approach would not be sustainable in the water sector as critical assets are widely distributed and often accessible to the public. This philosophy is reflected in the vision statement and a series of goals and objectives that seek to balance the need for traditional security measures and preparedness actions that seek to capture the NIPP's risk management framework and other supporting HSPD initiatives. The WSCC's security vision is to develop a secure and resilient drinking water and wastewater infrastructure that provides clean and safe water as an integral part of daily life. This Vision assures the economic vitality of and public confidence in the nation's drinking water and wastewater through a layered defense of effective preparedness and security practices in the sector" (WSCC, 2006).

The supporting goals and objectives were developed through a consensus process to ensure that they strategically focus on key priorities as follows:

- Goal 1: Sustain protection of the public health and environment—the nation relies on a sustained amount of safe drinking water and on the treatment of wastewater to maintain public health and environmental protection. To help better protect and secure public and environmental health, the water sector will work to ensure the continuity of both drinking water and wastewater services.

The following three principle objectives support this goal:

1. Encourage the integration of security concepts into daily business operations at water sector utilities to foster a security culture;

2. Evaluate and develop security-related surveillance, monitoring, warning, and response capabilities to recognize risks introduced into water sector systems that affect public health and economic viability; and

3. Develop a nationwide laboratory network for water quality security that integrates federal and state laboratory resources and uses standardized diagnostic protocols and procedures, or develop a supporting laboratory network capable of analyzing security threats to water quality.

The latter objectives are driven by the water sector's recognition of the potential contamination threat and the provisions of HSPD-9, which is the driver for U.S. EPA's Water Security Initiative (formerly known as *Water Sentinel*).

- Goal 2: Recognize and reduce risks in the water sector—with an improved understanding of the vulnerabilities, threats, and consequences, owners and operators of water sector utilities can continue to thoroughly examine and implement risk-based approaches to better protect, detect, respond to, and recover from manmade and natural events.

The following three principle objectives support this goal:

1. Improve the identification of vulnerabilities based on knowledge and best available information, with the intent of increasing the sector's overall security posture;

2. Improve the identification of potential threats through water sector partners' (i.e., water sector utilities, national associations, and federal, state, and local governments) knowledge base and communications with the intent of increasing the sector's overall security posture; and

3. Identify and refine public health and economic impact consequences of manmade or natural incidents to improve utility risk assessments and to enhance the sector's overall security posture.

The primary basis for these objectives is encompassed in the NIPP. The water sector is well ahead of other sectors because of both mandates under the Bioterrorism Act and voluntary actions to assess vulnerabilities through the development of standards.

- Goal 3: Maintain a resilient infrastructure—the water sector will investigate how to optimize continuity of operations to ensure the economic vitality of communities and the utilities that serve them. Response and recovery from an incident in the water sector will be crucial to maintaining public health and public confidence.

Four principle objectives support this goal:

1. Emphasize continuity of drinking water and wastewater services as it pertains to water sector utility emergency preparedness, response, and recovery planning;
2. Explore and expand the implementation of mutual aid agreements/compacts in the water sector;
3. Identify and implement key response and recovery strategies; and
4. Increase the understanding of how the water sector is interdependent with other critical infrastructure sectors.

Sectors such as public health and emergency services are largely dependent on the water sector for their continuity of operations, while the water sector is dependent on sectors such as chemical and electricity for the continuity of its operations.

The water sector has significantly enhanced its resilience through mutual aid agreements among utilities and will be described further in a subsequent section of this chapter. The functional objective is to increase the number and scope of these agreements such that the resiliency of the sector and the communities they serve are enhanced. These objectives support key priorities for National Preparedness (PDD-8) and support the principles of NIMS and the National Response Framework (both are under HSPD-5; PDD-8 National Preparedness was issued March 30, 2011, and supersedes HSPD-8) (DHS, http://www.dhs.gov/xabout/laws/editorial_0607.shtm).

While the events of September 11, 2001, were more drivers for security activities, the experiences of the water sector during the 2005 hurricane season are equally and, in some instances, of greater significance in shaping the priorities developed by WSCC. The sector had been a leader in promoting greater emphasis on actions and programs that address "response and recovery" as opposed to just basic "prevention."

- Goal 4: Increase communication, outreach, and public confidence—safe drinking water and water quality are fundamental to everyday life. An incident in the sector could have significant effects on public confidence. Fostering and enhancing the relationships between utilities, government, and the public can mitigate negative perceptions in the face of an incident.

The following three principle objectives support this goal:

1. Communicate with the public about the level of security and resilience in the water sector and provide outreach to ensure the public's ability to be prepared and respond to a natural disaster or manmade incident;

2. Enhance communication and coordination among utilities and federal, state, and local officials and agencies to provide information about threats and other hazards; and

3. Improve relationships among all water sector security partners through a strong public–private partnership characterized by trusted relationships.

Many of the initiatives that support these objectives are within the mission of WaterISAC. The WSCC continues to collaborate with DHS and U.S. EPA to enhance the information available to utilities to help inform risk and resilience management decisions. In addition, HSPD-10 calls for the development of an effective risk communication strategy to facilitate emergency preparedness for a biological attack.

Several reports and initiatives have resulted from the Water SSP. Examples of these reports and initiatives are as follows:

- Water sector metrics,

- Decon strategy,

- Roadmap for securing industrial control systems in the water sector,

- All-hazards consequence management guide, and

- The WSCC priorities strategic roadmap.

7.0 VULNERABILITY ASSESSMENT TOOLS AND RESOURCES FOR WASTEWATER UTILITIES

7.1 Risk Analysis and Management for Critical Asset Protection Standard for Risk and Resilience Management of Water and Wastewater Systems

A joint standard developed by ASME Innovative Technologies Institute, LLC (ASME-ITI) and AWWA was completed in July 2010 entitled, *Risk Analysis and Management for Critical Asset Protection (RAMCAP) Standard for Risk and Resilience Management of Water and Wastewater Systems* (J100-10 standard [ANSI et al., 2010]. This standard provides a consistent and technically sound methodology to identify, analyze, quantify, and communicate the risks of specific terrorist attacks and natural hazards against critical water and wastewater systems, and establishes requirements for the risk and resilience assessment and management process that inform decisions on allocation of resources to reduce risk and enhance resilience through countermeasures and mitigation strategies. The standard documents a process for identifying security vulnerabilities and provides methods to evaluate options for improving these weaknesses.

The sector has developed two voluntary consensus-based standards to further support utilities in becoming more secure and resilient, specifically ANSI/AWWA G430: Security Practices for Operations and Management (G430 standard) and ANSI/ASME-ITI/AWWA J-100 RAMCAP Standard for Risk and Resilience Management of Water and Wastewater Systems (J100 standard).

The G430 standard defines the minimum requirements for a protective security program at drinking water or wastewater utilities to promote employee safety and the protection of public health, public safety, and public confidence. This standard is part of the Utility Management G-Series, which is designed to cover the principal activities of a typical water and/or wastewater utility. This standard is intended to apply to all water or wastewater utilities, regardless of size, location, ownership, or regulatory status. This standard builds on the long-standing practice among utilities of using a multiple barrier approach for the protection of public health and safety. The requirements of this standard are designed to support a protective utility-specific security program that will result in consistent and measurable outcomes (McLaughlin, 2010). One key requirement is updating vulnerability assessments to address any changes that have occurred.

To address this requirement, the J100 standard was developed by ASME-ITI and AWWA to provide a consistent and technically sound methodology to identify, analyze, quantify, and communicate the risks of specific malevolent attacks and natural hazards against critical water and wastewater systems. The J100 standard provides a significant update to the methodologies applied in response to the requirements of the 2002 Bioterrorism Act by establishing an all-hazards risk and resilience assessment and management process. The standard supports decision-making needs for prioritizing resource allocations to reduce risk and enhance resilience through countermeasures and mitigation strategies.

7.1.1   Risk Analysis and Management for Critical Asset Protection Overview

The RAMCAP process is a process for analyzing and managing risks associated with malevolent attacks and naturally occurring hazards against critical infrastructure. When applied to the water sector, it provides a consistent, efficient, and technically sound methodology to identify, analyze, quantify, and communicate the level of risk and resilience (i.e., the ability to withstand disruption or to quickly return to an acceptable level of service after an interruption) and the benefits of risk reduction and resilience enhancement. Because of the rigor and consistency in estimating risks, resilience, and benefits quantitatively, results of the evaluation can also be used by utilities to inform their own planning process.

The RAMCAP process is composed of seven inter-related analytic steps, as illustrated in Figure 12.3. These steps provide a foundation for data collection and interpretation, analysis, and decision-making valuable for understanding and managing risk and resilience.

There are three key upgrades in RAMCAP that differentiates it from earlier methodologies that may have been applied in the water sector. These are as follows:

1. Provides guidance for calculating the Probability of Attack (or P_A in the Risk Assessment Methodology for Water Utilities [RAM-W] equation) in a more granular fashion in that it is not assumed to be 100% or 1;

2. Provides guidance for calculating the probability of a specific natural hazard occurring at a given utility (i.e., earthquake, tornado, and hurricane); and

3. Provides guidance for calculating asset and utility resilience.

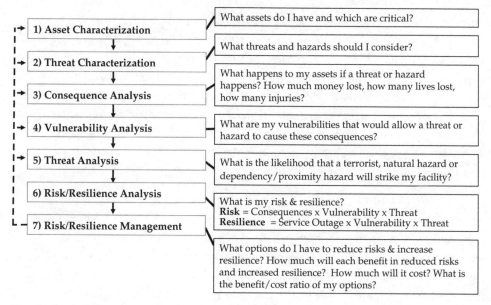

FIGURE 12.3   The seven-step RAMCAP process.

7.1.2   Probability of Attack

In a RAMCAP analysis, specific reference threat scenarios, included in this standard, are provided to the user. Use of these threats is essential to establishing comparability. The utility may also apply threats other than those provided given unique local condition or circumstances. Of the key changes in methodology, however, is the all-hazards balance that RAMCAP provides to place various threats in appropriate context. Previously, utilities lacked any credible justification for using a P_A value other than one for malevolent incidents such as terrorism. As a result, the findings of early risk assessment were heavily biased toward countermeasures aimed at thwarting acts of physical intrusion or destruction. In addition, historical data provide a robust ability to assess the probability of various natural disasters (such as flooding in the Midwest or hurricanes on the coasts) that any given utility must be prepared to handle. Therefore, the standard provides a reasoned approach to the malevolent incident threat such that the P_A value is less than 1, but greater than zero, as such acts cannot, unfortunately, be ruled out completely. The method also provides for some separation between utilities based on community size and annual natural occurrences (e.g., flooding).

7.1.3   Natural Hazards

At the urging of utility owners and operators, the new standard provides a means to incorporate natural hazard into the risk equation. The rationale as noted before is the simple reality of historical frequency and the fact that a strictly "guns, gates, and guards" approach to risk management will fail in a decentralized asset sector like water. The need to include preparedness in the risk assessment became clear in the aftermath of Hurricane Katrina (i.e., "fences and guards are no match"). An all-hazards risk management approach is necessary and, in the long term, more sustainable as most of the actions taken to prepare for natural hazards are applicable in responding to most malevolent incidents.

7.1.4   Resilience

Also missing from early risk assessment was a characterization of *resilience,* meaning the ability of an asset or system to withstand an attack or natural hazard without interruption of performing the asset or system's function or, if the function is interrupted, to restore the function rapidly (see Section 2.2). At the asset level, resilience is driven by time or severity of a service outage, which translates into lost revenue. In addition, the standard includes a URI that provides a macro-level assessment of the utility's resilience as an entity and, therefore, indicator of gaps and needs to become better prepared.

The Roadmap to Secure Control Systems in the Water Sector was developed by the Water Sector Coordinating Council Cyber Security Working Group, sponsored by AWWA and the DHS.

7.2   Risk Assessment Resources

Several decision support tools have been developed to facilitate preparation of vulnerability assessments; they include RAM-W, Vulnerability Self-Assessment Tool, and SEMS Corporation software. Although other resources are available for small or specialized water and wastewater utilities, this overview will consider these three tools.

7.2.1   Risk Assessment Methodology for Water Utilities

Risk Assessment Methodology for Water Utilities was developed by a partnership between the AWWA Research Foundation, Sandia National Laboratories, and U.S. EPA. This methodology assists utilities and security professionals and provides a plan for the utility to balance risk reduction measures by appropriately applying valuable water utility resources. This methodology also can be applied to wastewater collection and treatment systems (Sandia Corporation, http://www.sandia.gov/ram/RAMW.htm). Additional RAM-W resources and references may be obtained at http://www.sandia.gov/ram/references.htm.

7.2.2   Vulnerability Self-Assessment Tool

The Vulnerability Self-Assessment Tool is a risk assessment software tool applicable to water, wastewater, and combined utilities of all sizes. This program, developed with funding from U.S EPA, is available at no cost to utilities and assists them in performing risk assessments and updating emergency response plans (U.S. EPA, http://yosemite.epa.gov/ow/SReg.nsf/description/VSAT).

7.2.3   SEMS Software

SEMS software is marketed by SEMS Technologies, Inc., as a total compliance resource for drinking water and wastewater utilities. In addition to recordkeeping associated with water and wastewater compliance issues, this software also addresses asset management, security, and emergency management and technical support capabilities (SEMS Technologies, http://www.semstechnologies.com/).

7.3   Gap Assessment

A study was funded by the Water Research Foundation and the Association of Metropolitan Water Agencies to perform a gap analysis between the joint ASME-ITI/AWWA J-100-10 RAMCAP Standard for Risk and Resilience Management of Water and Wastewater Systems (J100-10 standard [ANSI et al., 2010]) and the three existing water/wastewater vulnerability assessment tools listed in Section 7.2 of this chapter (WRF and AMWA, 2011).

This report provides a comprehensive review of the deficiencies between the three vulnerability assessment methodologies and the J100-10 standard (J100-10 standard [ANSI et al., 2010]). The primary deficiency with all three approaches is that none of them incorporate a resilience calculation as discussed in the standard. Details of the deficiencies and recommendations to address these deficiencies can be found in the report (WRF and AMWA, 2011).

8.0   EMERGENCY RESPONSE PLANNING AND MANAGEMENT FOR WASTEWATER UTILITIES

8.1   U.S. Environmental Protection Agency Wastewater Response Protocol Toolbox

The U.S. EPA published the Response Protocol Toolbox in 2003 to address emergency response preparedness. The following is an excerpt from the "Overview and Application" document written by U.S. EPA that provides an overview of the six modules, as shown in Figure 12.4. This overview is presented to educate the reader about the emergency response process for wastewater collection and treatment systems. However, the authors advocate use of the comprehensive document published by U.S. EPA.

8.1.1   Module 1: Water Utility Planning Guide

Module 1 provides a brief discussion of the nature of the contamination threat to the public water supply. The module also describes planning activities that a utility may undertake to effectively manage contamination threats and incidents.

The objectives of Module 1 are to

1. Familiarize the reader with the nature of water contamination threats and incidents and
2. Provide an understanding of the various planning activities associated with the management of water contamination threat or incident.

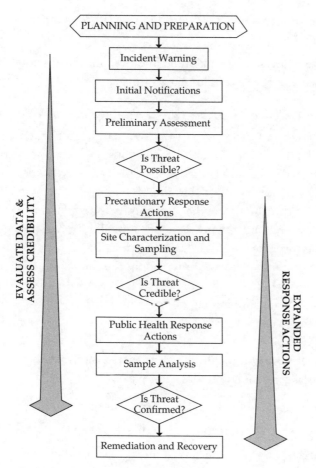

FIGURE 12.4   Overview of response to a contamination threat.

While the planning aspects of this module are targeted at drinking water utilities, much of the information provided will be of interest to any user that might support a drinking water utility during response to a contamination threat. This extended audience might include drinking water primacy agencies, law enforcement agencies, public health agencies, or crisis management organizations.

Module 1 consists of the following topics:

- Provides an overview of contamination threats;
- Describes the various warning signs of a potential contamination incident;

- Discusses the concept of "due diligence" in responding to contamination threats; and

- Lists several areas where planning and preparation are necessary to the effective management of a contamination threat.

8.1.2   Module 2: Contamination Threat Management Guide

The threat management process involves two parallel and interrelated activities: (1) evaluating the threat and (2) making decisions regarding appropriate actions to take in response to the threat. The first step of the threat evaluation process involves collection of information to help determine if the threat is "possible"; that is, do the circumstances of a threat indicate the opportunity for contamination? Following the determination that the threat is possible, additional information is gathered to help determine if the threat is "credible"; that is, does the additional information corroborate the information already known about the threat? Finally, efforts are taken to "confirm" the contamination incident; that is, is there definitive evidence that the water has actually been contaminated with a harmful substance? This is a progressive evaluation in which more serious response actions are considered as the threat is elevated through these three stages.

There are a number of difficult management decisions that must be made before, during, and after a contamination threat, such as

- How to decide if an incident has occurred, as opposed to a hoax;

- What actions to take in response to a threat;

- How to determine that a perceived threat is not credible and can be dismissed; and

- How to manage a confirmed contamination incident.

The objectives of Module 2 are to

- Present a framework for evaluating a water contamination threat and making decisions at key points in the process;

- Describe the type of information that may be useful for conducting a threat evaluation; and

- Describe the actions that might be implemented in response to a contamination threat, giving consideration to the potential consequences of various actions.

The primary audience for this module is the water utility emergency response manager, who will likely have some role in the threat management process throughout the response. Furthermore, other individuals that might be involved in the management of a contamination threat, such as members of law enforcement, the drinking water primacy agency, and the public health department, should also review this module.

Module 2 of the response protocol toolbox

- Describes the three stages of a threat evaluation: possible, credible, and confirmed;

- Describes the information that might support both the threat evaluation and the response actions that might be considered at each of these stages;

- Identifies the types of individuals and organizations that might become involved at various stages of the contamination threat management process;

- Provides examples regarding the manner in which the threat management process is applied to different incident warnings; and

- Contains various forms that might aid in the documentation of incident warnings and the subsequent threat evaluation process. The reader may find these forms useful in preparing his or her own response guidelines.

8.1.3   Module 3: Site Characterization and Sampling Guide

Site characterization is defined as the process of collecting information from the site of a suspected contamination incident at a drinking water system. Site characterization activities include the site investigation, field safety screening, rapid field-testing of the water, and sample collection.

The objectives of Module 3 are to

- Describe considerations for personnel involved in the planning or execution of site characterization activities in response to a water contamination threat; and

- Present protocols and procedures for the site investigation, field safety screening, rapid field testing, and sample collection.

Any individuals involved in planning or implementing site characterization activities are encouraged to review this module in its entirety. Laboratories that may tend to focus on Module 4 ("analytical guide") may also find the information in Module 3 useful, particularly with respect to the screening activities that occur in the field that directly affect the safety considerations of the laboratory.

Module 3 highlights the following:

- Provides an overview of planning for safe and effective site characterization;

- Describes the qualifications of individuals sent to the site and the steps taken to ensure the safety of the site characterization team;

- Contains various sample forms that may be useful for planning and documenting the results of site characterization and sampling activities, including chain of custody. The reader may find these forms useful in preparing his or her own response guidelines;

- Describes field safety screening and the contents of a core and an expanded field test kit;

- Lists the contents of a model sample collection kit; and

- Presents considerations for shipping the collected samples to the laboratory for analysis.

8.1.4   Module 4: Analytical Guide

The analytical guide presents an approach to the analysis of samples that may be collected from the site of a suspected contamination incident. The purpose of the analytical guide is *not* to provide a detailed protocol. Rather, it describes a framework for developing an approach for the analysis of water samples collected during site characterization. The framework is flexible and will allow the approach to be crafted based on available information about the threat and requirements of the specific situation. The framework is also designed to promote the effective and defensible performance of laboratory analysis.

The objectives of Module 4 are to

- Describe special laboratory considerations for handling and processing emergency water samples suspected of contamination with a harmful substance;

- Present model approaches and procedures for analysis of water samples suspected of contamination with a known or unknown substance(s); and

- Encourage planners to develop site-specific analytical approaches that follow the general principles of the framework and model analytical approaches presented in Module 4.

This module is applicable to laboratory personnel and utility planners.

Module 4 highlights the following:

- Describes existing laboratory infrastructure for the analysis of water contaminants, including a link to a compendium of laboratories that might support utilities in the analysis of emergency water samples;

- Discusses considerations for the analysis of water samples collected during an emergency, including safety, quality assurance, and legal admissibility of scientific evidence;

- Summarizes those aspects of site characterization issues that relate to laboratory safety and analysis;

- Introduces a general approach for the analysis of unknowns, which integrates site characterization results to produce a rapid, defensible, and comprehensive analysis;

- Presents an analytical approach for chemicals and pathogens based on two forms of screening for specific classes of contaminants. This approach uses a combination of standardized methods and sound exploratory techniques; and

- Provides examples of the customization of the analytical approach to specific laboratory objectives.

8.1.5   Module 5: Public Health Response Guide

Module 5 deals with public health response measures that would potentially be used to minimize public exposure to potentially contaminated water. It discusses the important issue of who is responsible for making the decision to initiate public health response actions, and considers the role of the water utility in this decision process. Specifically, it examines the role of the utility during a public health response action and the interactions between the utility, the drinking water primacy agency, the public health community, and other parties with a public health mission.

The objectives of Module 5 are to

- Identify the organizations and officials responsible for making and implementing public health response decisions for drinking water;

- Describe the role of the drinking water utility in the public health response to a water contamination threat;

- Develop communication protocols and structures within the responding public health agencies and also for communication with the public and the media;
- Identify resources and techniques to aid in evaluation of public health consequences associated with specific contaminants;
- Consider acute and chronic effects via ingestion, inhalation, and dermal exposure pathways;
- Develop response options, including containment and public notification; and
- Identify potential short-term alternative water supplies.

The primary intended users of this module include water utility staff and entities that will assist small water utilities (e.g., drinking water primacy agencies). In addition, public health response agencies (e.g., public health departments) are encouraged to read this module because they will likely make the decisions regarding public health response actions that are taken (e.g., public notification) during a water contamination threat.

Module 5 addresses the following topics:

- Describes the organizations that may be involved in making public health decisions, various response options that may be considered, and the need for an effective communication plan;
- Describes contaminant characteristics that should be considered when making public health decisions;
- Describes methods of estimating the spread of contaminated water and containment options;
- Discusses public notification, including applicable regulatory requirements, as a means of reducing or mitigating exposure and avoiding public panic, types of notifications, and information that is readily available or may be developed to educate the public (e.g., fact sheets);
- Discusses alternate water supply issues pertaining to domestic consumption, sanitation, firefighting, and the needs of critical customers.

8.1.6 Module 6: Remediation and Recovery Guide

Following a confirmed water contamination incident, it will be necessary to remediate the system and demonstrate that it has been successfully restored prior to resuming normal operation. This process involves a sequence of activities, including system characterization and selection of remedy options. Following implementation of the remediation plan, steps must be taken to demonstrate that the system can be returned to normal operation. Furthermore, plans will need to be made for the long-term supply of alternate drinking water during remediation. Module 6 describes the planning and implementation of these remediation and recovery activities, the types of organizations that would likely be involved in this stage of a response, and the utility's role during remediation and recovery.

The objectives of Module 6 are to

- Identify the organizations and officials responsible for making and implementing decisions regarding remediation and recovery activities for contaminated drinking water;

- Describe the role of the drinking water utility during the remediation and recovery stage of a contamination incident;

- Describe how a systematic planning process can be applied to ensure that the right type, quantity, and quality of data are obtained to support remediation and recovery activities;

- Describe the process for selecting a remedial technology, both for treatment of contaminated drinking water and remediation of contaminated system components; and

- Present the issues and considerations associated with returning to normal operation following remediation and recovery activities.

The target audience for this module includes individuals that will be involved in system characterization, risk assessment, and remedial response action activities following a confirmed contamination incident. The target audience also includes decision-makers who will determine the need for long-term alternate water supplies, select remedial technologies, determine when to return to normal operations, and communicate with the public.

Module 6 highlights the following:

- Presents procedures for characterization of the contaminated area;

- Describes considerations for providing a long-term alternate supply of drinking water during the remediation and recovery stage;

- Describes a flexible sequence of steps designed to select the appropriate remedial response to address a contaminated drinking water system;

- Describes regulations that must be considered when managing wastes generated from the remediation of a contaminated waste system; and

- Presents special considerations for system restart with emphasis on public outreach and communication.

A second and equally useful guidance document aimed specifically at wastewater systems is the *Emergency Response Plan Guidance for Wastewater Systems* written by the Water Environment Research Foundation in collaboration with U.S. EPA (WERF, 2004). The document provides a template for emergency response planning and presents essential vocabulary and concepts such as *chain-of-command, communication and notification plans, personnel safety provisions, plan initiation and decision-making process, emergency operations centers, emergency response training,* and *plan evaluation* (WERF, 2004). The guidance document also addresses terrorist threats related to wastewater systems.

8.2 Water/Wastewater Agency Response Networks

Transformative events like Hurricane Katrina and the Japanese earthquake test boundaries of our physical resilience, but society's capacity to cope is amazing. During such times, utilities have repeatedly demonstrated that the water sector has a significant capacity to help their neighbors. While mutual aid and assistance is not a new concept, formulation on intrastate mutual aid and assistance is because, previously, such agreements were localized. The intrastate initiative, called the water/wastewater agency response network (WARN), has been successful and already has numerous success stories (Blankenship and Morley, 2008).

Water/wastewater agency response network agreements expand the resource sharing capability between utilities to all signatories in the entire state. They also ensure that all stakeholders have a clear understanding of the operational rules of engagement in terms of liability and reimbursement, which are not issues a utility wants to be considering during a crisis situation. The WARN agreement can be activated by any member in need of assistance and response is optional because a utility would not respond if that response to a WARN agreement could put its own operations in jeopardy.

Water/wastewater agency response network programs have been established in nearly all 50 states and have expanded into Canada. The model agreement for the WARN initiative was first issued as part of an action plan (Morley and Riordan, 2006) based on an agreement in place in California, Florida, and Texas and key elements of

NIMS. This agreement was updated in 2007 to reflect the growing knowledge and limitation of various state laws. Each state WARN agreement is adopted to meet their own legislative code. However, the majority of current agreements are largely identical to the baseline model agreement. The rapid growth and adoption of WARN across the country has led to development of several key supporting guidance documents including resource typing (Morley, 2007), a sample operations plan (http://water.epa.gov/infrastructure/watersecurity/techtools/index.cfm) (U.S. EPA), and table-top exercise materials(http://water.epa.gov/infrastructure/watersecurity/techtools/ttx.cfm) (U.S. EPA).

8.3 Water Contamination Information Tool

The water contaminant information tool (WCIT) is a secure, online database that provides information to select personnel from drinking water and wastewater utilities on chemical, biological, and radiological contaminants of concern for water security. Access to this password-protected tool is granted by U.S. EPA by applying to the following Web site: http://cdx.epa.gov/. More information on WCIT is available at http://water.epa.gov/scitech/datait/databases/wcit/index.cfm.

9.0   REFERENCES

American National Standards Institute; American Water Works Association (2009) Security Practices for Operation and Management, 1st ed.; ANSI/AWWA G430-09, American Water Works Association: Washington, D.C.

American National Standards Institute; ASME Innovative Technologies Institute; American Water Works Association (2010) *Risk Analysis and Management for Critical Asset Protection (RAMCAP) Standard for Risk and Resilience Management of Water and Wastewater Systems*, 1st ed.; ANSI/ASME-ITI/AWWA J100-10.

Blankenship, L.; Morley, K. M. (2008) Building a Business Case for WARN Participation. *J. – AWWA,* **100** (11), 36–38, 40.

Department of Homeland Security (2008) *Water Sector-Specific Plan in Support of the National Infrastructure Protection Plan.*

Federal Emergency Management Agency, Ready America. http://www.ready.gov/america/index.html (accessed Jan 2012).

http://www.awwa.org/Advocacy/Govtaff/Documents/Utilities_Helping_Utilities.pdf (accessed Jan 2012).

McLaughlin, J. (2010) Going "All In" on All Hazards. *J.—Am. Water Works Assoc.*, **102** (1), 33.

Morley, K. M. (2007) A Vision and Direction for Water Sector Security and Preparedness Initiative. *J.—Am. Water Works Assoc.*, **99** (2) 38.

Morley, K. M.; Riordan, R. (2006) Utilities Helping Utilities: An Action Plan for Mutual Aid and Assistance Networks for Water and Wastewater Utilities.

Powell, A. E. (2010) Special Report: The Infrastructure Roundtables: Seeking Solutions to an American Crisis, *Civ. Eng.—Am. Soc. Civ. Eng.*, **80** (4), 62–70.

Sandia Corporation (2011) Security Risk Assessment Methodologies for Critical Infrastructures ™, Sandia National Laboratories Security Risk Assessment Methodologies. http://www.sandia.gov/ram/RAMW.htm (accessed Jan 2012).

SEMS Technologies, Inc. http://www.semstechnologies.com/ (accessed Jan 2012).

Suburban Emergency Management Project, Biot Report #356: May 03, 2006. http://www.semp.us/publications/biot_reader.php?BiotID=356 (accessed Jan 2012).

UK Centre for the Protection of National Infrastructure. http://www.cpni.gov.uk/ (accessed Jan 2012).

U.S. Department of Homeland Security, Homeland Security Presidential Directives. http://www.dhs.gov/xabout/laws/editorial_0607.shtm (accessed Jan 2012).

U.S. Department of Homeland Security (2008) *Water Sector Specific Plan in support of the National Infrastructure Protection Plan;* U.S. Department of Homeland Security: Washington, D.C.

U.S. Environmental Protection Agency; Association of Metropolitan Water Agencies; American Public Works Association; American Water Works Association; National Association of Clean Water Agencies; National Association of Water Companies; Water Environment Federation (2008) *Effective Utility Management: A Primer for Water and Wastewater Utilities.*

U.S. Environmental Protection Agency, Response Protocol Toolbox. http://www.epa.gov/safewater/watersecurity/tools/trainingcd/Pages/ws-documents.html (accessed Jan 2012).

U.S. Environmental Protection Agency (1996) http://www.epa.gov/owm/wquality/index.htm; http://www.epa.gov/owm/faq.htm (accessed Jan 2012).

U.S. Environmental Protection Agency (2002) http://www.epa.gov/waterinfrastructure/infrastructuregap.html..

U.S. Environmental Protection Agency (2006) Sustaining our Nation's Water Infrastructure. http://www.epa.gov/waterinfrastructure/pdfs/brochure_si_sustainingournationswaters.pdf

U.S. Environmental Protection Agency, VSAT Web Site. http://yosemite.epa.gov/ow/SReg.nsf/description/VSAT (accessed Jan 2012).

Water Environment Research Foundation (2004) *Emergency Response Plan Guidance for Wastewater Systems*. http://www.werf.org/pdf/03CTS4S.pdf (accessed Jan 2012).

Water Research Foundation; Association of Metropolitan Water Agencies (2011) Gap Assessment for ASME-ITI/AWWA J100-10 Standard and Leading Vulnerability Assessment Tools, Web Report #4358.

Water Sector Coordinating Council (2006) First Annual Report. http://www.awwa.org/Advocacy/Govtaff/Documents/WSCC_Annual_Report.pdf (accessed Jan 2012).

10.0 SUGGESTED READINGS

Morley, K. (2010) Advancing the Culture of Security and Preparedness in the Water Sector. *J.—Am. Water Works Assoc.*, **102** (6), 34.

Roberson, J. A.; Morley, K. M. (2005) We Need to Get Strategic on Water Security. *J.—Am. Water Works Assoc.*, **97** (10), 42.

Roberson, J. A.; Morley, K. M. (2006) Water Security: Shifting to an All-Hazards Resiliency Approach. *J.—Am. Water Works Assoc.*, **98** (5) 46.

Appendix A

Glossary of Terms

abatement—The actions taken to reduce the amount, degree of the hazard, or intensity of the release or threatened release of a hazardous material.

absorbent material—A material designed to pick up and hold liquid hazardous material to prevent contamination spread.

absorption—(1) The process of absorbing or "picking up" a liquid hazardous material to prevent enlargement of the contaminated area. (2) Movement of a toxicant into the circulatory system by oral, dermal, or inhalation exposure.

acceptable risk—A risk judged to be outweighed by corresponding benefits or one that is of such a degree that it is considered to pose minimal potential for adverse effects.

access control point—The point of entry and exit which regulates traffic to and from control zones.

ACGIH—See *American Conference of Governmental Industrial Hygienists*.

acid—A hydrogen-containing corrosive material that reacts with water to produce hydrogen ions; a proton donor.

acute effect—An adverse action on a human or animal, generally after a single significant exposure, which may be mild or severe (see *chronic effect*).

acute exposure—Exposure that is short in duration.

acute release—Release of a hazardous material that is short in duration.

acute toxicity—Any harmful effect produced by a single short-term exposure that may result in severe biological harm or death. Normally, a toxic effect that appears within a day of the exposure or dose.

adjutant—A substance used in pesticide formulation to aid its action. (Also used in the manufacture of drugs.)

administering agency The designated unit of a county or city tasked to administer local implementation of the state and federal hazardous material emergency planning and community right-to-know programs.

adsorption—The process or accumulation of molecules, in various states, on specific substances or surfaces.

aerosols—Liquid droplets or solid particles dispersed in air that are of fine enough particle size (0.01 to 100 microns) to remain dispersed for a period of time.

after action report—A post-incident analysis report generated by a responsible party or responding agency after termination of a hazardous material incident describing actions taken, materials involved, impacts, and so on.

agency specific plan—An emergency plan written by and addressing an individual agency's response actions, capabilities, and resources.

AIHA—See *American Industrial Hygiene Association*.

airborne pollutants—Contaminants that are carried and released into the atmosphere or air.

air modeling—Mathematical models used to predict movement and concentrations of chemicals in the atmosphere.

air monitoring—To measure, record, and/or detect pollutants in ambient air, typically with direct-reading instruments.

air-purifying respirators (APR)—Personal protective equipment; a breathing mask with specific chemical cartridges designed to either filter particulates or absorb contaminants before they enter the worker's breathing zone. They are intended to be used only in atmospheres where the hazards and concentrations are known. Some filtering face pieces are referred to as *dust masks*.

air-purifying respirator (APR)—powered—An APR with a portable motor to force air through the filtering/ purifying cartridges for use only in atmospheres where the chemical hazards and concentrations are known.

air quality management district (AQMD)—A local/regional air pollution agency responsible for regulation and monitoring of air quality.

air sampling—To measure, record, and/or detect pollutants in ambient air, typically with laboratory analysis of samples (e.g., a detector tube).

alkali—A hydroxide-containing (-OH) corrosive material that is soluble in water, neutralizes acids, and is irritating or destructive to tissue. A material can also be alkaline if it reacts in water to increase the concentration of hydroxide ions.

ambient air quality—Quality of the surrounding atmosphere or circulating air.

American Conference of Governmental Industrial Hygienists (ACGIH)—A professional society of persons responsible for full-time industrial hygiene programs who are employed by official governmental units. Its primary function is to encourage the interchange of experience among governmental industrial hygienists and to collect and make available information of value to them. The society promotes standards and techniques in industrial hygiene and coordinates governmental activities with community agencies.

American Industrial Hygiene Association (AIHA)—An organization of professionals trained in the recognition and control of health hazards and the prevention of illness related thereto. It promotes the study and control of environmental factors affecting the health of industrial workers and provides information and communication services pertaining to industrial hygiene.

American National Standards Institute (ANSI)—The institute serves as a clearinghouse for nationally coordinated voluntary safety, engineering, and industrial standards developed by industrial firms, trade associations, technical societies, consumer organizations, and government agencies.

American Society for Testing and Materials (ASTM)—The society establishes voluntary consensus standards for materials, products, systems, and services. Sponsors research projects and develops standard test methods, specifications and recommended practices now in use.

anhydrous—Free from water, dry.

asbestos—A silicate of calcium or magnesium mineral, the friable form occurring in threadlike fibers; non-combustible and a nonconductor of electricity; a known carcinogen.

asbestosis—A disease of the lungs caused by the inhalation of fine airborne fibers of asbestos.

asphyxiant—A vapor or gas that can cause unconsciousness or death by suffocation (lack of oxygen).

assessment—The process of determining the nature and degree of hazard of a hazardous material or hazardous materials incident.

assisting agencies—Any agency that assists the agency having jurisdiction at the scene of a hazardous materials incident by providing a service or support not within the immediate responsibility or capability of the agency having jurisdiction.

Association of American Pesticide Control Officials, Inc.—This association consists of officials charged by law with active execution of the laws regulating the sale of economic poisons and of deputies designated by these officials employed by state, territorial, dominion, or federal agencies.

Association of American Railroads (AAR)—A central coordinating and research agency of the American railway industry.

authority having jurisdiction—Provides for the position of Incident Commander/ Scene Manager at the scene of a hazardous materials incident occurring within their jurisdictional response boundaries. The organization, office, or individual responsible for approving the equipment, an installation, or a procedure (National Fire Protection Association).

base (chemical)—An hydroxide-containing (-OH) corrosive material that, when in a water solution, is bitter, more or less irritating, or caustic to the skin. A material can also be basic if it reacts in water to increase the concentration of hydroxide ions.

base (incident command system)—Location at which additional equipment, apparatus, and personnel are assembled for primary support of activities at the incident scene. The command post may be located at the base.

bioaccumulation—Absorption and storage of toxic chemicals from the environment in an organism, typically in body fat.

bioassay—Determination of the relative strength and toxicity of a substance (such as a drug) by comparing its effect on a test organism with that of a standard preparation.

biohazard—Infectious agents presenting a risk or potential risk to living organisms, either directly through infection or indirectly through disruption of the environment.

biohazard area—Any area in which work has been, or is being performed, with infectious agents or materials.

biological agents—Biological materials that are capable of causing acute or long-term damage to living organisms.

biological half-life—The time required for a living organism to eliminate half of a substance which it takes in.

biological treatment—A process by which waste is rendered less hazardous or is reduced in volume by relying on the action of microorganisms.

blasting agent—A material designed for blasting that has been tested and found to be so insensitive that there is little probability of accidental initiation to explosion or of transition from deflagration to detonation.

boiling liquid expanding vapor explosion (BLEVE)—Container failure with a release of energy, often rapidly and violently, which is accompanied by a release of gas to the atmosphere and propulsion of the container or container pieces because of an overpressure rupture.

boom—A floating physical barrier serving as a continuous obstruction to the spread of a contaminant.

bootie—A sock-like overboot protector worn to minimize contamination. *Boot cover* is the preferred term.

breakthrough time—The elapsed time between initial contact of the hazardous chemical with the outside surface of a barrier, such as protective clothing material, and the time at which the chemical can be detected at the inside surface of the material.

breathing zone air sample—A sample collected in the breathing area of a worker to assess exposure to airborne contaminants.

buddy system—A system of organizing employees into work groups in such a manner that each employee of the work group is designated to be observed by at least one other employee in the work group.

buffer zone—The area of land that surrounds a hazardous waste facility on which certain usage and activities are restricted to protect public health and safety and the environment from existing or potential hazards caused by the migration of hazardous waste.

Bureau of Alcohol, Tobacco and Firearms (ATF)—The federal agency that enforces and administers firearms and explosives laws and those covering the production, use, and distribution of alcohol and tobacco products.

Canadian Transport Emergency Center (CANUTEC)—A 24-hour, government-sponsored hotline for chemical emergencies (the Canadian version of CHEMTREC).

carboy—A container, typically encased in a protective basket or crate, used to ship hazardous materials, particularly corrosives.

carcinogen—An agent that produces or is suspected of producing cancer.

cascade system—Several air cylinders attached in a series to fill self-contained breathing apparatus bottles.

catastrophic incident—An event that significantly exceeds the resources of a jurisdiction.

cease and desist order—Legal direction to stop any and all activities.

Celsius (centigrade) °C—The internationally used scale for measuring temperature, in which 100° is the boiling point of water at sea level (1 atmosphere) and 0° is the freezing point.

Centers for Disease Control (CDC)—The federally funded research organization tasked with disease control and research.

CFR—*Code of Federal Regulations;* enforced by federal and state agencies and contains statutes for the function of federal government.

CGA—See *Compressed Gas Association.*

Chemical Abstracts Service (CAS) Number—A numbering system assigned by the American Chemical Society often used by local and state hazardous materials compliance legislation for tracking chemicals in the workplace and in the community.

chemical hazards response information system/Hazard Assessment Computer System (CHRIS/ HACS)—Developed by the U.S. Coast Guard, HACS is a computerized model of the CHRIS manuals (containing chemical-specific data), and is used by federal on-scene coordinators during a chemical spill response.

chemical protective clothing material—Any material or combination of materials used in an item of clothing for the purpose of isolating parts of the wearer's body from contact with a hazardous chemical.

chemical protective suit—Single or multipiece garment constructed of chemical protective clothing materials designed and configured to protect the wearer's torso, head, arms, legs, hands, and feet.

chemical resistance—The ability to resist chemical attack. The attack is dependent on the method of test and its severity is measured by determining the changes in physical properties. Time, temperature, stress, and reagent may all be factors that affect the chemical resistance of a material.

chemical-resistant materials—Materials that age and are specifically designed to inhibit or resist the passage of chemicals into and through the material by the processes of penetration, permeation, or degradation.

Chemical Transportation Emergency Center (CHEMTREC)—The Chemical Transportation Center, operated by the American Chemistry Council, provides information and technical assistance to emergency responders (telephone number: 1-800-424-9300).

Chemnet—A mutual aid network of chemical shippers and contractors. It is activated when a member shipper cannot respond promptly to an incident involving chemicals (contact is made through CHEMTREC).

Chlorep—The chlorine emergency plan, established by the Chlorine Institute, enables the nearest producer of chlorine to respond to an incident involving chlorine (contact is made through CHEMTREC).

chlorine kits—Standardized kits commercially manufactured by contract with the Chlorine Institute to provide equipment to control or stop leaks in chlorine cylinders, tanks, and transportation tank cars.

chronic effect—Delayed or slowly developing harm resulting from a chemical exposure that is often hard to recognize.

clandestine laboratory—An operation consisting of a sufficient combination of apparatus and chemicals that either have been or could be used in the illegal manufacture/synthesis of controlled substances.

Clean Air Act—A set of national standards for ambient air quality, which defines the principal types and levels of pollution that should not be exceeded. This law requires states to develop "state implementation plans" for achieving the ambient air standards in each air quality control region in the state.

cleanup—Incident scene activities directed toward removing hazardous materials, contamination, debris, damaged containers, tools, dirt, water, and road surfaces in accordance with proper and legal standards and resuming the site to as near a normal state as existed prior to the incident.

cleanup company (hazardous waste)—A commercial business entity available for hire to specifically remove, transport, and/or dispose of hazardous wastes; when appropriate, must meet California Highway Patrol and Department of Toxic Substances Control requirements.

cleanup operation—An operation where hazardous substances are removed, contained, incinerated, neutralized, stabilized, cleared up, or in any other manner processed or handled with the goal of making the site safer for people or the environment.

Clean Water Act (CWA)—Federal legislation to protect the nation's water and set state water quality standards for interstate navigable waters as the basis for pollution control and enforcement. The main objective is to restore and maintain the chemical, physical, and biological integrity of the nation's waters.

cold zone—The area outside of the warm zone. Equipment and personnel are not expected to become contaminated in this area. This is the area where resources are assembled to support the hazardous materials operation.

colorimetric tubes—Glass tubes containing a chemically treated substrate that reacts with specific airborne chemicals to produce a distinctive color. The tubes are calibrated to indicate approximate concentrations in air.

combined liquid waste sampler (coliwassa)—A tool designed to provide stratified sampling of a liquid container.

combustibility—The ability of a substance to undergo rapid chemical combination with oxygen with the evolution of heat.

combustible liquid—Liquids with a flashpoint above 38 °C (100 °F) (49 CFR 173.120 [b][2]).

combustion product—Byproducts produced or generated during the burning or oxidation of a fuel.

command—The act of directing, ordering, and/or controlling resources by virtue of explicit legal, agency, or delegated authority.

command post—The location from which all incident operations are directed and planning functions are performed. The communications center is often incorporated into the command post.

community awareness and emergency response (CAER)—A program developed by the Chemical Manufacturers Association to provide guidance for chemical plant managers to assist them in taking the initiative in cooperating with local communities developing integrated hazardous materials response plans.

community right-to-know—Legislation requiring business establishments to provide chemical inventory information to local agencies or the public.

company (fire usage)—Any piece of fire response equipment having a full complement of personnel.

compatibility—The matching of protective chemical clothing to the hazardous material involved to provide the best protection for the worker.

compatibility charts—Permeation and penetration data supplied by manufacturers of chemical protective clothing to indicate chemical resistance and breakthrough time of various garment materials as tested against a slew of chemicals. This test data should be in accordance with American Society for Testing and Materials and National Fire Protection Association standards.

Comprehensive Environmental Response, Compensation and Liability Act (CERCLA)—Known as CERCLA or SUPERFUND, it addresses hazardous substance releases into the environment and the cleanup of inactive hazardous waste sites. It also requires those who release hazardous substances, as defined by the U.S. Environmental Protection Agency, above certain levels (known as "reportable quantities") to notify the National Response Center.

compressed gas—Any material or mixture having an absolute pressure exceeding 2.7 atm (40 psi) in 21 °C (70 °F), having an absolute pressure exceeding 7 atm (104 psi) at 54 °C (130 °F); or, any liquid flammable material having a vapor pressure exceeding 2.7 atm (40 psi) absolute at 37 °C (100 °F) as determined by testing. Also includes cryogenic or "refrigerated liquids" (U.S. Department of Transportation) with boiling points lower than -90 °C (-130 °F) at 1 atm.

Compressed Gas Association (CGA)—Firms producing and distributing compressed, liquefied, and cryogenic gases; also manufacturers of related equipment submit recommendations to appropriate government agencies to improve safety standards and methods of handling, transporting, and storing gases; acts as advisor to regulatory authorities and other agencies concerned with safe handling of compressed gases; collaborates with national organizations to develop specifications and standards of safety.

computer aided management of emergency operations (CAMEO)—A computer database storage-retrieval system of preplanning and emergency data for on-scene use at hazardous materials incidents.

confinement—Procedures taken to keep a material in a defined or localized area.

consignee—The addressee to whom the item is shipped.

contact—Being exposed to an undesirable or unknown substance that may pose a threat to health and safety.

container—Any device in which a hazardous material is stored, transported, disposed of, or otherwise handled.

container, intermodal, ISO—An article of transport equipment that meets the standards of the International Organization for Standardization (ISO) designed to facilitate and optimize the carriage of goods by one or more modes of transportation without intermediate handling of the contents and equipped with features permitting ready handling and transfer from one mode to another. Containers may be fully enclosed with one or more doors and feature open-top, tank, refrigerated, open-rack, gondola, flatrack, and other designs. Included in this definition are modules or arrays that can be coupled to form an intrinsic unit regardless of intention to move single containers in multiplex configurations.

containment—All activities necessary to bring the incident to a point of stabilization and to establish a degree of safety for emergency personnel greater than existed upon arrival.

contamination—An uncontained substance or process that poses a threat to life, health, or the environment.

contamination control line—The established line around the contamination reduction zone that separates it from the support zone.

contamination reduction zone—Term used by the U.S. Coast Guard to identify the area of moderate hazard where threat of contamination spread to the immediate surrounding area is low. It is the area immediately outside of the timer hot zone (see *warm zone*).

contingency—A preplanned document presenting an organized and coordinated plan of action to limit potential pollution in case of fire, explosion, or discharge of hazardous materials; defines specific responsibilities and tasks.

control—The procedures, techniques, and methods used in the mitigation of a hazardous materials incident, including containment, extinguishment, and confinement.

control zones—The designation of areas at a hazardous materials incident based on safety and the degree of hazard (see *support zone, warm zone, hot zone,* and *decontamination corridor*).

coordination—To bring together, in a uniform and controlled manner, the functions of all agencies on scene.

corrosive—The ability to cause destruction of living tissue or many solid materials surfaces by chemical action.

cost recovery—A procedure that allows for the agency having jurisdiction to pursue reimbursement for all costs associated with a hazardous materials incident.

Council on Environmental Alternatives (CEA)—Encourages people to conserve, rather than consume, their environment. The council concentrates on the area of energy and provides specific recommendations that encourage individuals to recognize and assume responsibility for environmentally sound choices available to them.

cryogenic—Gases, usually liquefied, that induce freezing temperatures of -100 °C (-150 °F) and below (liquid oxygen, liquid helium, liquid natural gas, and liquid hydrogen, etc.).

damage assessment—Gathering information on the type, extent, and costs of damage after an incident.

damming—A procedure consisting of constructing a dike or embankment to totally immobilize a flowing waterway contaminated with a liquid or solid hazardous substance.

dangerous when wet—A label required for water reactive materials (solid) being shipped under US DOT, ICAO, and IMO regulations. A labeled material that is in contact with water or moisture may produce flammable gases. In some instances, these gases are capable of spontaneous combustion (49 CFR 171.8).

declared emergency—An action taken by a jurisdiction according to the California Emergency Services Act and local ordinances in response to the effect of a real or threatened hazard that exceeds local resources.

decon—Popular abbreviation referring to the process of decontamination.

decontamination—The physical and/or chemical process of reducing and preventing the spread of contamination from persons and equipment used at a hazardous materials incident (also referred to as *contamination reduction*).

decontamination corridor—A distinct area within the warm zone that functions as a protective buffer and bridge between the hot zone and the cold zone, where decontamination stations and personnel are located to conduct decontamination procedures.

decontamination officer—A position within the FIRESCOPE ICS HM-120 that has responsibility for identifying the location of the decontamination corridor, assigning stations, managing all decontamination procedures, and identifying the types of decontamination necessary.

decontamination team (decon team)—A group of personnel and resources operating within a decontamination corridor.

degradation—The loss in physical properties of an item of protective clothing because of exposure to chemicals, use, or ambient conditions.

delayed toxic exposure effect—The condition in which symptoms of an exposure are not present immediately after the exposure, but are delayed for a relatively short period of time (such as pulmonary edema a few hours after an inhalation exposure).

deleterious substances—Substances not typically harmful to humans that may be harmful to the environment.

Department of Commerce (DOC)—A federal agency whose primary mission is to encourage, serve, and promote economic development and technological advancement.

Department of Defense (DOD)—The federal entity that provides the military forces needed to deter war and protect the security of our country.

Department of Energy (DOE)—The federal agency that provides the framework for a comprehensive and balanced national energy plan through coordination and administration of the energy functions of the federal government; responsible for long-term, high-risk research, development, and demonstration of energy technology, the marketing of federal power, energy conservation, the nuclear weapons program, regulation of energy production and use, and a central energy data collection and analysis program.

Department of Justice (DOJ)—The federal department that serves as counsel for the citizens of the nation; represents them in enforcing the law in the public interest; through its thousands of lawyers, investigators, and agents, it plays a key role in protection against criminals and subversion, in ensuring healthy competition of business in our free enterprise system, in safeguarding the consumer, and in enforcing drug, immigration, and naturalization laws; plays a significant role in protecting citizens through its efforts for effective law enforcement, crime prevention, crime detection, and prosecution and rehabilitation of offenders; conducts all suits in the Supreme Court in which the United States is concerned; and represents the government in legal matters.

Department of Labor (DOL)—The purpose of the Department of Labor is to foster, promote, and develop the welfare of the wage earners of the United States, to improve their working conditions, and to advance their opportunities for profitable employment.

Department of State (DOS)— This department advises the president in formulation and execution of foreign policy; promotes long-range security and well-being of the United States; determines and analyzes the facts relating to American overseas interest, makes recommendations on policy and future action, and takes the necessary steps to carry out established policy; engages in continuous consultation with the American public, Congress, other U.S. departments and agencies, and foreign governments.

Department of Transportation (DOT)—This agency ensures the coordinated, effective administration of the transportation programs of the federal government and develops national transportation policies and programs conducive to the provision of fast, safe, efficient, and convenient transportation at the lowest possible cost.

desiccant—A substance, such as silica gel, that removes moisture (water vapor) from the air to maintain a dry atmosphere in containers of food or chemical packaging.

detectors—

- *combustible gas indicator (CGI) detector*—Measures the presence of a combustible gas or vapor in air.

- *corrosive, (pH)*—A meter or paper that indicates the relative acidity or alkalinity of a substance, generally using an international scale of 0 (acid) through 14 (alkali/caustic) (see *pH*).

- *flame ionization detector (FID)*—A device used to determine the presence of hydrocarbons in air.

- *gas chromatograph/mass spectrometer detector*—An instrument used for identifying and analyzing organics.

- *heat detector*—An instrument used to detect heat by sensing infra-red waves.

- *photoionization detector (PID)*—A device used to determine the presence of gases/vapors in low concentrations in air.

- *radiation beta survey detector*—An instrument used to detect beta radiation.

- *radiation dosimeter detector*—An instrument that measures the amount of radiation to which a person has been exposed.

- *radiation gamma survey detector*—An instrument used for the detection of ionizing radiation, principally gamma radiation, by means of a gas-filled tube.

- *temperature detector*—An instrument, either mechanical or electronic, used to determine the temperature of ambient air, liquids, or surfaces.

dike—An embankment or ridge, natural or man-made, used to control the movement of liquids, sludges, solids, or other materials.

dike overflow—A dike constructed in a manner that allows uncontaminated water to flow unobstructed over the dike while keeping the contaminant behind the dike.

dike underflow—A dike constructed in a manner that allows uncontaminated water to flow unobstructed under the dike while keeping the contaminant behind the dike.

dispersion—To spread, scatter, or diffuse through air, soil, surface, or groundwater.

disposal drum—A reference to a specially constructed drum used to overpack damaged or leaking containers of hazardous materials for shipment.

diversion—The intentional, controlled movement of a hazardous material to relocate it into an area where it will pose less harm to the community and the environment.

division—That organizational level within the incident command system having responsibility for operations within a defined geographic area. The *division* officer directs approximately five companies and answers to the "operations" officer.

dose—The amount of substance ingested, absorbed, and/or inhaled per exposure period.

double gloving—A set of gloves worn over those already in place for enhanced protection.

downwind—In the direction in which the wind blows.

dust—Solid particles generated by handling, crushing, grinding, rapid impact, detonation, and decrepitation of organic or inorganic materials such as rock, ore, metal, coal, wood, and grain. Typically applied to particles small enough to remain airborne for a minute or more.

ecology—A branch of science concerned with the interrelationship of organisms and their environments.

economic poison—As defined in the Federal Insecticide, Fungicide, and Rodenticide Act, an economic poison is "any substance or mixture of substances intended for preventing, destroying, repelling, or mitigating any insects, rodents, nematodes, fungi, or weeds, or any other forms of life declared to be pests … any substance intended for use as a plant regulator, defoliant, or desiccant." As defined, economic poisons are generally known as pesticides."

ecosystem—A habitat formed by the interaction of a community of organisms with their environment.

edema—The swelling of body tissues resulting from fluid retention.

Emergency Medical Services (EMS)—Functions as required to provide emergency medical care for ill or injured persons by trained providers.

Emergency Medical Services Authority (EMSA)—The state agency responsible for developing general guidelines for triage and handling of contaminated/exposed patients; develops and promotes hazardous materials training for emergency medical responders in the field and hospital emergency rooms; identifies and coordinates the procurement of medical assistance, supplies, and hospital beds when local and/or regional resources are depleted; and coordinates the evaluation of casualties to other areas of the state.

emergency operations center (EOC)—The secured site where government officials exercise centralized direction and control in an emergency. The EOC serves as a resource center and coordination point for additional field assistance. It also provides executive directives to and liaison for state and federal government representatives, and considers and mandates protective actions.

emergency operations plan—A document that identifies the available personnel, equipment, facilities, supplies, and other resources in the jurisdiction, and states the method or scheme for coordinated actions to be taken by individuals and government services in the event of natural, man-made, and attack-related disasters.

emergency response—Response to any occurrence that has or could result in release of a hazardous substance.

emergency response organization—An organization that uses personnel trained in emergency response.

emergency response personnel—Personnel assigned to organizations that have the responsibility to respond to different types of emergency situations.

empty packaging—Any packaging having a capacity of 110 gal or less that contains only the residue of a hazardous material.

endothermic—A process or chemical reaction that consumes or absorbs heat.

engine (fire usage)—Any emergency response vehicle providing specified levels of pumping, water, hose capacity, and personnel.

entry point—A specified and controlled location where access into the hot zone occurs at a hazardous materials incident.

entry team leader—The entry leader is responsible for the overall entry operations of assigned personnel within the hot zone.

Environmental Protection Agency (EPA)—The purpose of EPA is to protect and enhance the environment today and for future generations to the fullest extent possible under the laws enacted by Congress. The agency's mission is to control and abate pollution in the areas of water, air, solid waste, pesticides, noise, and radiation. The EPA's mandate is to mount an integrated, coordinated attack on environmental pollution in cooperation with state and local governments.

EOC liaison—Person designated to establish communications between the incident scene and the emergency operations center.

EPA—See *Environmental Protection Agency*.

etiologic agent—Any material or energy (such as a viable microorganism or its toxin) that causes or may cause human disease.

evacuation—The removal of potentially endangered, but not yet exposed, persons from an area threatened by a hazardous materials incident.

explosive ordnance disposal (EOD)—Military or civilian bomb squads.

extremely hazardous substances (EHS)—The Environmental Protection Agency uses this term for chemicals that must be reported pursuant to Superfund Amendments and Reauthorization Act, Title III. The list of these substances and the threshold planning quantities are identified in 40 CFR 355. Releases of extremely hazardous substances as defined by EPA must be reported to the National Response Center.

extremely hazardous waste—Any hazardous waste or mixture of hazardous wastes which, if human exposure should occur, may likely result in death, disabling injury, or serious illness caused by the hazardous waste or mixture of hazardous wastes because of its quantity, concentration, or chemical characteristics.

exclusion zone—See *hot zone*.

exothermic—A process or chemical reaction that produces or releases heat.

explosion-proof equipment—Instruments whose enclosure is designed and constructed to prevent the ignition of an explosive atmosphere. Certification for explosion-proof performance is subject to compliance with American Society for Testing and Materials standards.

explosive—Any chemical compound, mixture, or device of which the primary or common purpose is to function by explosion, that is, with substantial instantaneous release of gas and heat (49 CFR 173.50).

explosive Class A—Any of nine types of explosives as defined in 49 CFR 173.53. A material which, when it detonates, creates a shock wave that travels faster than the speed of sound.

explosive Class B—Those explosives which generally function by rapid combustion rather than by detonation and include some explosive devices such as special fireworks, flash powders, some pyrotechnic signal devices and liquid or solid propellant explosives including some smokeless powders (49 CFR 173 RR).

explosive Class C—Certain types of manufactured articles that contain Class A or Class B explosives or both as components, but in restricted quantities, and certain types of fireworks. This includes small arms ammunition (49:173.100).

exposure—The subjection of a person to a toxic substance or harmful physical agent through any route of entry.

Fahrenheit (°F)—The scale of temperature in which 212° is the boiling point of water at 760 mm Hg and 32° is the freezing point.

Federal Insecticide, Fungicide, and Rodenticide Act (FIFRA)—An act that requires pesticides to be registered and labeled, makes it illegal to detach or destroy pesticide labels, and provides for pesticide inspections. An amendment to FIFRA now requires the Environmental Protection Agency to determine whether a pesticide "will perform its intended function without causing unreasonable adverse effects on the environment" or human health.

Federal Water Pollution Control Act (1972) WPCA—See *Clean Water Act*.

fibrosis—A condition marked by an increase of interstitial fibrous tissue.

filter canister—A container filled with sorbents and catalysts that removes gases and/or vapors from air drawn through the unit. The canister may also contain an aerosol (particulate) filter to remove solid or liquid particles.

first responder—The first trained person(s) to arrive at the scene of a hazardous materials incident; may be from the public or private sector of emergency services.

first responder, awareness level—Individuals who are likely to witness or discover a hazardous substance release who have been trained to initiate an emergency response sequence by notifying the proper authorities of the release. They would take no further action beyond notifying the authorities of the release.

first responder, operations level—Individuals who respond to releases or potential releases of hazardous substances as part of the initial response to the site for the purpose of protecting nearby persons, property, or the environment from the effects of the release. They are trained to respond in a defensive fashion without actually trying to stop the release. Their function is to contain the release from a safe distance, keep it from spreading, and prevent exposures.

flammable liquid—Any liquid having a flash point below 37.8 °C (100 °F) (49 CFR 173.115[a]).

flammable range—A mixture of flammable gas, as mixed with air, expressed as a percent. Each gas has a range, including a lower limit and upper limit, and between these limits the mixture is flammable (explosive).

flammable solid—Any solid material, other than one classified as an explosive, that, under conditions normally incident to transportation, is likely to cause fires through friction, retains heat from manufacturing or processing, or that can be ignited readily and when ignited burns so vigorously and persistently as to create a serious transportation hazard. Included in this class are spontaneously combustible and water-reactive materials.

flashpoint—The minimum temperature of a liquid at which it gives off vapors of sufficient concentration to form an ignitable mixture with air that will flash when subjected to an external ignition source.

Food and Drug Administration (FDA)—Performs, directs, and coordinates detection and control activities that protect consumers against adulterated, misbranded, or falsely advertised foods, drugs, medical devices, and hazardous products.

full protective clothing—Protective clothing worn primarily by firefighters that includes helmet, coat, pants, boots, gloves, and a self-contained breathing apparatus designed for structural firefighting. It does not provide specialized chemical protection.

fully encapsulating suits—Chemical protective suits that are designed to offer full body protection, including a self-contained breathing apparatus, are gas tight, and meet the design criteria as outlined in National Fire Protection Association Standard 1991.

fume—Airborne dispersion consisting of minute solid particles arising from the heating of a solid material such as lead, in distinction to a gas or vapor. This physical change is often accompanied by a chemical reaction such as oxidation. Fumes flocculate and sometimes coalesce. Odorous gases, smokes, and vapors should not be called fumes.

gas—A state of matter in which the material has low density and viscosity; can expand and contract greatly in response to changes in temperature and pressure; easily diffuses into other gases; readily and uniformly distributes itself throughout any container. A gas can be changed to a liquid or solid state by the *combined* effect of increased pressure and/or decreased temperature.

gelling—A process of adding a specific material that is designed to coagulate a liquid facilitating its isolation and removal.

grounding—Method whereby activities that may generate static electricity will be prevented from discharging a spark and thereby not produce an ignition point.

group—That organization level within the incident command system having responsibility for operations within a specific functional area, that is, salvage, ventilation, hazardous materials.

habitat—The native environment of an animal or plant; the natural place for life and growth of an animal or plant.

halogens—A chemical family that includes fluorine, chlorine, bromine, and iodine.

halons—Fire-suppressing gases that are composed of straight chain carbon atoms with a variety of halogen atoms attached.

hazard—The characteristic of having a potential for causing damage to life, property, and/or the environment.

hazard assessment—A process used to qualitatively or quantitatively assess risk factors to determine incident operations.

hazard class—The eight classes of hazardous materials as categorized and defined by the Department of Transportation in 49 CFR.

hazardous air pollutant—An airborne pollutant that may cause or contribute to an increase in mortality or serious illness. Some hazardous air pollutants can be listed specifically depending on the authority having jurisdiction. Please contact your local agency for specific hazardous air pollutants.

hazardous chemical—A term used by the Occupational Safety and Health Administration to denote any chemical that would be a risk to employees if they were exposed to it in the workplace.

hazardous material—A substance (solid, liquid, or gas) capable of posing an unreasonable risk to health, safety, environment, or property.

hazardous material categorization—A field analysis process to determine basic hazardous materials hazard classification and some chemical and physical properties of unknowns.

hazardous materials emergency—The release or threatened release of a hazardous material that may affect public health, safety, and/or the environment.

hazardous materials safety officer/official—A person at a hazardous materials incident responsible for ensuring that all operations performed at a hazardous materials incident, by all members present, are done so with respect to the highest levels of safety. The hazardous materials safety officer has full authority to alter, suspend, or terminate any activity that may be judged to be unsafe; advises the hazardous materials group supervisor; and reports to the incident commander through the site safety officer.

hazardous substance—(1) As used by the U.S. Department of Transportation, describes the chemicals and materials on the list in 49 CFR 172.101 (Attachment B); (2) as used by the California Department of Toxic Substances Control, encompasses every chemical regulated by both the Department of Transportation (hazardous materials) and the Environmental Protection Agency (hazardous waste), including emergency response.

hazardous waste—(1) Waste materials or mixtures of waste that require special handling and disposal because of their potential to damage health and/or the environment; (2) the Environmental Protection Agency uses the term, *hazardous waste,* for chemicals that are regulated under the Resource Conservation and Recovery Act and are listed in 40 CFR 261.33 (d). Environmental Protection Agency or California Toxic Substances Control regulated hazardous waste, when in transport, must also meet 49 CFR parts 170 through 179.

hazardous waste facility—Any location used for the treatment, transfer, disposal, or storage of hazardous waste as permitted and regulated.

hazardous waste generation—The act or process of producing hazardous waste.

hazardous waste leachate—Any liquid that has percolated through or drained from hazardous waste placed in or on the ground.

hazardous waste management—Systematic control of the collection, source separation, storage, transportation, processing, treatment recovery, and disposal of hazardous wastes.

hazardous waste manifest, uniform (EPA usage)—The shipping document, originated and signed by the waste generator or an authorized representative, that contains the information required by law and must accompany shipments of hazardous waste (40 CFR 262, Subpart B).

hazardous waste site—A location where hazardous wastes are located.

HAZCAT—See *hazardous materials categorization.*

hazmat—Acronym used for *hazardous materials.*

health hazard, chemical—Any chemical or chemical mixture whose physical or chemical properties may cause acute or chronic health effects.

heavy metal—A high density metallic element that may demonstrate health hazards as a result of exposure and may contribute to contamination of the environment; this includes chromium (Cr), beryllium (Be), lead (Pb), mercury (Hg), zinc (Zn), copper (Cu), cadmium (Cd), and other elements.

hepatotoxic—A substance that negatively affects the liver.

herbicide—An agricultural chemical intended for killing plants or interrupting their normal growth (see *pesticides*).

high performance liquid chromatography (HPLC)—A procedure used in organic analysis to separate chemical mixtures based on differential ionic absorption to various substrates.

hot tapping—A sophisticated method of welding on and then cutting holes through liquid, compressed gas vessels, and piping for the purpose of relieving pressure and/or removing product without compromising the containment of the material of energy.

hot zone—An area immediately surrounding a hazardous materials incident that extends far enough to prevent adverse effects from hazardous materials releases to personnel outside the zone. This zone is also referred to as the *exclusion zone*, the *red zone*, and the *restricted zone* in other documents.

hygroscopic—A substance that has the property of absorbing moisture from the air such as silica gel.

hypergolic—Two chemical substances that spontaneously ignite upon mixing. It literally means "very energetic," and is typically applied to a mixture.

ignitable material—Any material having, as a liquid, a flash point less than 59 °C (140 °F) or, if not a liquid, is capable of causing firs through friction, absorption of moisture, or spontaneous chemical changes.

ignition temperature—The minimum temperature at which a material will initiate or maintain combustion.

immediately dangerous to life or health (IDLH)—An atmospheric concentration of any toxic, corrosive, or asphyxiant substance that poses an immediate threat to life or would cause irreversible or delayed adverse health effects or would interfere with an individual's ability to escape from a dangerous atmosphere.

incident—An event involving a hazardous material or a release or potential release of a hazardous material.

incident action plan—A plan that is initially prepared at the first meeting of emergency personnel who have responded to an incident. The incident action plan contains general control objectives reflecting overall incident strategy and specific action plans.

incident command—A disciplined method of management established for the specific purpose of control and direction of resources and personnel.

incident commander (IC)/scene manager (SM)—The person responsible for all decisions relating to management of the incident.

incident command post—See *command POSL*.

incident command system (ICS)—An organized system of roles, responsibilities, and standard operating procedures used to manage and direct emergency operations.

incompatible waste—Waste unsuitable for commingling with another waste or material. One waste can be incompatible *with* another. No chemical has this characteristic by itself.

industrial wastes—Unwanted materials produced in or eliminated from an industrial operation.

infectious waste—Waste containing pathogens; *may* consist of tissues, organs, body parts, blood, and body fluids.

ingestion—The process of taking substances such as food, drink, and medicine into the body through the mouth.

inhibitor—A chemical added to another substance to prevent or slow down an unwanted or sudden occurrence of chemical change.

inorganic compounds——Chemical compounds that do not contain the element, carbon, with the exception of carbon oxides and carbon sulfides.

insecticide—A chemical product used to kill and control insects (see *pesticides*).

International Air Transport Association (IATA)—An association of air carriers that develops guidelines for transportation of cargo.

International Civil Aviation Organization (ICAO)—An organization that develops the principles and techniques of international air navigation and fosters planning and development of international air transport to ensure safe and orderly growth.

investigate—To systematically search or inquire into the particulars of an incident and collect the necessary evidence to seek criminal and/or civil prosecution.

irritant— A reversible inflammatory health effect; exposure by inhalation or by skin or eye contact (29 CFR 1910.1200).

isolating the scene—Preventing persons and equipment from becoming exposed to a release or threatened release of a hazardous material by establishment of site control zones.

jurisdiction specific plan—A plan that details emergency activities, capabilities, responsibilities, and resources within an area, agency, facility, or political subdivision.

labpack—Putting multiple small containers of chemicals with compatible chemical characteristics in a disposal drum with absorbent material.

lacrimation—Tearing produced by eye irritation.

LC_{50} (lethal concentration, 50%)—The amount of a toxicant in air that is deadly to 50% of the exposed laboratory animal population within a specified time. Most LC_{50} tests last a day, at most.

LD_{50} (lethal dose, 50%)—The amount of a toxicant administered other than by inhalation, which is deadly to 50% of the exposed laboratory animal population within a specified time. Most LD_{50} tests last a day, at most.

leak—The uncontrolled release of a hazardous material that could pose a threat to health, safety, and/or the environment.

leak control compounds—Substances used for the plugging and patching of leaks in nonpressure containers.

leak control devices—Tools and equipment used for the plugging and patching of leaks in nonpressure and some low-pressure containers, pipes, and tanks.

level of protection—In addition to appropriate respiratory protection, designations of types of personal protective equipment to be worn based on National Fire Protection Association standards.

- Level A—vapor protective suit for hazardous chemical emergencies.
- Level B—liquid splash protective suit for hazardous chemical emergencies.
- Level C—limited use protective suit for hazardous chemical emergencies.

local disaster plan—A plan developed and used by local government for extraordinary events.

local emergency planning committee (LEPC)—A committee appointed by a state emergency response commission, as required by Superfund Amendments and Reauthorization Act Title III, to formulate a comprehensive emergency plan for its corresponding office of emergency services mutual aid region.

local government—A political subdivision within a state.

localized exposure—Contact with a limited area, typically an external body surface.

logistics chief—That organizational position within the incident command system having responsibility for summoning and managing support, apparatuses, equipment, and personnel.

lower explosive limit (LEL)—The lowest concentration of the material in air that can be detonated by spark, shock, flame, and so on.

macro-encapsulation—The isolation of a waste by embedding it in, or surrounding it with, a material that acts as a barrier to water or air (e.g., clay and plastic liners).

manifest, uniform hazardous waste—A document required by 40 CFR 262 to accompany any shipment of hazardous waste from the point of generation to the point of final disposal/destruction (see *shipping papers* and *hazardous waste manifest, uniform*).

marking—The required descriptive name, instructions, cautions, weight, specifications, or combination thereof on containers of hazardous materials/hazardous waste.

material safety data sheet (MSDS)—A document that contains information regarding the specific identity of hazardous chemicals, including information on health effects, first aid, chemical and physical properties, and emergency phone numbers. The Hazard Communication Standard requires the creation of MSDSs, their use, content, and format.

melting point—The temperature at which a material changes from a solid to a liquid.

microorganism—A living organism not discretely visible to the unaided eye.

mist—Suspended liquid droplets generated by condensation from the gaseous to the liquid state or by breaking up a liquid into a dispersed state, such as by splashing, foaming, or atomizing. A mist is formed when a finely divided liquid is suspended in air.

mitigation—Any action used to contain, reduce, or eliminate the harmful effects of a spill or release of a hazardous material.

monitoring—The act of systematically checking to determine contaminant levels and atmospheric conditions.

monitoring environmental contamination—Use of instruments and other techniques to determine the presence or levels of hazardous materials.

monitoring equipment—Instruments and devices used to identify, qualify, and/or quantify contaminants.

MSDS—See *material safety data sheet*.

Multihazard functional planning—The California format used for developing disaster and emergency plans.

mutagen—A substance capable of causing genetic damage.

mutual aid—An agreement to supply specifically agreed upon aid or support in an emergency situation between two or more agencies, jurisdictions, or political subdivisions.

narcosis—Stupor or unconsciousness produced by chemical substances.

National Contingency Plan (NCP)—Created by Comprehensive Environmental Response, Compensation and Liability Act to define the federal response authority and responsibility for oil and hazardous material spills.

National Fire Protection Association (NFPA)—An international voluntary membership organization to promote improved fire protection and prevention and establish safeguards against loss of life and property by fire; writes and publishes the American National Standards.

National Institute for Occupational Safety and Health (NIOSH)—A federal agency that, among other activities, tests and certifies respiratory protective devices, air sampling detector tubes, and recommends occupational exposure limits for various substances.

National Interagency Incident Management System (NIIMS)—A standardized systems approach to incident management that consists of five significant subdivisions collectively providing a total systems approach to all-risk incident management.

National Oceanic and Atmospheric Administration (NOAA)—The agency responsible to serve as scientific support coordinator for a federal on-scene coordinator. Assists in oil spill and air toxics modeling and meteorological monitoring and oceanic research.

National Pesticide Telecommunications Network (NPTN)—A 24-hour national hotline (1–800/858-PEST) operated by Texas Tech University School of Medicine providing toll-free information about pesticide safety, application, chemistry, and toxicology to callers in the United States, Puerto Rico, and the Virgin Islands. Questions are answered directly or via next-day mail.

National Response Center (NRC)—A communications center operated by the U.S. Coast Guard headquarters located in Washington, D.C. They provide information on suggested technical emergency actions, and must be notified by the spiller within 24 hours of any spill of a reportable quantity of a hazardous substance.

necrosis—Death in a particular part of a living tissue.

nephrotoxic—A substance that negatively affects the kidneys.

neurotoxic—A substance that negatively affects the nervous system.

neutralization—The process by which acid or alkaline properties of a solution are altered by addition of certain reagents to bring the hydrogen and hydroxide concentrations to equal value (pH 7 is neutral). Oxidizers and reducers can also neutralize each other.

nonflammable gas—Any material or mixture in a cylinder or tank, other than poison or flammable gas, having an absolute pressure in the container exceeding 2.7 atm (40 psi) at 21 °C (70 °F) or having an absolute pressure exceeding 7 atm (104 psi) at 54 °C (130 °F). (49 CFR).

North American (NA) number—A four-digit number used in the United States and Canada to identify a hazardous material or group of hazardous materials in transportation.

not otherwise specified (NOS or n.o.s.)—In shipping regulations, the term is used for classes of substances to which restrictions apply, but for which the individual members of the class are not listed in the regulations.

Occupational Safety and Health Administration (OSHA)—Component of the U.S. Department of Labor, an agency with safety and health regulatory and enforcement authorities for most industries, businesses, and states in the United States.

odor threshold—The lowest concentration in the atmosphere that can be detected by the human sense of smell. Often a poor indicator of toxicity risk.

Office of Hazardous Materials Safety (OHMS)—A federal agency tasked with providing research and recommended revisions to 49 CFR.

oil—Any of numerous mineral, vegetable, and synthetic substances and vegetable and animal fats that are generally slippery, combustible, viscous, liquid or liquefiable at room temperature.

oil spill cleanup agent—Any material used in removing oil from the environment, including inert sorbent materials, approved chemical dispersants, surface collecting agents, sinking agents, and biological additives.

olfactory—Pertaining to the sense of smell.

on-scene coordinator (OSC)—As explained in the National Contingency Plan, it is the pre-designated federal official who coordinates federal activities at a hazardous material incident and monitors the incident for compliance with federal pollution laws.

operations—That organizational level within the Incident Command System immediately subordinate to the incident commander. When established, this position is responsible for the direct management of all incident tactical activities.

oral toxicity—Adverse effects resulting from taking a substance into the body through the mouth.

organic peroxide—Strong oxidizers, often chemically unstable, containing the -O-O structure. They react readily with solvents or fuels resulting in an explosion or fire.

other regulated materials A (ORM A)—A material that has an anesthetic, irritating, noxious, toxic, or other similar property and can cause extreme annoyance or discomfort to passengers and crew in the event of leakage during transportation (49 CFR 173.500[b][1]).

other regulated materials B (ORM B)—A material (including a solid when wet with water) capable of causing significant damage to a transport vehicle from leakage during transportation (49 CFR 173.500[b][2]).

other regulated materials C (ORM C)—A material that has other inherent characteristics not described as an ORM A or ORM B, but which make it unsuitable for shipment unless properly identified and prepared for transportation (49 CFR 173.500[b][4]).

other regulated materials D (ORM D)—A material, such as a consumer commodity, which presents a limited hazard during transportation because of its form, quantity, and packaging (49 CFR 173.500[b][4]).

other regulated materials E (ORM E)—A material that is not included in any other hazard class, but is subject to the requirements of 49 CFR 173.500; this includes hazardous waste.

overpack—An enclosure used to consolidate two or more packages of hazardous material. *Overpack* does not include a freight container.

oxidizer—A chemical, other than a blasting agent or explosive, that initiates or promotes combustion in other materials thereby causing fire either of itself or through the release of oxygen or other gases (49 CFR 173.151). (The reader should note that this is a practical, not scientific, definition.)

oxygen deficiency—A concentration of oxygen insufficient to support life.

oxygen-deficient atmosphere—An atmosphere that contains an oxygen content less than 19.5% by volume at sea level.

pallets—A low portable platform constructed of wood, metal, plastic, or fiberboard, built to specified dimensions, on which supplies are loaded, transported, or stored in units.

parts per billion (ppb)—A unit for measuring the concentration of a particular substance equal to one unit combined with 999,999,999 other units.

parts per million (ppm)—A unit for measuring the concentration of a particular substance equal to one unit combined with 999,999 other units.

pathogen—Any disease-producing organism including viruses.

PCB contaminated electrical equipment—Any electrical equipment, including transformers, that contains at least 50 ppm (50 mg/L) but less than 500 ppm (500 mg/L) of polychlorinated biphenyls (40 CFR 761.3).

PCB item—An item containing polychlorinated biphenyls at a concentration of 5 ppm (5 mg/L) or greater (40 CFR 761.3). See *polychlorinated biphenyl*.

PCB transformer—Any transformer that contains 500 ppm (500 mg/L) of polychlorinated biphenyls or greater (40 CFR 761.3).

penetration—The movement of liquid molecules through a chemical protective clothing, suit, garment, or material.

permeation—The movement of vapor or gas molecules through a chemical protective garment material.

permeation kits—Kits assembled for the purpose of testing an unknown liquid substance on-site for permeability of chemical protective clothing.

permissible exposure limit (PEL)—The employees' permitted exposure limit to any material listed in Table Z1, Z2, or Z3 of Occupational Safety and Health Administration regulations, section 1910.1000, "Air Contaminants."

persistent toxic substance—A material or waste that resists natural degradation or detoxification and may present long-term health and environmental hazards.

personal protective equipment (PPE)—Equipment provided to shield or isolate a person from the chemical, physical, and thermal hazards that are near or may be encountered at a hazardous materials incident. Adequate personal protective equipment should protect the respiratory system, skin, eyes, face, hands, feet, head, body, and hearing. Personal protective equipment includes personal protective clothing, self-contained positive pressure breathing apparatus, and air-purifying respirators.

pesticides—A chemical or mixture of chemicals used to destroy, prevent, or control any living organism considered to be a pest.

pH—A numerical designation of the negative logarithm of hydrogen ion concentration. A pH of 7.0 is neutrality; higher values indicate alkalinity and lower values indicate acidity.

plugging and patching kits—Kits commercially available, or privately assembled, for the purpose of providing capabilities for emergency plugging patching of leaking containers, pipes, and tanks.

plume—A vapor, liquid, dust or gaseous cloud formation that has shape and buoyancy.

pneumonitis—Inflammation of the lungs characterized by an outpouring of fluid in the lungs.

poison Class A—Poisonous gases or liquids of such a nature that a very small amount of the gas, or vapor of the liquid, mixed with air is dangerous to life. (49 CFR 173.326) This is a good place for a hyperlink.

poison Class B—Substances, liquids, or solids other than poison Class A or irritating materials, which are known to be toxic to man and a hazard to health (49 CFR 173.343).

Poison Control Centers (PCC)—Each Poison Control Center is available 24 hours a day and can provide immediate health effects, scene management, victim decontamination, and other emergency medical treatment advice for hazardous materials emergencies. A physician specializing in medical toxicology is available for backup consultation. The national number for poison control is 1-800-222-1222.

pollution—Contamination of air, water, land, or other natural resources that will, or is likely to, create a public nuisance and cause health and environmental harm.

polychlorinated biphenyl (PCB)—One of several aromatic compounds containing two benzene nuclei with two or more chlorine atoms. Material is classified as toxic.

polymerization—A chemical reaction, typically carried out with a catalyst, heat, or light and often under high pressure, which generates high temperature and, when uncontrolled, may be violent.

post-emergency response—That portion of an emergency response performed after the immediate threat of a release has been stabilized or eliminated and cleanup of the site has begun.

post-incident analysis—The termination phase of an incident that includes completion of the required forms and documentation for conducting a critique.

pre-incident planning—The process associated with preparing for the response to a hazard by developing plans, identifying resources, conducting exercises, and other techniques to improve an agency's or organization's response capabilities.

prevention plan—See *risk management prevention program*.

product substitution—Replacing a hazardous substance in a process with a less hazardous substance.

proper shipping name—The U.S. Department of Transportation-designated name for a commodity or material (49 CFR 172.101).

protective clothing—See *personal protective equipment (PPE)*.

public information officer (PIO)—The individual assigned to act as the liaison between the incident commander and the news media.

pulmonary—Pertaining to the lungs.

pyrophoric—A substance that ignites spontaneously in dry or moist air at or below 130 °F (49 CFR 173.115[c]).

qualitative fit test—A physical testing of a breathing apparatus face piece to the wearer, performed in an atmosphere of amyl acetate or irritant smoke to evaluate whether the wearer can detect the contaminant, indicating mask leakage and improper fit.

Radiation Absorbed Dose (RAD)—A basic unit of absorbed dose of ionizing radiation (1 rad = 100 grays).

radioactive—The spontaneous disintegration of unstable nuclei accompanied by emission of nuclear radiation.

radioactive material (RAM)—Any material, or combination of materials, that spontaneously emits ionizing radiation and has a specific activity greater than 0.002 microcuries μciper gram (49 CFR 173.389).

recovery drum——See *disposal drum.*

reference library—A selection of chemical text books, reference books, microfiche, and computer data programs typically carried by a hazardous materials response team.

regional plan—A hazardous material plan developed pursuant to Superfund Amendments and Reauthorization Act Title III.

regional response team—Composed of representatives of federal agencies and a representative from each state in the 10 federal Environmental Protection Agency regions as specified in the National Contingency Plan.

Regional Water Quality Control Board (RWQCB)—The agency charged with managing statewide water quality. California only.

release, threatened release—The actual or potential spilling, leaking, pumping, pouring, emitting, emptying, discharging, injecting, escaping, leaching, dumping, or disposing into the environment, including the abandonment or discarding of barrels, containers, and other closed receptacles of any hazardous material.

remedial action—Actions taken to mitigate the effects of a release or threatened release of a hazardous material to protect health or the environment.

removal action—See *mitigation.*

reportable incident—Any incident that has or may affect public health, safety, or the environment, or is otherwise required by law to be reported.

reportable quantity (RQ)—The designated amount of a specific material that, if spilled or released, requires immediate notification to the National Response Center (49 CFR 172.101, 40 CFR 117.3, 173. and 302.6).

rescue——The removal of victims from an area determined to be contaminated or otherwise hazardous by appropriately trained and equipped personnel.

residue—A material remaining in a package after its contents have been emptied and before the packaging is refilled, cleaned, and purged of vapor to remove any potential hazard.

Resource Conservation and Recovery Act (RCRA)—The federal framework for proper management and disposal of hazardous wastes. This program is administered by the Environmental Protection Agency and may be delegated to the states.

respiratory protective equipment—See *self-contained breathing apparatus* and *air-purifying respirators*.

response—That portion of incident management where personnel are involved in controlling a hazardous material incident.

responsible party (RP)—A legally recognized entity (person, corporation, business, or partnership, etc.) that has a legally recognized status of financial accountability and liability for action necessary to abate and mitigate adverse environmental and human health and safety effects resulting from a non-permitted release or discharge of hazardous material; the person or agency found legally accountable for the cleanup of the incident.

risk—The potential for harm, which incorporates both probability and severity. The inverse of *safety*.

risk analysis—A process to analyze the probability that harm may occur to life, property, and the environment and to note the risks to be taken to identify the incident objectives.

risk management—Decision-making process that involves such considerations as risk assessment, technological feasibility, economic information about costs and benefits, statutory requirements, public concerns, and other factors.

risk management prevention plan (RMPP-RMP, outside California)—

- A plan that encompasses, among other appropriate elements, a structured assessment of hazards.

- A formal personnel training program for the prevention of, and response to, emergencies.

  o Procedures for periodic safety reviews of operating equipment and procedures.

  o Schedules for regular testing of the program.

  o Procedures for the purpose of reducing the probability of accidents.

roentgen—A measure of the charge produced in air created by ionizing radiation, typically in reference to gamma radiation (1 R = 100 coulomb/kilogram).

roentgen equivalent man (REM)—The unit of dose equivalent; takes into account the effectiveness of different types of radiation (1 rem = 100 Sieverts).

rupture—The physical failure of a container or mechanical device releasing or threatening to release a hazardous material.

safety—Freedom from harm, which incorporates both probability and severity. The inverse of *risk*.

safety data sheet (SDS)—The new format for Global Harmonization and creating chemical specific data sheets. This new sheet will replace the older material safety data sheet format and will meet global codes within the updated Occupational Safety and Health Administration HAZCOM program.

safety officer—Selected by the incident commander, a person at an emergency incident responsible for ensuring that all overall operations performed at the incident by all agencies present are done so with respect to the highest levels of safety and health. The safety officer reports directly to the incident commander.

salivation—An excessive discharge of saliva; ptyalism.

salvage drum—See *recovery drum*.

sample—To take a representative portion of the material for evidence or analytical purposes.

sampling kits—Kits assembled for the purpose of providing adequate tools and equipment for taking samples and documenting unknowns to create a "chain of evidence."

SARA—See *Superfund Amendments and Reauthorization Act*.

SARA Title III Regional Plan—Regional and local plan.

SCBA—See *self-contained breathing apparatus*.

scenario—An outline of a natural or expected course of events.

scene—The location affected or potentially affected by hazard.

scene manager—See *incident commander*.

secondary materials—Spent materials, sludges, byproducts, scrap metal, and commercial chemical produces recycled in ways that differ from their normal use.

selective toxicity—The capacity of a chemical to injure one kind of living matter without harming another, even though the two may be in intimate contact.

self-contained breathing apparatus (SCBA)—A positive-pressure, self-contained breathing apparatus or combination SCBA/supplied air breathing apparatus certified by the National Institute for Occupational Safety and Health and the Mine Safety and Health Administration or the appropriate approval agency for use in atmospheres that are immediately dangerous to life or health.

sensitizer—A substance that, on first exposure, causes little or no reaction in humans or test animals, but, upon repeated exposure, may cause a marked response not necessarily limited to the contact site. An adverse effect may occur immediately, as in anaphylactic shock or in an asthmatic reaction, depending upon the person's genetics. It can be researched in the Occupational Safety and Health Administration's specific chemical list Z table.

sheltering in place/in place protection—To direct people to quickly go inside a building and remain inside until the danger passes.

shipping papers—Generic term used to refer to documents that must accompany all shipments of goods for transportation. These include hazardous waste manifests, bills of lading, consists, and so on. Shipping papers are intended to describe what hazardous materials are contained within the shipment, if any.

short-term exposure limit (STEL)—A 15-minute time-weighted coverage exposure that should not be exceeded at any time during a work day, nor repeated more than 4 times per day, even if the 8-hour time-weighted average is within the threshold limit value.

skimmer—Physical systems whereby a liquid phase is recovered from another liquid phase because of polarity differences and stored or transferred for further processing. Typical use is to remove petroleum products floating on a waterbody.

sludge—Accumulated solids, semisolids, or liquid waste generated from wastewaters, drilling operations, or other fluids.

smoke—An air suspension (aerosol) of liquid droplets, often originating from combustion or sublimation.

solidification—Process whereby a contaminant is permanently immobilized in a substrate to prevent future migration away from the container.

solubility—The ability or tendency of one substance to blend uniformly with another.

solvents—A liquid substance capable of dissolving or dispersing one or more other substances to form a uniformly dispersed mixture.

spill—The release of a liquid, powder, or solid hazardous material in a manner that poses a threat to air, water, ground, and the environment (see *incident*).

spiller—See *responsible party*.

spontaneously combustible—See *pyrophoric*.

stabilization—The period of an incident where the adverse behavior of the hazardous material is controlled.

staging area—The safe area established for temporary location of available resources closer to the incident site to reduce response time.

state warning center—The center within the state's office of emergency services that monitors seismic activities and receives reports of any release or threatened release of a hazardous material or spill.

stationary source—A fixed facility from which a release of hazardous materials may originate.

storage—Containment of hazardous materials on a temporary basis in such a manner as to not constitute disposal of such materials.

strict liability—The responsible party is liable even though they have exercised reasonable care.

Superfund Amendments and Reauthorization Act (SARA)—Created for the purpose of establishing federal statutes for right-to-know standards and emergency response to hazardous materials incidents, reauthorizing the federal Superfund, and mandating states to implement equivalent regulations/requirements.

support zone—See *cold zone*.

surface impoundment—A natural depression, man-made excavation, or diked area designed to hold an accumulation of liquid wastes or waste containing free liquids.

synergistic effect—The combined effect of two chemicals that is greater than the sum of the effect of each agent alone.

Systemic—Pertaining to the internal organs and structures of the body.

systemic toxic exposure—Toxic effects to the body as a whole spreading via the bloodstream and often displaying delayed symptoms.

team leader—See *entry team leader*.

technical specialist—Hazardous materials reference person assigned to document activities of the hazardous material team and gather information relevant to the chemicals involved and their hazards.

teratogen—A substance or agent that can result in malformations of a fetus. Also used to describe agents that disrupt reproductive functions.

teratogenicity—Ability to produce birth defects.

termination—That portion of incident management where personnel are involved in documenting safety procedures, site operations, hazards faced, and lessons learned from the incident. Termination is divided into three phases: debriefing, post-incident analysis, and critique (see *post-incident analysis*).

thieving rod—A glass tube used like a coliwassa, except the liquid is contained in the tube by a vacuum pressure.

threshold—The point where a physiological or toxicological effect begins to be produced by the smallest degree of stimulation.

threshold limit value (TLV)—The value for an airborne toxic material that is used as a guide in the control of health hazards and represents the concentration to which nearly all workers may be exposed 8 hours per day over extended periods of time without adverse effects. The TLV is a recommended exposure limit issued by the American Conference of Governmental Industry Hygienists.

threshold limit value-ceiling (TLV-C)—The concentration that should not be exceeded during any part of the working exposure.

threshold limit value-time weighted average (TLV-TWA)—An exposure level under which most people can work consistently for 8 hours a day, day after day, with no harmful effects.

threshold planning quantity (TPQ)—The quantity designated for each extremely hazardous substance that triggers a required notification by facilities to the state emergency response commission that such facilities are subject to reporting under Superfund Amendments and Reauthorization Act Title III.

totally encapsulated suits—Special protective suits made of materials that prevent toxic or corrosive substances or vapors from coming in contact with the body (see *fully encapsulated suit*).

toxic—Poisonous; relating to or caused by a toxin; able to cause injury by contact or systemic action to plants, animals, or people.

toxic chemicals—The Environmental Protection Agency uses this term for chemicals whose total emissions and releases must be reported annually by owners and operators of certain facilities that manufacture, process, or otherwise use a listed toxic chemical as identified in Superfund Amendments and Reauthorization Act Title III.

toxicity—A relative property of a chemical agent that refers to its harmful effect on some biological mechanism and the conditions under which this effect occurs.

traffic control/crowd control—Action(s) by law enforcement to secure and/or minimize exposure of the public to unsafe conditions resulting from emergency incidents, impediments, and congestion.

treatment—Any method, technique, or process which changes the physical, chemical, or biological character or composition of any hazardous waste or removes or reduces its harmful properties or characteristics for any purpose.

United Nations Identification Number (UN)—When "UN" precedes a four-digit number, it indicates that this identification number is used internationally to identify a hazardous material.

upper explosive limit (UEL)—The highest concentration of the material in air that can be detonated.

upwind—In or toward the direction from which the wind blows.

vapor—An air dispersion of molecules of a substance that is typically a liquid or solid at standard temperature and pressure.

vapor dispersion—The movement of vapor clouds in air caused by turbulence, gravity, spreading, and mixing.

vapor protective suit—See *level of protection*.

vulnerability—The susceptibility of life, the environment, and/or property to damage by a hazard.

warm zone—The area where personnel and equipment decontamination and hot zone support takes place. It includes control points for the access corridor and thus assists in reducing the spread of contamination. This is also referred to as *decontamination, contamination reduction, yellow zone, support zone,* or *limited access zone* in other documents.

water reactive—Having properties of, when contacted by water, reacting violently, generating extreme heat, burning, exploding, or rapidly reacting to produce an ignitable, toxic, or corrosive mist, vapor, or gas.

Appendix B

Abbreviations and Acronyms

AAR	Association of American Railroads
ACGIH	American Conference of Governmental Industrial Hygienists
ACM	asbestos-containing material
ACP	asbestos-containing pipe
AED	automated external defibrillator
AHA	activity hazard analysis
AIHA	American Industrial Hygiene Association
ANSI	American National Standards Institute
APR	air-purifying respirator
AQMD	Air Quality Management District
ASTM	American Society for Testing and Materials
AWWA	American Water Works Association
BBS	behavior-based safety
BCIS	Bureau of Citizenship and Immigration Service
BLEVE	boiling liquid expanding vapor explosion
BMP	best management practices
B of M	Bureau of Mines
BOD	biochemical oxygen demand
BTX	benzene, toluene, xylene
CAA	Clean Air Act
CAER	community awareness and emergency response
CAMEO	computer-aided management of emergency operations
CANUTEC	Canadian Transport Emergency Center
CAS	Chemical Abstracts Service
CBC	complete blood count

CD	compact disk
CDC	Centers for Disease Control
CDL	commercial driver's license
CERCLA	Comprehensive Environmental Response, Compensation and Liability Act
CESQG	conditionally exempt small quantity generator
CFR	*Code of Federal Regulations*
CGA	Compressed Gas Association
CGI	combustible gas indicator
CHEMTREC	Chemical Transportation Emergency Center
CHRIS	chemical hazard-response information system
cc	cubic centimeter
CMA	Chemical Manufacturers Association
CMV	commercial motor vehicles
CNS	central nervous system
CO	carbon monoxide
CPR	cardiopulmonary resuscitation
CRC	contamination reduction corridor
CRT	cathode ray tube
CRZ	contamination reduction zone
CUPA	California Certified Unified Program Agency
CWA	Clean Water Act
DECON	decontamination
DHHS	Department of Health and Human Services
DOE	Department of Energy
DOL	Department of Labor
DOT	Department of Transportation
DTSC	California Department of Toxic Substance Control
DVD	digital versatile disk
EAP	emergency action plan
EERU	Environmental Emergency Response Unit
EHS	extremely hazardous substances
EMOD (EMR)	experience modification rate
EMS	Emergency Medical Services
EMSA	Emergency Medical Services Authority
EOC	emergency operations center

EOD	explosive ordinance disposal
EPA	Environmental Protection Agency
EPCRA	Environmental Planning and Community Right-to-Know Act
ERCS	Emergency Response Cleanup Services, under EPA contract
ERT	environmental response team
ESLI	end-of-service-life indicator
FBI	Federal Bureau of Investigation
FDA	Food and Drug Administration
FEMA	Federal Emergency Management Agency
FID	flame ionization detector
FIFRA	Federal Insecticide, Fungicide, and Rodenticide Act
FIT	field investigation team under contract to EPA
FMCSA	Federal Motor Carrier Safety Administration
FMEA	failure mode effect analysis
GC	gas chromatograph or gas chromatography
GCWR	gross combination weight rating
GHS	Global Harmonized System
GSA	General Service Administration
GVW	gross vehicle weight
GVWR	gross vehicle weight rating
H2S	hydrogen sulfide
HACS	Hazard Assessment Computer System
HAZCAT	hazardous materials categorization
HAZMAT	hazardous materials
HAZOP	hazard and operability study
HEPA	high-efficiency particulate air filter
HM	hazardous material
HMRT	hazardous materials response team
HMSO	hazardous materials safety officer
HMSP	hazardous materials safety permit
HSIF	hazardous substance information form
IATA	International Air Transport Association
ICAO	International Civil Aviation Organization
ICS	incident command system
IDLH	immediately dangerous to life or health
IR	infrared radiation

IUPAC	International Union of Pure and Applied Chemists
JHA	job hazard analysis
JSA	job safety analysis
kPA	kilopascal
LD$_{50}$	lethal dose, 50%
LCD	liquid crystal display
LC$_{50}$	lethal concentration, 50%
LEL	lower explosive limit
LEPC	local emergency planning committee
LFL	lower flammable limit
LPG	liquefied petroleum gas
LQG	large quantity generator
LTI	lost time injury
MBR	membrane bioreactor
mg/L	milligrams per liter
mg/m^3	milligrams per cubic meter
mr/hr	milliroentgens per hour
MSDS	material safety data sheet
MSHA	Mine Safety and Health Administration
MUC	maximum use concentration
MUL	maximum use limit
NBR	nitrile-butadiene rubber (syn. Buta-N)
NDR	National Driver Registry
NESC	National Environmental Services Association
NFPA	National Fire Protection Association
NIIMS	National Interagency Incident Management System
NIOSH	National Institute for Occupational Safety and Health
NOAA	National Oceanic and Atmospheric Administration
NOS or n.o.s.	not otherwise specified
NPF	National Priority List
NPTN	National Pesticide Telecommunications Network
NRC	National Response Center
NRC	Nuclear Regulatory Commission
O$_2$	oxygen
OHMTADS	Oil and Hazardous Materials Technical Assistance Data System
ORM	other regulated material

OSC	on-scene coordinator
OSHA	Occupational Safety and Health Administration
OVA	organic vapor analyzer
PAPR	powered air-purifying respirator
PCB	polychlorinated biphenol
PCC	Poison Control Center
PEL	permissible exposure limit
PF	protection factor
PFD	personal flotation device
pH	relates to corrosivity (acids and bases)
PHA	process hazard analysis
PID	photoionization detector
PIO	public information officer
PIV	powered industrial vehicle
ppb	parts per billion
PPE	personal protective equipment
ppm	parts per million
POTW	publicly owned treatment works
psi	pounds per square inch
PVC	polyvinyl chloride
QLFT	qualitative fit test (subjective)
QNFT	quantitative fit test (measured or numbered)
RAM	radioactive material
RAS	return activated sludge
RBC	rotating biological contactor
RCRA	Resource Conservation and Recovery Act
RDD	radiological dispersion event
REM	Roentgen equivalent man
RMP	risk management plan
RO	reverse osmosis
ROE	routes of entry or exposure
RQ	reportable quantity
SAR	supplied air respirator
SARA	Superfund Amendments and Reauthorization Act
SBR	styrene-butadiene rubber
SCADA	supervisory control and data acquisition

SCBA	self-contained breathing apparatus
SDS	safety data sheet
SOPs	standard operating procedures
SOSG's	standard operating safety guidelines
SQG	small quantity generator
SSOHC	Safety, Security and Occupational Health Committee
STEL	short-term exposure limit
TAT	technical assistance team under contract to EPA
TCE	trichloroethylene
TECP	totally encapsulated chemical protective (suit or clothing)
TLV	threshold limit value
TLV-C	threshold limit value-ceiling
TPQ	threshold planning quantity
TRI	Toxics Release Inventory
TSDF	treatment storage and disposal facility
TWA	time-weighted average
µCI	micro curie
UEL	upper explosive limit
UL	Underwriters Laboratories
USCG	United States Coast Guard
USGS	United States Geological Survey
UV	ultraviolet
VPP	voluntary protection program
VPPPA	Voluntary Protection Program Participants Association
VQ	verification questionnaire
VSAT	vulnerability self-assessment tool
WARN	water/wastewater agency response network
WAS	waste activated sludge
WEF	Water Environment Federation
WWTP	wastewater treatment plant

Index